Checkbook's 2018 Guide to Health Plans for Federal Employees

39th Edition

By Walton Francis and the Editors of
Washington Consumers' Checkbook

D1264176

	Checkbook—Health Insurance
For more copies of this book:	1625 K Street, NW, 8th Floor, Washington, DC 20006 Phone: 202-347-7283 Send $12.95 per copy (price includes shipping) Make checks payable to "Checkbook" ***Or visit Checkbook.org***

This book is a special publication of the Center for the Study of Services, which publishes *Washington Consumers' Checkbook* magazine and Checkbook.org. The Center is a nonprofit organization dedicated to giving consumers the information they need to find high quality, reasonably priced services. We cannot promise that the health plan you choose using this book will be satisfactory to you. However, we believe that our advice is sound. Employees may want to encourage their agencies to purchase copies in bulk for broad distribution, as many agencies have done with previous editions of the *Guide*.

Contents

Chapter 1: Introduction, Basics, and Changes for 2018...............4

Chapter 2: Comparing Plan Costs.............................17

**Chapter 3: Cost Comparisons and Advice for Employees
and Former Employees**...........................28

Costs for Employees Under 55 Who Pay General Schedule Premiums.................32
Costs for Employees Under 55 Who Pay Postal Premiums 38
Costs for Employees Age 55 to 64 Who Pay General Schedule Premiums............50
Costs for Employees Age 55 to 64 Who Pay Postal Premiums 54
Costs for Part-Time Employees..62
Costs for Persons Who Pay Full Premiums.....................................68

Chapter 4: Cost Comparisons and Advice for Annuitants...........73

Costs for Annuitants without Medicare 76
Costs for Annuitants with Medicare Parts A and B................................79
Costs for Annuitants with Medicare Part A Only 82

Chapter 5: Cost Sharing...............................94

Chapter 6: Coverage Features................................99

Chapter 7: Dental, Vision, and Hearing....................................105

Chapter 8: Plan Types and Flexibility....................................118

Chapter 9: Quality and Service...............................126

Chapter 10: Premiums and Taxes.................................143

Chapter 11: Key Tips and Final Plan Selection.....................148

Cost and Coverage Features of All Plans................................134

Appendix: Our Methods and Data Sources.......................188

Chapter 1

Introduction, Basics, and Changes for 2018

What the Guide Does

Checkbook's Guide to Health Plans for Federal Employees gives you vital shopping information that you cannot get from any other source. It tells you how much money you can save by changing—or by staying in—your health insurance plan. It summarizes thousands of facts about the plans to simplify your choice. The *Guide* comes in both print and Internet versions. They are almost identical but the print version is more convenient for many, and the online version allows more depth and details. The online version is particularly useful for Federal agencies that subscribe for all their employees, giving the employees invaluable money-saving advice while saving the agencies money as well, since they pay most of the premium cost. We show employees how to save thousands of dollars in unnecessary costs. Federal agencies also save, over a thousand dollars on average, for every employee who switches to a lower-cost plan using our advice. In both versions:

- Our ratings cover **all** of over 250 health insurance plans available to Federal employees and retirees, including about 20 national plans, over 200 health maintenance organization (HMO) and other local options, and about two dozen Consumer-Driven and High Deductible plan options. Wherever you live, we rate all the plans in **your community**.
- Our **ratings** of plan costs take into account premiums, catastrophic limits, and estimates of likely out-of-pocket costs for medical expenses of every kind.
- We compare plans for **insurance value** in dealing with unforeseen medical expenses, not just for the routine costs you can predict.
- We **compare** limits on out-of-pocket costs based on the actual coverage allowed by each plan, not just what the plan seems to say before you read the fine print.
- We rate plans for **each coverage group**—employees in different pay systems, annuitants with or without Medicare, former spouses, families of various sizes, children at age 26, part-time employees, and former employees.
- We rate plans according to how well each covers **low, average, or high medical expenses**, analyzing coverage of all major types of cost.

- We adjust our estimates for the **tax advantages** that reduce the after-tax premium cost to most employees (but not retirees) by about one third.
- We provide information on **coinsurance, copays and other cost sharing**, so you can quickly determine whether a plan pays well for a benefit you need.
- We provide **accurate estimates of potential exposure to catastrophic expense** by adjusting plans' claimed limits on out-of-pocket expenses so they don't omit important categories of cost.
- We give you data on **coverage features** of each plan, including skilled nursing, dental, and hearing aid coverage.
- We address **plan quality**, and provide data on **enrollee satisfaction** with each plan's service. We provide in-depth results from an annual survey in which plan members rate their plans on ease of getting needed care, customer service, claims processing, and other factors.
- We **rate dental and vision** plans as well. We provide dollar estimates of likely dental costs, taking into account both premiums and out-of-pocket expense. We compare dental coverage in all plans, not just standalone plans.
- We provide up-to-date information on changes in the FEHB program, including the **effects of health reform**, of **Medicare premium changes**, and of the **Self plus One option**.
- We provide detailed **consumer advice** on which plan options work best in different situations, on plan advantages you may not have thought about, and on mistakes to avoid.

As a result, the *Guide* gives you a solid basis for selecting the best health or dental plan for you and your family. Hundreds of thousands of employees and annuitants have followed our advice over the years, and many of them have saved thousands of dollars a year by finding better coverage for lower premiums. **There is no other source of plan comparisons or Open Season advice that provides even half of these features.**

The Setting

Every Federal employee and annuitant can choose from twenty plans or more. Choices include well-known national plans, such as Blue Cross/Blue Shield; local plans available in many areas, such as the Aetna, Humana, UnitedHealthcare and Kaiser plans; and plans sponsored by unions and employee associations, such as the American Postal Workers Union (APWU) and the Government Employees Health Association (GEHA). You are free to join most union and association plans, regardless of your employing agency and whether you are an employee or annuitant. At most you must pay annual dues, which are generally near $30. However, a few plans restrict enrollment. For example, two plans are open only to those involved in foreign affairs, intelligence, or defense—a pool, however, that is very large and covers many agencies.

You can switch plans for the coming year during the annual Open Season, scheduled from November 13 through December 11, 2017. You are also free to switch among plans at certain other times—for instance, if you marry. You are allowed to switch from plan to plan regardless of preexisting conditions, even if you are in the hospital when the new plan enrollment year begins.

Hundreds of thousands of employees and annuitants are still enrolled in plans that are much more expensive than average, and that give them no needed extra

benefits. In Open Season almost all of these persons will be able to reduce premium costs greatly while maintaining or even improving benefits.

As always, this year's *Guide* reflects changes as plan options have been added or dropped, benefits modified, and premiums gone up in some plans and down in others. For newly hired employees, and those who can change plans after Open Season, the information in the *Guide* applies throughout the year.

The Savings

Whether your family's circumstances are "average" or unusual, some HMOs, some national plans such as Blue Cross Basic and GEHA Standard option, and a number of High-Deductible plans offer big savings compared to other plans. To help decide which is best, we estimate likely, and not so likely, costs to you under each plan, and compare coverage features of the plans and several aspects of customer service. In addition to dollar costs, customer service is an important element of plan choice, particularly for HMOs. We present customer survey data on plan satisfaction, data on which plans are least likely to have claims disputes, and data on accreditation.

Our tables rate each plan on total expenses—including premium and out-of-pocket costs. The tables show what each plan will cost you in an "average" year and in years when your medical costs are much higher or lower than average. As our tables show, **likely savings available to most employees and annuitants range from hundreds to thousands of dollars a year**.

You should not pick a plan on the basis of its premium, benefit coverage, or catastrophic expense guarantee alone. We help you avoid these traps by including all of these complex factors in our ratings.

The information we give you is especially important if you expect a major change in your medical or financial situation. If you plan to have a baby next year, or face heavy dental bills, the plan that was best for you last year may not be best this year. Also, if you will retire, divorce, leave Federal employment, or join Medicare, you should review your choices very carefully.

Even if your plan satisfies you, why not consider switching to another? Those who switch in Open Season save hundreds of millions of dollars every year for themselves and their employing agencies, through migration to lower-cost plans that offer better value. You, too, can share in these savings.

Consider the following examples. If you are a single employee in the Washington, DC area, our estimates show that you are likely to save over well over $1,000 next year by joining the Kaiser HMO Standard Option instead of the Blue Cross Standard Option, the most popular plan. If you are unwilling to make such a drastic departure from fee-for-service medicine, you can save almost $1,000 by enrolling in the Blue Cross Basic plan rather than the Standard Option. We rate a half dozen Consumer-Driven (CD) and High Deductible (HD) options as equal to or better than even Blue Cross Basic for most enrollees. All of these estimates include your premium cost, your savings from tax preferences, and your likelihood of a range of expenses up to and including a catastrophically expensive illness.

Perhaps you are a retired couple with Medicare parts A and B. The great majority of such retirees select the Blue Cross Standard Option. But we rate the APWU Consumer-Driven plan, Blue Cross Basic, GEHA Standard Option, and Kaiser Standard Option plan as likely to save you about $2,000, or even more. The Aetna Direct plan can save you about $4,000. Why? Most of these plans, like Blue Cross Standard Option, allow you to pay nothing for hospital and physician charges when you have Medicare parts A and B. In some of them their prescription drug coverage is not quite as good, but their premiums are far lower. So, you start the year with major savings in hand. The Consumer-Driven plans have "Personal Care Accounts" that you can spend on dental costs and drugs that Medicare doesn't cover to offset the cost of the Medicare premium, and Blue Cross Basic now offers a similar arrangement. In the Consumer-Driven plans, and most High Deductible plans, you have the potential for even larger savings in future years if you build up your account. These comparisons show that even the most popular plans may not be the best buys.

Using the Guide

We prepared the *Guide* because we know that choosing the right plan can be difficult, even if you have time to read hundreds of pages in plan brochures. The coverage details are hard to understand, and trying to compare multiple benefit details simultaneously is very difficult. As a result, it is often hard to determine which plan is best for you. Many employees depend on advice from their friends, or stick with a "name brand" or the plan sponsored by their own union. However, that choice can waste hundreds or thousands of dollars.

The Office of Personnel Management (OPM), which administers the program, sets standards for plan benefits and for information in plan brochures, and also presents summary plan comparison information on its Web site. The complexity of comparing plans is substantial. We have studied and restudied each plan and have checked many details with plan officials. But we have undoubtedly missed a few limitations or special coverages. So, before making a final choice, you should compare the brochures of several plans.

We structure the *Guide*'s advice and information as follows:

- You are reading the "Introduction, Basics, and Changes for 2018."
- "Comparing Plan Costs" explains how and why some choices can save so much money.
- "Cost Comparisons and Advice" for Employees and Former Employees explains and provides our cost ratings for each plan, organized separately by eligibility group.
- "Cost Comparisons and Advice" for Annuitants provides cost ratings that take into account higher costs for the elderly, and the effects of enrolling in Medicare Part A or Parts A and B.
- "Cost Sharing" provides basic information on plan benefits for hospital, medical, and prescription drug expenses.
- "Coverage Features" addresses features such as skilled nursing and mental health coverage.
- "Dental, Vision, and Hearing" compares standalone plans with each other and with the dental, vision, and hearing aid coverage in the health insurance plans.
- "Plan Types and Flexibility" explains the various types of plans and how they affect your ability to use the provider of your choice and to achieve additional savings.
- "Quality and Service" describes several measures of quality of plan service, and presents quality ratings for all plans.
- "Premiums and Taxes" explains how premiums and out of pocket spending can be tax advantaged and how much employees can save.
- "Key Tips and Final Plan Selection" reminds you of factors vital to you and gives advice on making a final decision among plans.
- "Our Methods and Data Sources" explains the information we use to create our ratings.

Protect Your Retirement

It is not expensive to enroll in the FEHBP for the five years before retirement. Several plans have annual self only premiums below $1,500. These plans cost under $1,000 after tax savings. Some plans give you savings accounts higher than the tax advantaged premium cost.

We rate health plans by their likely cost to you, taking into account your pay system, employment or retirement status, family size, age, health status, location, and other factors. For example, we present information on premium cost to employees using the "premium conversion" tax-advantaged basis available to employees, but not retirees. Online *Guide* users reach the table applicable to them by answering questions regarding family size, age, retirement status, health status, zip code, pay system, and several other factors. They see a summary ratings table for their area and then have the option to choose whether to look at tables providing detailed cost comparisons, cost sharing, coverage features, plan flexibility, or plan quality for plans in their area. Readers of the print *Guide* turn to applicable cost comparison and other tables within each of the book chapters. Information on the cost, coverage, and features for local plans in all States is available online simply by entering your zip code, and in the print *Guide* provided in summary in a table at the end of the "Key Tips and Final Plan Selection" chapter.

Be Sure to Elect a Survivor Annuity for Your Spouse

If you die and your spouse receives no Federal pension, your spouse will lose FEHBP coverage forever. If you die while enrolled as self-only, your spouse will also lose coverage.

The information contained in our print and online versions is almost identical. Both versions allow users to compare plans based on their pay system, age, family size, and health status. Many people prefer to use paper copies. However, the online *Guide* makes the customization, selection, and presentation of comparative information exceptionally fast and convenient, and you can print out plan comparisons customized to your needs. In the Washington, D.C. area, you can use the online version to see which plan networks include your doctors. Not everyone uses the Internet, so we publish both versions and let individual purchasers decide which they want. In addition, many Federal Departments and agencies provide free access to the online version for all their employees. You can check to see if your agency provides free access, at our Web site at *www.guidetohealthplans.org*.

General FEHB Program Procedures

The Federal Employees Health Benefits Program (FEHB) is an unconventional government program. Instead of giving you one "take it or leave it" choice, the government authorizes plans to compete for your premium dollar. It pays most of the premium cost—up to 75 percent for annuitants and most employees—and even more for Postal employees and employees of some other agencies, such as the FDIC and SEC. Taking into account tax advantages, the government pays between 80 and 90 percent of premium costs for most plans for employees (but not retirees). Nationally, over 250 plan options are offered, with most employees and retirees eligible to join 20 or more. You decide which plan you want to join. If you are not satisfied, you can switch in the next Open Season.

The FEHB program enrolls about 8 million persons. Enrollees spend about $50 billion a year through their health plans. About five percent of enrollees switch among plans in most Open Seasons. Until the Medicare Advantage program, which was modeled on the FEHB program, it was the largest "managed competition" system for harnessing consumer choices to contain health insurance costs. Studies have shown that it outperforms both Original Medicare and private employer plans in coverage, cost control, and consumer satisfaction.

OPM sets minimum financial, administrative, and benefit terms and conditions for every plan participating in the program. Insurance companies and OPM agree each year on contracts setting forth both benefits and costs. A few key points about FEHB plans are:

- All employees and annuitants can enroll in whatever plan they choose, or not enroll at all.
- Everyone can change plans once per year in Open Season. You also may switch plans or options in circumstances such as marriage, birth of a child, or geographic transfer. If you belong to an HMO and move out of its service area, you may enroll in a new plan.
- A family or self plus one enrollment covers only immediate family members: your spouse and children. Coverage for children now lasts until they reach age 26, unless they are severely handicapped. In that case they may be eligible at any age.
- **Plans cannot exclude coverage for any preexisting conditions or illnesses your family may have when you switch plans**. You may switch to gain the best coverage for your condition, and use the new plan without penalty.
- Plans must publish brochures in a common format that provides a clear explanation of their benefits and your cost for covered services, how you access plan services, how you get approvals, and your rights in disputes.
- Each plan must pay for the medical and related costs as explained in its brochure—no more and no less. If a brochure says that a particular category of service is limited or excluded, believe it.
- Plan brochures may word the same benefits differently. Sometimes the wording used is not clear to a layperson. However, **you can often figure out what specific benefit language really means by comparing two or three brochures to see how they differ**.

Getting Information

Our website includes a great deal of useful information including not only uniquely informative plan comparisons, but a great deal of advice including Questions and Answers addressing more than one hundred problems. OPM has a website with plan brochures and a great deal of other useful information at *www.opm.gov/insure*. You can access this site at most libraries if you do not use the Internet in your home or office. Unlike many government websites, OPM's are user friendly and easy to navigate. You can also visit plan websites directly. This is especially useful if you want to check how a particular plan covers your medicines.

You change plans by filling out OPM's form SF 2809 or an online equivalent. Personnel offices have copies and will give you form SF 2809 if you decide to change your enrollment. In many agencies, an online service such as "Employee Express" can be used to change plans. Annuitants are mailed only abbreviated

Contacting National and DC Area Plans

Plan code(s)	Plan name	Plan telephone	Website	Enrollment limitations
22, F5, N6	Aetna HealthFund	888-238-6240	aetnafeds.com	None
JN	Aetna Open Access	800-537-9384	aetnafeds.com	Limited areas
47	APWU	800-222-2798	apwuhp.com	Pay dues
10, 11	Blue Cross	Phone book*	fepblue.org	None
2G, B6	CareFirst	888-789-9069	carefirst.com/fedhmo	None
42	Compass Rose	888-438-9135	compassrosebenefits.com	Intel/Foreign Aff/DOD
40	Foreign Service	202-833-4910	afspa.org/fsbp	Intel/Foreign Aff/DOD
31, 34	GEHA	800-821-6136	geha.com	None
E3	Kaiser Mid-Atlantic	877-574-3337	kp.org/feds	None
JP	MD-IPA	877-835-9861	uhcfeds.com	None
41, 45	MHBP	800-410-7778	mhbp.com	Pay dues
48	MHBP HDHP	800-694-9901	mhbp.com	Pay dues
32, KM	NALC	888-636-6252	nalchbp.org	Pay dues
38	Rural Carrier	800-638-8432	rcbphealth.com	Rural carrier
44	SAMBA	800-638-6589	sambaplans.com	None
L9, LR, V4	UnitedHealthcare	877-835-9861	uhcfeds.com	None

* The DC area number for Blue Cross is 202-484-1650

information and should use the Internet to get more details. A special OPM procedure provides an easy way for annuitants to order paper copies of plan brochures.

If you have a problem getting information from these normal channels, you can call OPM for help. There is an automated phone system, called "Open Season Express" at 800-332-9798 to help annuitants get brochures, change plans, or get other help. In addition, the retirement information office number is 1-888-767-6738. This office can answer many questions, and help you with enrolling in a Medicare-participating HMO. We caution, however, that these numbers are often overburdened with calls—don't wait until the last minute.

Of course, Checkbook provides information on contacting each plan directly, including its telephone number and website, along with information on enrollment limitations. On our website at *www.guidetohealthplans.org* you can download plan brochures and access the provider list and drug formulary for each plan. You can also purchase online access to the *Guide*, and obtain other consumer information, including national ratings of hospitals and doctors in *Consumers' Guide to Hospitals* and *Consumers' Guide to Top Doctors*, as well as online articles rating physicians, dentists, and other health care providers for quality and price.

Enrollment Limitations

Many plans are open to all employees. However, HMOs require that you live in a particular area, and a few plans require that you work for a particular agency or join a specific union. Most of the union plans allow any Federal employee to join. This generally means that you can enroll in the plan no matter what agency you work for, but you may have to pay annual dues and become an "associate" member

Check Your Brochure!

Do not stay in the same plan without reading at least "How We Change" for next year or join a new plan without checking any benefits of particular importance to your health care.

of the union. These dues are modest, and our cost tables include them. Some plans are restricted to particular agencies or categories of employees. For example, the Foreign Service and Compass Rose plans enroll employees who serve in foreign affairs, defense, or intelligence functions (both plans interpret these limitations broadly, but they differ in details as explained in their brochures).

Use and Trust Plan Brochures

Plan brochures are necessary to determine what benefits each plan covers, or does not cover. In some cases, a plan does not mention a service at all in its brochure, but has assured us that its claims manual (which is not available to employees) says the service is covered. You cannot fully rely on this, however, since OPM has stated that the brochure "is the only official description of the benefits provided by each plan. Do not rely on statements not contained in the brochure. Study the brochures carefully." We agree, and endorse OPM efforts to assure that brochures are consistently and clearly written. Indeed, compared to most public and private insurance, the FEHB brochures are models of clarity. They are particularly well organized to facilitate comparisons of particular topics, such as surgery or maternity.

Unfortunately, health plan brochures have mushroomed in length. In 1990 the average national plan had a brochure 29 pages in length; by ten years later the average grew to 77 pages. For local plans, brochures grew over the same period from 16 to 65 pages, on average. Some of the increase represents increased clarity through "plain English," some is due to increased complexity in plan benefits, and some is due to unnecessary detail. Nonetheless, downloading brochures as PDF files either from our Web site or from OPM's is easily accomplished, and vital to final plan selection. Once you have an electronic version, you can easily use "find" to search the brochure for any topic of concern to you.

Why Premiums Differ

The General Schedule (GS) employee and retiree share of the annual premium varies widely among plans. In national plans it ranges from about $1,500 to almost $5,000 for individuals, and from about $2,500 to over $10,000 for self plus one or larger families. What explains these vast premium differences?

First, plans vary in the kinds of enrollees they attract. Some plans attract families who expect higher expenses. Some have a disproportionate share of high-cost annuitants who joined when premiums were lower and do not realize that their plan is no longer a good buy. Unfortunately, Federal agencies all too often neglect to encourage sensible Open Season choices, and employees and retirees are all too often dilatory about looking for savings. Despite repeated urging over the years, the Congress has failed to address this problem, which could easily be accomplished by a technique called "risk adjustment" and long used by Medicare. Plans that face higher costs have to cover those costs through higher premiums. Premiums in such plans far exceed the fair value of their benefits.

Comparison of Total Cost, Enrollee Cost, and Government Share Under Four Family Plans in 2018 (GS Premiums, Before Tax Savings)

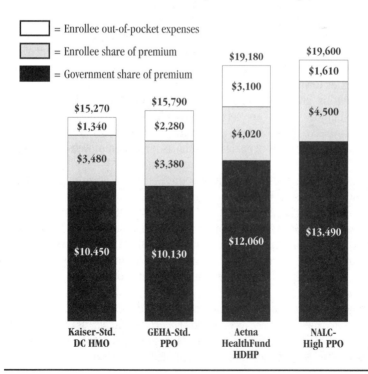

Second, plans differ in the generosity of benefits they offer. Variations include coverage of different expenses; coinsurance, the percentage of each expense you pay; and deductibles, the amount you have to pay before the plan will reimburse any expenses for a service. Plans with higher cost sharing can charge lower premiums. This is one reason the new Consumer-driven plans have such low premiums.

Third, plans vary in how well they manage costs. A well-run HMO can reduce hospital costs by 25 percent or more compared to traditional insurance through case management. Fee-for-service plans review utilization and use panels of preferred providers. "Disease management" techniques are powerful tools to contain costs.

Fourth, cost sharing creates incentives for doctors and patients to be less wasteful. High deductibles discourage unnecessary visits, while 100 percent reimbursement of psychiatric or laboratory and imaging costs encourages overuse of these "free" services. High Deductible and Consumer-Driven plans' premiums benefit somewhat from slightly younger and healthier enrollees, but mainly from their incentives to reduce unnecessary care. Also, the time and trouble to file claims for expenses slightly above the deductible discourages some enrollees from applying for them.

Fifth, variations in the proportion of enrollees with Medicare Parts A and B has a big effect on plan premiums, since Medicare is "primary" (pays first) for retirees, and covers over four-fifths of hospital and doctor costs. Most HMO benefits are so good that retired enrollees often do not sign up for Part B, which puts these plans at a major disadvantage in keeping premiums low.

Sixth, the formula for sharing premium costs magnifies the differences in what you pay. For GS employees and annuitants, the government pays 75 percent of the overall cost of each plan, up to a maximum amount. This varies each year according to a complex formula. The maximum contribution in 2018 for GS employees and annuitants is about $6,000 for singles, $12,800 for self plus one, and $13,600 for families. There are separate formulas for most postal employees, and for employees of the SEC, FDIC, and several other agencies, with higher government shares. A few types of enrollees, such as former employees, get no government contribution and must pay the full premium.

Employees pay the entire premium amount above the government's share. This employee share is far higher for the more expensive plans because the government contribution is capped by an all-plan average. For example, the total premium cost of the GEHA High option for self-only is about $8,600. The government pays the maximum contribution of about $6,000 for GS employees and you pay the extra $2,600. In contrast, under the GEHA Standard option and some other plans, you pay about $1,400 after the government contribution, a premium saving of almost half.

In summary, you pay modestly for insurance from a well-run plan, but you pay more for a plan's inefficiencies, its unusually generous benefits, or its disproportionate share of high-cost enrollees. Your ability to switch among plans during Open Season gives you a major tool for obtaining the best deal.

The chart "Comparison of Total Cost, Enrollee Cost, and Government Share" shows how the employee's premium, the total premium (employee and government share), and the employee's out-of-pocket costs compare for a family of four under several family plans. All these factors contribute to premium differences, and explain why some plans are such bargains. Of course, some of the differences are offset by what you may have to spend out-of-pocket if you pick a plan with less comprehensive benefits. That is why our ratings tables include both the cost of insurance and the cost of medical bills that are not covered. It would be foolish to select a plan just because it has the lowest premium. It would be equally foolish to pick a plan just because it seems to have the best benefits if you wind up paying more in premiums than those extra benefits are worth to you.

For 2018, many plans' premiums are about the same as this year and a few are lower, but premiums in several plans have risen dramatically. Many plans have changed benefits. As is true every year, opportunities for big savings by switching plans are significant.

Changes for 2018

In recent years, there have been significant program-wide changes to the FEHB program. For example, under Affordable Care Act (ACA) rules have had to expand coverage and eliminate all cost sharing for preventive benefits. The effect on plan premiums has been small, because coverage was already so good in the FEHB program.

The ACA change that has been by far the most important to Federal employees is the new coverage of adult children until age 26. One effect of this change has been to raise slightly the cost of FEHB premiums, probably by about one percentage point. Importantly, adult children enrolled in their parents' FEHB plans will also benefit from future eligibility for temporary continuation of coverage for three years after they turn age 26. Of course, this only benefits a small fraction of Federal employee and retiree families, and then only if they pay for a self plus one or self plus family plan option. For single parents, it will in most cases be far less expensive for the adult child to enroll in his or her own employer's plan, if available, or in a private marketplace exchange plan.

Also, both private and public employees are subject to a legal obligation to enroll in health plans. At present, a substantial number of Federal employees, possibly several hundred thousand, are uninsured. They are probably disproportionately younger and healthier, and over time their participation in the FEHB program would tend to lower premiums. Penalties for failure to enroll are growing sharply.

Under another recent change, a very small group of employees—members of Congress and their personal staffs—were forced by a provision of the ACA to join marketplace exchange plans for coverage. An OPM regulation requires them to enroll in Gold plans on the DC exchange (many of these have national networks), and allows them to be reimbursed "as if" these were FEHB plans.

The FEHB statute now requires each plan to offer separate premiums to families with only two members ("self plus one") and to families with two or more members ("self plus family"). Couples with no dependents and single parents with one dependent can enroll in either variation, depending on which premium is less costly. Plan benefits are usually identical under both. The fall 2015 Open Season offered eligible families the first opportunity to switch from self plus family to self plus one. Only about half of those eligible changed to self plus one plans.

Most self plus one premiums are lower than family premiums, primarily because fewer persons incur fewer expenses. The differences are small (and in some cases self plus one costs more) because "empty nesters" are typically much older and average health care costs rise rapidly with age. The proportion of annuitants in each plan, and the proportion of these with Medicare Parts A and B, also influence resulting premiums. In 2018, the yearly premiums for those who enroll in self plus one will be on average about $200 a year less than for those enrolled in family plans, but the variations are wide, and in well over ten percent of the plans self plus one actually costs more than self plus family. Hence, it is very important to check which premium is lower to decide on which way to enroll, or whether to remain in the more expensive option.

The savings under self plus one are relatively small compared to the multi-thousand dollar savings that can be achieved by switching to lower cost plans. The two sets of savings in combination, however, offer spectacular savings possibilities for the majority of federal employees and annuitants.

Finally, OPM has asked plans to adopt cost-saving coordination with Medicare, a reform that saves money for the program because Medicare usually pays first, which reduces FEHB premiums, and also offers savings for annuitants because their out-of-pocket costs are reduced. Most national plans already have such "wraparound" benefits. Dozens of local plans have now added them. Most annuitants now can enroll in a wide range of all plan types—PPO, HDHP, CDHP, and HMO—that provide these savings.

An excise tax of 40% on health plan premiums in "high cost" plans above a certain amount (not on the entire cost of the plan) was previously scheduled to take effect in 2018, but was postponed by the Congress. This is also known as the "Cadillac plan" tax. The amount of premium excluded from the tax will not grow as fast as health care costs, so if and when this tax goes into effect, it would create major incentives for plans to take cost reducing steps in the future to avoid the excise tax.

Longer-term effects of these and other changes are impossible to predict with precision, and by definition do not affect individual enrollee decisions for the coming year, since premiums and benefit levels are already set. For now, the effects of health reform are minor and for most Federal employees and retirees, with only minimal effects on plan costs or benefits. Our advice is to focus on making wise Open Season choices this fall, and to put aside concerns over future changes.

Chapter 2

Comparing Plan Costs

We rate and compare health plans based on their likely cost to you, taking into account your pay system, employment or retirement status, family size, age, health status, location, and other factors. A key element of our ratings are estimates of likely out-of-pocket costs under each plan, based on actuarial estimates of the size and likelihood of low, average, and high spending for families of different sizes and ages. Our ratings also reflect varying premium levels and tax situations faced by different eligibility groups. Full time employees pay lower premiums than annuitants because of tax advantages, and far lower premiums than those who must pay the entire premium. Postal union members and Federal Deposit Insurance Corporation (FDIC) and Securities and Exchange Commission (SEC) employees pay less because the government pays a higher share than for GS employees and annuitants. Neither annuitants nor those who pay full premiums obtain "Premium Conversion" tax advantages. These premium cost differences can reach thousands of dollars a year. We provide separate ratings for each group.

Online *Guide* users see a summary cost comparison table for their group, and then have the option to look at tables providing more detailed cost comparisons. Readers of the printed *Guide* see both summary and detailed cost comparison information for their group in one set of tables for all national plans and local plans available in the DC area, and summary cost comparison information on all local plans in a table covering "Cost and Special Features of All Plans" in all states at the end of *Guide*. The online information is by far more detailed and complete than we can provide in the print version.

Our comparisons take into account not only premiums and potential health care costs, but also plan financial features such as Health Savings Accounts and Wellness benefits that involve cash rewards. We also include dental benefits built into some health plans and, in our separate Chapter on "Dental, Vision, and Hearing," the costs and benefits of standalone dental plans. For annuitants, our estimates and comparisons also take into account both Medicare benefits and Medicare premiums, depending on choices about Medicare enrollment. Online, we also allow for comparisons for those using Flexible Spending Accounts (FSAs). In summary, we provide a comprehensive set of financial comparisons that allow users to make "apple to apple" comparisons of costs for both premiums and likely health care expenses under each plan and across all plans.

Understanding Health Insurance

Individuals and families buy automobile, life, fire, and health insurance policies to protect themselves from catastrophic financial harm from rare events. No one buys "food insurance" because food costs, though large, are unavoidable and predictable. Why pay a middle-man overhead costs to reimburse us for our grocery bills? Nor do we buy rent insurance, or clothes insurance.

We buy life insurance during our working years, because death is very unlikely but financially ruinous to our families if it occurs. For a few hundred dollars a year we can buy support for our families worth hundreds of thousands of dollars if we die. We buy automobile liability insurance because we can protect ourselves from losing huge amounts if we cause an accident.

True health insurance protects our families from ruinous costs of illness. Like most employers, the Federal Government does not offer employees this kind of insurance alone. Instead, it offers various combinations of true insurance and "prepaid" health care. The part of your premium that prepays health care by making advance payment for routine bills will generally equal about what you would have spent by paying the bills directly. However, you wind up paying far less than this because prepaid health care isn't counted as taxable income. Most Federal employees save about one-third of their health care costs because of this exclusion, as explained in our chapter on "Premiums and Taxes."

Unfortunately, prepaid health care creates incentives for enrollees to waste money because the insurance company pays the bill. Prepaid health care may be the single largest cause of wasteful health care spending which, according to some estimates, may be as high as one third of all health care expenditures. There are two major ways to reduce waste. First, health maintenance organizations (HMOs) and other managed care arrangements such as preferred provider organizations (PPOs) use payment incentives for doctors and hospitals to contain costs. Second, high deductible (HDHP) and consumer-driven plans with savings accounts create incentives for enrollees to save costs through prudent shopping decisions. We analyze the advantages and disadvantages of these plans in our analysis of "Plan Types and Flexibility."

How much and what kind of coverage is true insurance? How much is prepaid health care? These questions have no simple answer. A policy protecting against catastrophic medical expense for one family is simply a prepaid health care policy for another family. To a GS-5 with three dependents, $5,000 is a hardship, and $20,000 a heavy burden. To a GS-15 with no dependents, even $20,000 may not be a hardship.

Risk, Premium, and Choice

Since you do not know in advance how high your medical bills will be, there is no way to know which plan will leave you with the lowest total costs. You have to gamble just as you do with any insurance, or indeed with many other choices you make. On sunny mornings you probably won't take an umbrella to work, and sometimes you get wet. In a good year the best policy, in hindsight, would have been no policy, and your total costs would have been zero. In an expensive year, the best policy would have been one that covered every dollar. But we usually don't know whether we'll have a good year or a bad year, which is precisely why we buy insurance. No one but you can decide how much risk you want to bear. Our cost comparisons give you a menu of risk as well as plan choices. They help you think about the level of risk each plan involves, and how much that will cost or save you.

Do not pick a plan either because it has the lowest premium (a seeming best buy) or the highest premium (a seeming set of terrific benefits). As our ratings show, a low premium may hide major coverage gaps, and a high premium may simply reflect expensive enrollees rather than the best benefits. Only some plans have both low premiums and excellent coverage. Pick one of these based on our ratings, which combine both premium and coverage in determining the best buys.

Also, do not pick a plan because it has a lower deductible despite a higher coinsurance amount, or vice versa, and do not try to compare these benefits directly. We use computer programs to perform these calculations, and there are many complexities. For example, whether a plan with a low deductible and a high coinsurance rate is better for you than a plan with the opposites depends on the amount of your expenses, which may not be what you expect. A large body of research shows that very few people are able to juggles cost-sharing variables to pick plans that are the best buys.

Our Ratings

Our cost comparisons cover medical, hospital, dental, and prescription drug costs. They show how you are likely to fare under every national and local plan available to Federal employees. We show how each plan handles various levels of financial risk for you.

Plans are of three main types—combined Preferred Provider Organization (PPO) and Fee-for-Service (FFS) plans, High Deductible (HDHP) and Consumer-Driven (CDHP) plans, and Health Maintenance Organization (HMO) plans, some of which have Point-of-Service (POS) benefits outside the plan network. Most of these options are available in both national and local area plans. Historically, PPO-FFS and HMO plans are distinct approaches. The decision as to which type to join involves service delivery as well as financial factors. The preferred provider or PPO approach now central to most Fee-for-Service plans goes part way toward the HMO model by reducing your cost if you restrict yourself to a network of providers. One national plan, the Blue Cross Basic option, is like most PPOs and HMOs in providing no coverage if you use out-of-network providers. The HDHP plans follow the PPO and FFS model of the national plans, even when they are local. Thus, the differences among plan types are blurring.

Our cost ratings tell you how much you are likely to pay for premiums and out-of-pocket (unreimbursed) medical expenses added together. The tables assume that your bills may be for almost any type or size of expense, including:

- Hospital room and board for surgical or medical care for any illness;
- Other types of hospital services (operating room, anesthesia);
- Surgery, in or out of a hospital;
- Diagnostic tests, X-rays, and lab tests in or out of a hospital;
- Doctor visits in or out of a hospital when you are ill;
- Mental health treatment, outpatient and inpatient;
- Mammograms, Pap smears, and routine immunizations;
- Maternity, even if you are in a self-only plan;
- Emergency care in or out of a hospital;
- Prescription drugs, including insulin and syringes for diabetics;
- Nursing care after an illness;
- Chemotherapy and radiation therapy;
- Physical and rehabilitation therapy;
- Cosmetic ("plastic") surgery or oral surgery—only after an accident;
- Dental care;
- Preventive care including physical examinations and vaccines; and
- **All of these expenses are covered even if you have a preexisting condition or are hospitalized on the date when your enrollment begins.**

With rare exceptions, no plan will pay for any of the following expenses and we do not cover them in our comparisons (however, some of these expenses are covered by Flexible Spending Accounts and Health Savings Accounts):

- Cosmetic or plastic surgery, except after accidents or a disfiguring illness;
- Custodial nursing home care, or any kind of rest care;
- Personal comfort items such as telephone or television while in the hospital;
- Care that is fully paid by another insurance provider;
- Care that is not medically necessary;
- Experimental care (clinical trials are partly excepted);
- Charges that are higher than the plan "allowance" or what the plan has determined to be "reasonable;" and
- Expenses incurred before joining or after leaving a plan.

All plans cover routine exams without deductibles or copayments. Only some plans cover dental care. And most plans expose you to significant out-of-pocket costs, such as not including all prescription drugs in their formularies. Even among plans that cover all services generously, however, there are always some limitations, such as coinsurance and deductibles. Our tables take the major benefit limitations such as these into account in estimating costs. However, we cannot deal with every single coverage nuance or difference (such as which organs are eligible for transplantation, which models of particular medical devices are covered, or which specific medicines are covered). Nor can we assure that all plans will make identical medical necessity decisions in close cases—and they won't. Nor can we reflect extra benefits the plan may provide if, for example, it can save money by giving you more home nursing than its normal limitation on this benefit.

Hence, all of our calculations should be considered approximations that will be broadly accurate in the great majority of situations but that cannot provide precise predictions that cover every possible situation. What our calculations can do, and you cannot do for yourself even if you try to predict your costs, is take into account the risks of ruinously high health care costs from an unexpected illness or accident.

Using the Cost Comparison Tables

There are many separate sets of comparisons, one for each major group facing different premiums, coverage, or likely medical costs. We generally provide comparisons for self-only, self plus one, and families of sizes two through five. However, we limit certain tables to conserve space and because some situations are very uncommon: for older employees, annuitants, part-time employees, and several small enrollment groups we present only self-only, self plus one, and families of two or three rather than larger family sizes. In all family comparisons, the rankings would not change substantially with an additional child. Comparisons for employees and annuitants include:

Be Wary of Misleading Catastrophic Cost Protection Claims in Plan Summaries

Some plans exclude deductibles, physician copayments, or drug costs in the figure they claim for catastrophic limits. This can understate your risk by thousands of dollars.

- Employees who pay **GS premiums** (e.g., General Schedule, special rate, Congressional, and Foreign Service employees).
- Employees who pay lower premiums, including **postal and FDIC employees**. We present rates for postal Category 1 employees (mainly bargaining unit union members) in our print Guide and online, and Category 2 online (Category 2 premiums are now the same as for GS employees).
- **Older employees,** whose costs are much higher on average.
- For **part-time employees**, we cover half-time workers and employees who work four days out of five. In almost all agencies, these employees pay part of the "employer share" as well as the regular employee share.
- Former spouses, children turning age 26 who are not covered by a parental FEHB plan, and other **persons who pay full premiums** (both employer and employee share). These persons are not eligible for tax sheltering, and we do not reduce premiums from the nominal rate.
- **Annuitants without Medicare**. Again, there are no tax savings in premium rates.

- **Annuitants with Medicare Parts A and B**. These tables include not only the FEHB plan premium, but also the Part B Medicare premium. No tax savings are available. We cover situations where enrollees pay more, often far more, than the regular Part B premium.
- Finally, we present tables for **annuitants who have only Part A of Medicare**, the hospital benefit. You can compare these with the preceding ratings to see how much you gain, or in many cases lose, by paying the Part B premium. Of course, there are no tax savings.

There are many comparisons, but **only one cost comparison table applies to your current situation**. Of course, your situation may change if your family changes, if you retire, and if you change your Medicare decisions—and you can compare tables to see those differences. Each cost comparison table presents several columns of cost data. Each column except the one for published premium assumes a different level and mix of medical bills, described in the heading. These columns show what your likely costs will be under each plan, including both premium costs and out-of-pocket costs not paid by the plan.

By looking at the different columns in a table, you can find how you will come out under each plan. The columns display:

The Extra Cost When a PPO Member Uses a Non-PPO Doctor

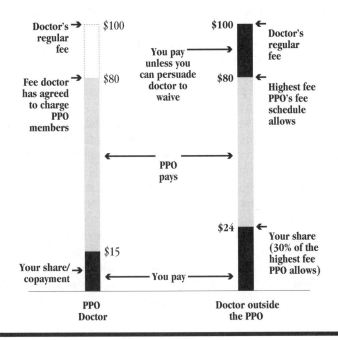

- The "Published premium" (including when applicable the Medicare Part B premium) that you will pay biweekly or monthly, expressed as an annual cost;
- The actual premium you will pay when you incur "No costs" for health care. This takes into account savings from premium conversion for employees, offsetting savings from money the plan puts in your Health Savings Account or Health Reimbursement Arrangement, and any dues;
- Your premium and out of pocket costs at "Low costs" usage with bills of about $1,000 (self-only) or $3,000 (families);
- Costs for "Average" usage with medical and dental bills averaged over a wide range of expense taking into account the statistical likelihood of costs at each level;
- Costs for "High" usage with bills of about $30,000; and
- The yearly "Limit to you" showing the maximum you will ever be expected to pay for medical (but not dental) bills, also reflecting both premium and out of pocket costs.

We present two different premium columns to reduce confusion over two issues. First, many employees do not understand Premium Conversion. For almost all employees, this tax preference creates about a one-third saving in premium cost. Your average tax rate is much lower, but for those "marginal" income dollars most employees pay about 33 percent, including Federal income tax, State income tax, and the employee share of Social Security and Medicare taxes. Annuitants are not eligible for Premium Conversion.

Second, many persons find High Deductible plans hard to understand. We believe that the best way to analyze them is to consider the Health Savings Account (HSA) as the equivalent of a reduction in premium. If you don't spend that account at the end of the year you will have a bank balance in that amount. It is therefore possible for you to have "free" health insurance in some High Deductible or Consumer-Driven plans. If your published premium is about $2,100 you actually pay only about $1,400 after Premium Conversion. However, the plan provides you with a savings account that is in your name. If that account is $1,500 you actually come out ahead if you have no medical expenses. In fact, since these plans all provide a free physical exam and routine vaccinations, you come out ahead this much even after your preventive care. The HSA is your money and can earn interest and grow like any other savings account (in this case, grow tax-free). You can save the HSA as an investment, or you can use it to pay your bills.

If you join a Consumer-Driven plan with a "personal account" or Health Reimbursement Arrangement (HRA), the account belongs to the plan, and must be spent rather than saved if you incur expense, but still has the effect of reducing your "up front and for sure" premium cost. In cases like these where you come out money ahead, we show this in our tables with a negative number in the "Net Premium" column. All HDHP and CDHP plans offer similar net savings, or greatly reduced premiums paid. Even retirees get an offset from these savings accounts if they join one of these plans.

Therefore, the "No costs" column includes your yearly premium adjusted, as pertinent, for Premium Conversion, HSA or HRA account, and any membership dues. These will be your only out-of-pocket costs if you have no medical bills.

We also indicate the percentage chance that you and your family will have bills that are "Low" or "High"—for instance, how likely you are to have bills of about $3,000 or less, or $30,000 or more.

We rank the plans in order of average cost to emphasize the importance of each plan's treatment of "average" expenses for a family of a particular size and type. Most families fall far below the average in most years, but very expensive cases pull the average up. Because almost all plans reimburse 80 percent or more of average or high expenses, the premium counts for most of this average cost, regardless of medical expenses. Very importantly, the "average" includes costs for the entirely unexpected medical problems that can affect any family, such as a heart attack, automobile accident, or onset of an expensive disease. Moreover, the "High costs" and "Limit to you" columns portray directly the insurance value of these plans. You should not select a plan based primarily on the relatively low costs that most of us can predict.

You begin by making profile choices to find the one table that relates to families of your age, premium category, and size. Assuming that you don't know something to the contrary, you should expect average expenses in the coming year. The plans that are likely to cost families the least have the lowest dollar figures in this column. **Our cost comparisons assume that you use preferred, network providers exclusively**. You should select a plan primarily based on using network providers, and plan to use non-network providers only in rare instances. You can see the financial consequences of using non-network providers in the online *Guide*, and in our table on "Coverages and Copays."

But do not choose the highest-ranked plan until you consider whether there is some reason the average column does not apply to you or your family.

Bargain with Out of Network Providers

Most plans have very low payments for non-preferred providers. You MUST negotiate with these doctors before any expensive procedure in order to protect yourself. One good tactic is to ask for either their "preferred" or Medicare rate.

First, **consider your particular health situation**. Medical problems are mostly a matter of good or bad luck. However, some people are much more likely than others to have high expenses. In these cases, you should compare plans using the "High cost" or "Limit to you" column. A hip replacement is a large expense. A diabetic may have several expensive ailments. A history of cancer or heart disease worsens your odds. You can use the $30,000 ("High") cost comparisons if you have information that suggests you are much likely to face much higher health expenses than others of your age and family size.

Second, **consider your attitude about risk**. If you are willing to spend a few hundred dollars extra to be sure you will not have heavy out-of-pocket expenses, you may want to pick one of the plans that is lowest cost for a person with high medical bills. However, **all plans have such good coverage that you are well protected from most catastrophic expenses**. Most have a dollar limit on the annual hospital, doctor, and prescription drug expenses you must pay—as noted under the heading "Limit to you." Even where there is a gap, the effect of the generous benefit structure is to create a *de facto* limit.

How We Adjust Catastrophic Limits to Make Them Comparable Across Plans		
Illustrative Plans	Brand X HDHP	Brand Y High Option Plan
Limit stated in plan's summary of benefits	$5,000	$3,000
Excluded amounts:		
Deductibles	None	None
Hospital copays*	None	$900
Prescription copays*	None	$1,000
Specialty drug limit	None	None
Physician copays*	None	$1,500
Subtotal	$5,000	$6,400
Premium	$1,000	$1,600
Health Savings Acct.	−$1,000	None
Total "limit to you"	$5,000	$8,000

* We assume three hospital stays at $300, 50 prescriptions at $20, and 50 physician visits at $30; typical values in many plans.

In your cost table you will notice that differences among closely ranked plans are often very small. Differences of $100 or less are not important. A different mix of bills from those we use to compare plans could overcome these. Differences of several hundred dollars, however, reflect significant variations in how expensively the plans handle most cases as well as the "for sure" premium expense.

Notice that most of the higher-ranked plans will save you money in every year—whether your expenses are high or low—compared to the plans ranked lower. Again, this is because you have to pay the premium whether your medical expenses are high or low.

Using Preferred Providers
We rate plan costs based on the assumption that you will always or almost always want to use preferred providers, also known as "staying in the network". Your cost is always lower, usually far lower, when you do. However, all but one of the national PPO plans and all CDHP and HDHP plans allow you to obtain care out of network. This can sometimes be a valuable flexibility. But you face not only a higher copayment, but also an additional risk. The plans set limits on the fee they will recognize. For example, the plan may charge a flat amount of $20 to PPO users. For doctors outside the PPO, the plan may pay 70 percent of the cost up to $80 for a particular procedure, but if the physician charges $100 you will pay $30 plus the extra $20, or half the total bill compared to only $20 if you use the preferred provider. You can sometimes negotiate fees down, and we urge this

strategy for non-preferred providers. This problem goes away if you have Medicare Parts A and B, since most of the national plans waive most doctor and hospital cost-sharing whether you obtain care in or out of the network. Even in HMOs that don't waive these costs, you can use Medicare to go out of network. Therefore, **for retirees who participate in Medicare Parts A and B preferred provider restrictions largely disappear when enrolled in any plan.** You can go to any hospital and almost any doctor without penalty. Moreover, persons over age 65 who are in any plan are by law guaranteed a Medicare rate and can use all doctors who have not opted out of Medicare with substantial protection, even if cost sharing is not eliminated.

Catastrophic Coverage

The most important reason for buying health insurance is to protect you against financial catastrophe. You may, therefore, wish to approach plan selection by comparing plans on the basis of potential financial risk, rather than average cost. To facilitate this, our cost comparisons include a "Limit to you" column. Our "Limit" calculation includes both the annual premium and the claimed guarantee provided by each plan for hospital, medical, and prescription drug expenses. We combine these two types of expenses because you are sure to incur premium costs and there is little point in picking a plan with $1,000 less in claimed limit if its premium is $2,000 higher. However, no plan includes dental expenses in its guarantee. The "Limits" column, therefore, cannot include these costs. Our figures use a 33 percent premium reduction for tax savings for employees under Premium Conversion (but not for retirees or those paying full premiums, who are ineligible). We also take account of the ability of enrollees in High Deductible plans to reduce costs by using their HSA or HRA accounts. We have not, however, included estimates for additional tax savings from funding high expenses through additional contributions to HSA accounts (see Cost and Taxes). Therefore, these are conservative estimates for High Deductible plans.

Because some plans present catastrophic limits in confusing ways, we attempt to make our limit calculations comparable among plans. For example, we take account of deductibles if these are not included in the claimed limit. A few plans put prescription drug payments under separate limits and we adjust for this difference. Plans calculate limits differently and the dollar numbers published in a plan's "Summary of Benefits" do not necessarily reflect the loopholes and exclusions listed under "Your cost for covered services"). The adjustments we make are necessary to make comparisons that are not inaccurate "apples to oranges." For plans that do not include certain hospital, doctor, or drug copayments in the limit we have assumed three hospital stays and 50 (single) or 100 (family) prescriptions or doctor visits, and presented the limit on this basis.

Although we included dental costs in most columns, we had to leave dental costs out of the "Limits" column because no plan includes dental costs in its guarantee. Most HMOs have a limit and cover nearly all hospital, medical, and prescription drug expenses. To compare HMOs, our estimates are based on the same number of hospital stays, doctor visits, and prescriptions as for national plans to make the figures comparable. However, the figures we present are not necessarily an actual guarantee by the plan.

The cost tables can be used to find those plans with the lowest limits. From this group, you can select plans with lower average costs. Or you might wish to select one of the plans with the best catastrophic coverage and accept somewhat higher out-of-pocket costs as the price of that guarantee.

If You Have Other Insurance

You cannot use our cost rankings directly if you have health insurance coverage from another source. The best FEHB plan for you depends on the cost and benefit structure of the other plan, though your best choice will almost always be a low premium plan to minimize unnecessary premium payments. But do not assume that you should not enroll in an FEHB plan just because you have other coverage.

If your spouse has a low-cost health plan through a private employer, or you have a health plan from prior employment, check to be sure that it covers you and your children, and has a benefit package as good as the Federal plans. Even if your spouse's plan is every bit as good as any of the Federal plans, consider the cost of this coverage compared to some of the lower-premium Federal plans. Remember that you must be covered under an FEHB plan continuously for the five years preceding retirement to continue enrollment after retirement (there are some very rare exceptions, such as certain agency downsizing situations). You don't have to be in the same plan in each year, but you must be covered continuously by some FEHB plan or, in the special case of former military, TRICARE.

Most importantly, if you should die while you are not enrolled in an FEHB family plan, your spouse will lose eligibility for the program. Since most employers do not continue coverage past retirement, or cannot be counted on to do so, your only guarantee that your spouse can keep this entitlement is to be continuously enrolled. There is an excellent strategy for doing so at minimum cost. All of the plans showing a very low or negative number in the "No Costs" column are Consumer-Driven or High Deductible plans that give you a savings account as large or larger than the premium. With double coverage, you will probably not ever reach the high deductible and will realize this saving in most circumstances. In other words, these plans really are almost "free" if they supplement other coverage from your spouse.

Chapter 3

Cost Comparisons and Advice for Employees and Former Employees

As explained in Chapter 2 on "Comparing Plan Costs," we rate and compare health plans based on their likely cost to you, taking into account your pay system, employment or retirement status, family size, age, health status, location, and other factors. A key element of our ratings are estimates of likely out-of-pocket costs under each plan, based on actuarial estimates of the size and likelihood of low, average, and high spending for families of different sizes and ages.

Online *Guide* users see a summary cost comparison table for their group, and then have the option to look at tables providing more detailed cost comparisons. Readers of the printed *Guide* see both summary and detailed cost comparison information for their group in one set of tables for all national plans and local plans available in the DC area, and summary cost comparison information on all local plans in a table covering "Cost and Special Features of All Plans" in all states at the end of *Guide*.

All of these comparisons take into account not only premiums and potential health care costs, but also plan features such as Health Savings Accounts and Wellness benefits that involve cash rewards. We also include dental benefits built into some health plans and, both online and in our separate Chapter on "Dental, Vision, and Hearing," compare the costs and benefits of standalone dental plans. Online, we also allow for comparisons for those using Flexible Spending Accounts (FSAs). In summary, we provide a comprehensive set of financial comparisons that allow users to make "apple to apple" comparisons of costs for both premiums and likely health care expenses under each plan and across all plans.

All of our calculations should be considered approximations that will be broadly accurate in the great majority of situations but that cannot provide precise predictions that cover every possible situation. What our calculations also do, therefore, is take into account the risks of ruinously high health care costs from an unexpected illness or accident, and compare the maximum out-of-pocket and premium costs under each plan.

28

Using the Cost Comparison Tables for Employees and Former Employees

There are many separate sets of comparisons, one for each major group facing different premiums, coverage, or likely medical costs. We generally provide comparisons for self-only, self plus one, and families of sizes two through five. However, in the print version of the *Guide* we limit certain tables to conserve space and because some situations are very uncommon: for older employees, annuitants, part-time employees, and several small enrollment groups we present only self-only, self plus one, and families of two or three rather than larger family sizes. In all family comparisons the rankings would not change substantially with an additional child. Comparisons for employees include:

- Employees who pay **GS premiums** (e.g., General Schedule, special rate, Congressional, and Foreign Service employees).
- Employees who pay lower premiums, including **postal, FDIC, and SEC employees**. We present plan comparisons for postal Category 1 and 2 employees (bargaining unit union members) in our print Guide as well as online (most postal management employees have the same premiums as GS employees and these rates are also shown both in print and online). FDIC and SEC results are shown only online.
- **Older employees,** whose costs are much higher on average.
- For **part-time employees**, we cover half-time workers and employees who work four days out of five. In almost all agencies, these employees pay part of the "employer share" as well as the regular employee share.
- Former spouses, children turning age 26 who are not covered by a parental FEHBP plan, and other **persons who pay full premiums** (both employer and employee share). These persons are not eligible for tax sheltering, and we do not reduce premiums from the nominal rate.

There are many comparisons, but **only one cost comparison table applies to your current situation**. Of course, your situation may change if your family changes, or if you retire—and you can compare tables to see those differences. Each plan cost comparison table presents several columns of cost data. Each column except the one for published premium assumes a different level and mix of medical bills, described in the heading. These columns show what your likely costs will be under each plan, including both premium costs and out-of-pocket costs not paid by the plan.

Avoid a Big Risk

Many people who are covered by their spouse's insurance drop FEHBP. This saves premium costs. However, if you are not enrolled and die suddenly, your spouse cannot ever enroll again. Your best option is to carry a family policy and drop the spousal insurance.

Is Self Plus One for You?

In most cases the self plus one premium is lower than the family premium by one or two hundred dollars a year. So check your plan to be sure it gives you this saving and, while you are at it, check our ratings to see if you can't save even more by changing plans.

By looking at the different columns in a table, you can find how you will come out under each plan if your expenses range from none to the maximum you could pay in a year. The details are explained in Chapter 2 on "Comparing Plan Costs." Very importantly, the columns other than "Published premium" all include the tax savings you get from Premium Conversion for employees. These columns also credit you with the savings you gain from a Health Savings Account (HSA) or personal care account or Health Reimbursement Arrangement (HRA) in plans that give you these benefits. HSAs and HRAs are the equivalent of a reduction in premium. If you don't spend that account at the end of the year you will have a bank balance in that amount that carries over to the next year. Therefore, the "No costs" column includes your yearly premium adjusted, as pertinent, for Premium Conversion, HSA or personal care account or HRA, and any membership dues. These will be your only out-of-pocket costs if you have no medical bills. We rank the plans in order of average cost to emphasize the importance of each plan's treatment of "average" expenses for a family of a particular size and type.

You begin by making profile choices to find the table that relates to families of your age, premium category, and size. Assuming that you don't know something to the contrary, you should expect average expenses in the coming year. The plans that are likely to cost families the least have the lowest dollar figures in this column. But do not choose the highest-ranked plan until you consider whether there is some reason the average column does not apply to you or your family.

In your cost table you will notice that differences among closely ranked plans are often very small. Differences of $100 or less are not important. A different mix of bills from those we use to compare plans could overcome these. Differences of several hundred dollars or more, however, reflect significant variations in how expensively the plans handle most cases.

Notice that most of the higher-ranked plans will save you money in every situation—whether your expenses are high or low—compared to the plans ranked lower. You can also see that most but not all HMO, CDHP, and HDHP plans will save you hundreds of dollars compared to most national PPO plans.

Savings for Couples Using Self Only Enrollments

For a husband and wife who are **both** employed by the Federal Government and who have no dependent children, it is possible to save on premium costs by enrolling separately as self only rather than together as a self plus one. The

30

premiums for two self only enrollments are usually less than the self plus one premium. This option can be particularly valuable in cases where each spouse prefers a different plan, perhaps because no one plan covers both family physicians in its network.

Be cautious, however, because each person will have to meet a separate catastrophic limit rather than the single limit that applies to self plus one. Most plans do not increase your risk because they include individual limits of about half the amount of the overall self plus one or family limit. Moreover, while you are still technically subject to meeting two catastrophic limits if you both enroll self-only, the fee structure of most HMOs makes it almost impossible to reach those limits. For these reasons you are usually safe with two self only enrollments. But do check the plan brochure's catastrophic limits carefully before making this decision.

Savings for Couples or Single Parents with One Child Under Self Plus One

Married couples with no children to cover, and single parents with one child to cover, can enroll as self plus one rather than as a family and, depending on the plan chosen, often save two or three hundred dollars a year in premium costs. Since the benefits of the plan are the same regardless of which enrollment type is chosen, this is a clear saving. You should use our comparison table for self plus one with adults of your age to make your initial plan comparison. **But before you make a final decision, check to make sure the premium for a family enrollment isn't lower for the plan you have chosen. And while you are at it, check our ratings to see other plans that offer even larger savings.**

If You or Your Spouse Has Other Employer Insurance

If your spouse has a low-cost health plan through a private employer, or you have a health plan from prior employment, check to be sure that it covers you and your children, and has a benefit package as good as the Federal plans. Even if your spouse's plan is every bit as good as any of the Federal plans, consider the cost of this coverage compared to some of the lower-premium Federal plans. Remember that you must be covered under the FEHBP continuously for the five years preceding retirement to be eligible for enrollment after retirement (there are some very rare exceptions, such as certain agency downsizing situations). You don't have to be in the same plan in each year, but you must be covered continuously by some FEHBP plan or, in the special case of military dependents, TRICARE.

If you should die while you are not enrolled in the FEHBP in a family plan, your spouse will lose eligibility for the program. Since most other employers do not continue coverage past retirement, or cannot be counted on to do so, your only guarantee that your spouse can keep this entitlement is to be continuously enrolled. There is an excellent strategy for doing so at minimum cost. All of the plans showing a very low or negative number in the "No Costs" column are Consumer-Driven or High

(Text continues on page 71)

Persons Under 55: GS Premiums				**Self Only**				
		Plan type	Published premium	Estimated yearly out-of-pocket costs, including premium and typical hospital, medical, drug, and dental bills near:				
Plan code	Plan name			No costs*	Low use: $1,000 or less	Average cost	High use: $30,000 or more	Limit to you
DC Area Plans When You Use Preferred Providers								
E34	Kaiser-Std	HMO	1510	1010	1080	1630	4510	4510
E31	Kaiser-Hi	HMO	1980	1320	1340	1720	3570	3570
T71	Kaiser-Basic	HMO	1380	920	1140	1820	4920	4920
B61	CareFirst HDHP	HDHP	1830	770	1280	1870	4630	5220
V41	UnitedHealthcare HDHP	HDHP	1700	380	980	1940	5430	5430
L91	UnitedHealthcare Choice Plus	PPO-FEE	1390	930	1460	2030	3930	3930
JN4	Aetna Open Access Basic	HMO	1990	1330	1430	2120	5870	6330
LR1	UnitedHealthcare Choice	HMO	1820	1220	1410	2140	6220	6220
2G4	CareFirst-Std POS	HMO-POS	2360	1580	2020	2300	4080	4080
F54	Aetna Value Plan	PPO-FEE	1750	1170	1420	2320	6470	6470
JP1	MD-IPA	HMO	2650	1770	1910	2580	6370	6770
F51	Aetna HealthFund CDHP	CDHP	3710	1430	2030	2750	6780	6780
2G1	CareFirst-Hi	HMO	4300	2870	3410	3770	5370	5370
JN1	Aetna Open Access-Hi	HMO	7280	4850	4920	5470	8340	8850
National Plans When You Use Preferred Providers								
324	NALC CDHP	CDHP	1390	-240	120	1380	7560	7560
341	GEHA HDHP	HDHP	1500	250	750	1590	5060	6000
474	APWU CDHP	CDHP	1660	-60	590	1760	6440	6440
N61	Aetna Direct CDHP	CDHP	1580	160	860	1840	6060	6060
224	Aetna HealthFund HDHP	HDHP	1820	470	990	1850	5220	5220
401	Foreign Service†	PPO-FEE	1720	1150	1430	1980	4920	6150
481	MHBP HDHP	HDHP	1700	280	1030	2090	6040	7180
314	GEHA-Std	PPO-FEE	1430	950	1180	2100	6950	6950
111	Blue Cross Basic	PPO	1920	1280	1400	2190	6490	6780
321	NALC-Hi	PPO-FEE	2050	1400	1620	2220	5370	8000
KM1	NALC Value Plan	PPO-FEE	1140	700	1070	2260	7400	7400
454	MHBP-Std	PPO-FEE	1750	1210	1490	2320	7160	7210
421	Compass Rose†	PPO-FEE	2390	1600	1910	2470	5540	7070
381	Rural Carrier†	PPO-FEE	2270	1510	2020	2540	5510	5510
414	MHBP Value Plan	PPO-FEE	1490	1040	1510	2610	7640	7640
471	APWU-Hi	PPO-FEE	2420	1650	2100	2740	7050	7150
311	GEHA-Hi	PPO-FEE	2690	1800	2020	2790	7300	7300
444	SAMBA-Std	PPO-FEE	2540	1690	2040	3030	8690	8690
104	Blue Cross-Std	PPO-FEE	2940	1960	2390	3110	6960	6960
441	SAMBA-Hi	PPO-FEE	4990	3330	3650	4520	9330	9330

* These are the premiums after tax savings, offset by savings accounts for plans that offer them. If you have no or low health-care costs with these plans, it can result in actual saving to you, which we indicate with a negative number.

Persons Under 55: GS Premiums		Self Plus One						
				Estimated yearly out-of-pocket costs, including premium and typical hospital, medical, drug, and dental bills near:				
Plan code	Plan name	Plan type	Published premium	No costs*	Low use: $3,000 or less	Average cost	High use: $30,000 or more	Limit to you
DC Area Plans When You Use Preferred Providers								
E36	Kaiser-Std	HMO	3480	2320	2720	3470	6160	9320
T73	Kaiser-Basic	HMO	3020	2010	2790	3700	7440	10010
B63	CareFirst HDHP	HDHP	3660	1540	3260	3730	6480	8940
L93	UnitedHealthcare Choice Plus	PPO-FEE	2710	1810	3320	4030	7680	7810
2G6	CareFirst-Std POS	HMO-POS	4160	2780	3720	4050	5750	7780
V43	UnitedHealthcare HDHP	HDHP	3660	940	3140	4190	9230	9890
JN6	Aetna Open Access Basic	HMO	4180	2790	3440	4200	7240	9640
JP3	MD-IPA	HMO	4210	2810	3500	4250	7330	12810
LR3	UnitedHealthcare Choice	HMO	3920	2620	3440	4280	7770	12620
E33	Kaiser-Hi	HMO	5460	3640	3920	4380	6070	8140
F56	Aetna Value Plan	PPO-FEE	3930	2620	3470	4730	9770	10070
F53	Aetna HealthFund CDHP	CDHP	9070	3950	6080	6460	9890	13500
2G3	CareFirst-Hi	HMO	7760	5170	6440	6870	9240	10170
JN3	Aetna Open Access-Hi	HMO	16700	11140	11670	12270	14570	17990
National Plans When You Use Preferred Providers								
326	NALC CDHP	CDHP	3010	-350	1340	2670	7740	15250
343	GEHA HDHP	HDHP	3230	660	2540	3280	6370	12160
476	APWU CDHP	CDHP	3660	80	2380	3600	8400	13080
N63	Aetna Direct CDHP	CDHP	3470	520	2920	3730	8360	9170
226	Aetna HealthFund HDHP	HDHP	3940	1130	3180	3900	7410	9480
316	GEHA-Std	PPO-FEE	3070	2050	2810	4040	8700	9550
483	MHBP HDHP	HDHP	3770	760	3270	4280	8290	14560
383	Rural Carrier†	PPO-FEE	3910	2600	3770	4300	7100	7100
403	Foreign Service†	PPO-FEE	4210	2810	3890	4350	6820	9810
456	MHBP-Std	PPO-FEE	4020	2720	3840	4520	7660	14720
KM3	NALC Value Plan	PPO-FEE	2470	1490	3180	4540	9580	14890
113	Blue Cross Basic	PPO	4470	2980	3690	4570	8060	13980
323	NALC-Hi	PPO-FEE	4860	3280	4010	4690	7420	12280
473	APWU-Hi	PPO-FEE	4830	3260	4460	5100	8150	12260
416	MHBP Value Plan	PPO-FEE	3530	2400	4400	5310	10150	15600
423	Compass Rose†	PPO-FEE	5620	3750	4920	5340	7940	9220
313	GEHA-Hi	PPO-FEE	6270	4180	4890	5820	9250	11180
446	SAMBA-Std	PPO-FEE	5930	3960	5100	6190	10590	17960
106	Blue Cross-Std	PPO-FEE	6700	4470	5780	6530	9990	14470
443	SAMBA-Hi	PPO-FEE	11330	7560	8620	9540	13320	19560

† Plan is open only to specific groups.

Family of Two

Plan code	Plan name	Plan type	Published premium	Estimated yearly out-of-pocket costs, including premium and typical hospital, medical, drug, and dental bills near:				
				No costs*	Low use: $3,000 or less	Average cost	High use: $30,000 or more	Limit to you
DC Area Plans When You Use Preferred Providers								
E35	Kaiser-Std	HMO	3480	2320	2720	3470	6160	9320
E32	Kaiser-Hi	HMO	4660	3110	3390	3850	5540	7610
T72	Kaiser-Basic	HMO	3310	2210	2990	3900	7640	10210
B62	CareFirst HDHP	HDHP	4350	2000	3720	4190	6940	9400
JN5	Aetna Open Access Basic	HMO	4640	3100	3750	4510	7550	9950
V42	UnitedHealthcare HDHP	HDHP	4250	1340	3540	4590	9630	10290
F55	Aetna Value Plan	PPO-FEE	4000	2670	3520	4780	9820	10120
LR2	UnitedHealthcare Choice	HMO	4680	3120	3940	4780	8270	13120
L92	UnitedHealthcare Choice Plus	PPO-FEE	3900	2600	4110	4820	8470	8600
2G5	CareFirst-Std POS	HMO-POS	6220	4150	5090	5420	7120	9150
F52	Aetna HealthFund CDHP	CDHP	8490	3560	5690	6070	9500	13110
JP2	MD-IPA	HMO	10590	7060	7750	8500	11580	17060
2G2	CareFirst-Hi	HMO	10820	7220	8490	8920	11290	12220
JN2	Aetna Open Access-Hi	HMO	16200	10800	11330	11930	14230	17650
National Plans When You Use Preferred Providers								
325	NALC CDHP	CDHP	3080	-310	1380	2710	7780	15290
342	GEHA HDHP	HDHP	3560	870	2750	3490	6580	12370
475	APWU CDHP	CDHP	3990	300	2600	3820	8620	13300
225	Aetna HealthFund HDHP	HDHP	4020	1180	3230	3950	7460	9530
N62	Aetna Direct CDHP	CDHP	3990	860	3260	4070	8700	9510
315	GEHA-Std	PPO-FEE	3380	2250	3010	4240	8900	9750
382	Rural Carrier†	PPO-FEE	3980	2660	3830	4360	7160	7160
402	Foreign Service†	PPO-FEE	4250	2830	3910	4370	6840	9830
482	MHBP HDHP	HDHP	3960	880	3390	4400	8410	14680
322	NALC-Hi	PPO-FEE	4500	3030	3760	4440	7170	12030
455	MHBP-Std	PPO-FEE	4060	2750	3870	4550	7690	14750
KM2	NALC Value Plan	PPO-FEE	2530	1520	3210	4570	9610	14920
112	Blue Cross Basic	PPO	4710	3140	3850	4730	8220	14140
415	MHBP Value Plan	PPO-FEE	3600	2450	4450	5360	10200	15650
422	Compass Rose†	PPO-FEE	6490	4330	5500	5920	8520	9800
445	SAMBA-Std	PPO-FEE	5980	3990	5130	6220	10620	17990
472	APWU-Hi	PPO-FEE	6550	4400	5600	6240	9290	13400
312	GEHA-Hi	PPO-FEE	7000	4670	5380	6310	9740	11670
105	Blue Cross-Std	PPO-FEE	7070	4720	6030	6780	10240	14720
442	SAMBA-Hi	PPO-FEE	12720	8490	9550	10470	14250	20490

* These are the premiums after tax savings, offset by savings accounts for plans that offer them. If you have no or low health-care costs with these plans, it can result in actual saving to you, which we indicate with a negative number.

Persons Under 55: GS Premiums				Family of Three				
				Estimated yearly out-of-pocket costs, including premium and typical hospital, medical, drug, and dental bills near:				
		Plan type	Published premium	No costs*	Low use: $3,000 or less	Average cost	High use: $30,000 or more	Limit to you
Plan code	Plan name							
DC Area Plans When You Use Preferred Providers								
E35	Kaiser-Std	HMO	3480	2320	2720	3650	6160	9320
E32	Kaiser-Hi	HMO	4660	3110	3390	3970	5540	7610
T72	Kaiser-Basic	HMO	3310	2210	2990	4160	7640	10210
B62	CareFirst HDHP	HDHP	4350	2000	3720	4440	6940	9400
JN5	Aetna Open Access Basic	HMO	4640	3100	3750	4730	7550	9950
V42	UnitedHealthcare HDHP	HDHP	4250	1340	3540	4990	9630	10290
LR2	UnitedHealthcare Choice	HMO	4680	3120	3940	5020	8270	13120
L92	UnitedHealthcare Choice Plus	PPO-FEE	3900	2600	4110	5090	8470	8600
F55	Aetna Value Plan	PPO-FEE	4000	2670	3520	5100	9820	10120
2G5	CareFirst-Std POS	HMO-POS	6220	4150	5090	5550	7120	9150
F52	Aetna HealthFund CDHP	CDHP	8490	3560	5690	6360	9500	13110
JP2	MD-IPA	HMO	10590	7060	7750	8720	11580	17060
2G2	CareFirst-Hi	HMO	10820	7220	8490	9110	11290	12220
JN2	Aetna Open Access-Hi	HMO	16200	10800	11330	12100	14230	17650
National Plans When You Use Preferred Providers								
325	NALC CDHP	CDHP	3080	-310	1380	3140	7780	15290
342	GEHA HDHP	HDHP	3560	870	2750	3800	6580	12370
475	APWU CDHP	CDHP	3990	300	2600	4260	8620	13300
225	Aetna HealthFund HDHP	HDHP	4020	1180	3230	4280	7460	9530
N62	Aetna Direct CDHP	CDHP	3990	860	3260	4440	8700	9510
315	GEHA-Std	PPO-FEE	3380	2250	3010	4530	8900	9750
382	Rural Carrier[†]	PPO-FEE	3980	2660	3830	4550	7160	7160
402	Foreign Service[†]	PPO-FEE	4250	2830	3910	4570	6840	9830
322	NALC-Hi	PPO-FEE	4500	3030	3760	4640	7170	12030
455	MHBP-Std	PPO-FEE	4060	2750	3870	4800	7690	14750
482	MHBP HDHP	HDHP	3960	880	3390	4800	8410	14680
112	Blue Cross Basic	PPO	4710	3140	3850	4980	8220	14140
KM2	NALC Value Plan	PPO-FEE	2530	1520	3210	4980	9610	14920
415	MHBP Value Plan	PPO-FEE	3600	2450	4450	5740	10200	15650
422	Compass Rose[†]	PPO-FEE	6490	4330	5500	6120	8520	9800
472	APWU-Hi	PPO-FEE	6550	4400	5600	6470	9290	13400
445	SAMBA-Std	PPO-FEE	5980	3990	5130	6530	10620	17990
312	GEHA-Hi	PPO-FEE	7000	4670	5380	6550	9740	11670
105	Blue Cross-Std	PPO-FEE	7070	4720	6030	7050	10240	14720
442	SAMBA-Hi	PPO-FEE	12720	8490	9550	10750	14250	20490

† Plan is open only to specific groups.

Persons Under 55: GS Premiums		Family of Four						
		Plan type	Published premium	Estimated yearly out-of-pocket costs, including premium and typical hospital, medical, drug, and dental bills near:				
Plan code	Plan name			No costs*	Low use: $3,000 or less	Average cost	High use: $30,000 or more	Limit to you
DC Area Plans When You Use Preferred Providers								
E35	Kaiser-Std	HMO	3480	2320	2720	3840	6160	9320
E32	Kaiser-Hi	HMO	4660	3110	3390	4090	5540	7610
T72	Kaiser-Basic	HMO	3310	2210	2990	4400	7640	10210
B62	CareFirst HDHP	HDHP	4350	2000	3720	4660	6940	9400
JN5	Aetna Open Access Basic	HMO	4640	3100	3750	4930	7550	9950
LR2	UnitedHealthcare Choice	HMO	4680	3120	3940	5260	8270	13120
L92	UnitedHealthcare Choice Plus	PPO-FEE	3900	2600	4110	5330	8470	8600
V42	UnitedHealthcare HDHP	HDHP	4250	1340	3540	5370	9630	10290
F55	Aetna Value Plan	PPO-FEE	4000	2670	3520	5410	9820	10120
2G5	CareFirst-Std POS	HMO-POS	6220	4150	5090	5680	7120	9150
F52	Aetna HealthFund CDHP	CDHP	8490	3560	5690	6620	9500	13110
JP2	MD-IPA	HMO	10590	7060	7750	8920	11580	17060
2G2	CareFirst-Hi	HMO	10820	7220	8490	9280	11290	12220
JN2	Aetna Open Access-Hi	HMO	16200	10800	11330	12260	14230	17650
National Plans When You Use Preferred Providers								
325	NALC CDHP	CDHP	3080	-310	1380	3540	7780	15290
342	GEHA HDHP	HDHP	3560	870	2750	4080	6580	12370
225	Aetna HealthFund HDHP	HDHP	4020	1180	3230	4580	7460	9530
475	APWU CDHP	CDHP	3990	300	2600	4660	8620	13300
382	Rural Carrier†	PPO-FEE	3980	2660	3830	4730	7160	7160
402	Foreign Service†	PPO-FEE	4250	2830	3910	4750	6840	9830
N62	Aetna Direct CDHP	CDHP	3990	860	3260	4790	8700	9510
315	GEHA-Std	PPO-FEE	3380	2250	3010	4820	8900	9750
322	NALC-Hi	PPO-FEE	4500	3030	3760	4840	7170	12030
455	MHBP-Std	PPO-FEE	4060	2750	3870	5020	7690	14750
482	MHBP HDHP	HDHP	3960	880	3390	5150	8410	14680
112	Blue Cross Basic	PPO	4710	3140	3850	5220	8220	14140
KM2	NALC Value Plan	PPO-FEE	2530	1520	3210	5370	9610	14920
415	MHBP Value Plan	PPO-FEE	3600	2450	4450	6090	10200	15650
422	Compass Rose†	PPO-FEE	6490	4330	5500	6310	8520	9800
472	APWU-Hi	PPO-FEE	6550	4400	5600	6680	9290	13400
312	GEHA-Hi	PPO-FEE	7000	4670	5380	6780	9740	11670
445	SAMBA-Std	PPO-FEE	5980	3990	5130	6830	10620	17990
105	Blue Cross-Std	PPO-FEE	7070	4720	6030	7300	10240	14720
442	SAMBA-Hi	PPO-FEE	12720	8490	9550	11010	14250	20490

* These are the premiums after tax savings, offset by savings accounts for plans that offer them. If you have no or low health-care costs with these plans, it can result in actual saving to you, which we indicate with a negative number.

Persons Under 55: GS Premiums				Family of Five				
				Estimated yearly out-of-pocket costs, including premium and typical hospital, medical, drug, and dental bills near:				
Plan code	Plan name	Plan type	Published premium	No costs*	Low use: $3,000 or less	Average cost	High use: $30,000 or more	Limit to you
DC Area Plans When You Use Preferred Providers								
E35	Kaiser-Std	HMO	3480	2320	2720	4010	6160	9320
E32	Kaiser-Hi	HMO	4660	3110	3390	4200	5540	7610
T72	Kaiser-Basic	HMO	3310	2210	2990	4640	7640	10210
B62	CareFirst HDHP	HDHP	4350	2000	3720	4870	6940	9400
JN5	Aetna Open Access Basic	HMO	4640	3100	3750	5130	7550	9950
LR2	UnitedHealthcare Choice	HMO	4680	3120	3940	5480	8270	13120
L92	UnitedHealthcare Choice Plus	PPO-FEE	3900	2600	4110	5570	8470	8600
F55	Aetna Value Plan	PPO-FEE	4000	2670	3520	5710	9820	10120
V42	UnitedHealthcare HDHP	HDHP	4250	1340	3540	5710	9630	10290
2G5	CareFirst-Std POS	HMO-POS	6220	4150	5090	5790	7120	9150
F52	Aetna HealthFund CDHP	CDHP	8490	3560	5690	6860	9500	13110
JP2	MD-IPA	HMO	10590	7060	7750	9120	11580	17060
2G2	CareFirst-Hi	HMO	10820	7220	8490	9430	11290	12220
JN2	Aetna Open Access-Hi	HMO	16200	10800	11330	12420	14230	17650
National Plans When You Use Preferred Providers								
325	NALC CDHP	CDHP	3080	-310	1380	3920	7780	15290
342	GEHA HDHP	HDHP	3560	870	2750	4340	6580	12370
225	Aetna HealthFund HDHP	HDHP	4020	1180	3230	4860	7460	9530
382	Rural Carrier†	PPO-FEE	3980	2660	3830	4900	7160	7160
402	Foreign Service†	PPO-FEE	4250	2830	3910	4920	6840	9830
475	APWU CDHP	CDHP	3990	300	2600	5020	8620	13300
322	NALC-Hi	PPO-FEE	4500	3030	3760	5020	7170	12030
315	GEHA-Std	PPO-FEE	3380	2250	3010	5100	8900	9750
N62	Aetna Direct CDHP	CDHP	3990	860	3260	5110	8700	9510
455	MHBP-Std	PPO-FEE	4060	2750	3870	5240	7690	14750
112	Blue Cross Basic	PPO	4710	3140	3850	5450	8220	14140
482	MHBP HDHP	HDHP	3960	880	3390	5470	8410	14680
KM2	NALC Value Plan	PPO-FEE	2530	1520	3210	5740	9610	14920
415	MHBP Value Plan	PPO-FEE	3600	2450	4450	6420	10200	15650
422	Compass Rose†	PPO-FEE	6490	4330	5500	6480	8520	9800
472	APWU-Hi	PPO-FEE	6550	4400	5600	6880	9290	13400
312	GEHA-Hi	PPO-FEE	7000	4670	5380	7000	9740	11670
445	SAMBA-Std	PPO-FEE	5980	3990	5130	7120	10620	17990
105	Blue Cross-Std	PPO-FEE	7070	4720	6030	7540	10240	14720
442	SAMBA-Hi	PPO-FEE	12720	8490	9550	11260	14250	20490

† Plan is open only to specific groups.

Persons Under 55: Postal Premiums (Category 1)			Self Only				
		Plan type	Published premium	Estimated yearly out-of-pocket costs, including premium and typical hospital, medical, drug, and dental bills near:			
Plan code	Plan name			No costs*	Low use: $3,000 or less	Average cost	High use: $30,000 or more	Limit to you

Plan code	Plan name	Plan type	Published premium	No costs*	Low use: $3,000 or less	Average cost	High use: $30,000 or more	Limit to you
DC Area Plans When You Use Preferred Providers								
E34	Kaiser-Std	HMO	1380	920	990	1540	4420	4420
E31	Kaiser-Hi	HMO	1800	1200	1220	1600	3450	3450
T71	Kaiser-Basic	HMO	1260	840	1060	1740	4840	4840
B61	CareFirst HDHP	HDHP	1660	660	1170	1760	4520	5110
V41	UnitedHealthcare HDHP	HDHP	1550	280	880	1840	5330	5330
L91	UnitedHealthcare Choice Plus	PPO-FEE	1260	840	1370	1940	3840	3840
JN4	Aetna Open Access Basic	HMO	1810	1210	1310	2000	5750	6210
LR1	UnitedHealthcare Choice	HMO	1660	1110	1300	2030	6110	6110
2G4	CareFirst-Std POS	HMO-POS	2110	1410	1850	2130	3910	3910
F54	Aetna Value Plan	PPO-FEE	1590	1060	1310	2210	6360	6360
JP1	MD-IPA	HMO	2400	1600	1740	2410	6200	6600
F51	Aetna HealthFund CDHP	CDHP	3460	1260	1860	2580	6610	6610
2G1	CareFirst-Hi	HMO	4050	2700	3240	3600	5200	5200
JN1	Aetna Open Access-Hi	HMO	7030	4690	4760	5310	8180	8690
National Plans When You Use Preferred Providers								
324	NALC CDHP	CDHP	1270	-320	40	1300	7480	7480
341	GEHA HDHP	HDHP	1370	160	660	1500	4970	5910
474	APWU CDHP	CDHP	1510	-160	490	1660	6340	6340
N61	Aetna Direct CDHP	CDHP	1440	60	760	1740	5960	5960
224	Aetna HealthFund HDHP	HDHP	1660	360	880	1740	5110	5110
401	Foreign Service†	PPO-FEE	1560	1040	1320	1870	4810	6040
481	MHBP HDHP	HDHP	1550	180	930	1990	5940	7080
314	GEHA-Std	PPO-FEE	1300	870	1100	2020	6870	6870
111	Blue Cross Basic	PPO	1740	1160	1280	2070	6370	6660
321	NALC-Hi	PPO-FEE	1820	1250	1470	2070	5220	7850
KM1	NALC Value Plan	PPO-FEE	1040	630	1000	2190	7330	7330
454	MHBP-Std	PPO-FEE	1590	1100	1380	2210	7050	7100
381	Rural Carrier†	PPO-FEE	1800	1200	1710	2230	5200	5200
421	Compass Rose†	PPO-FEE	2150	1430	1740	2300	5370	6900
414	MHBP Value Plan	PPO-FEE	1360	950	1420	2520	7550	7550
471	APWU-Hi	PPO-FEE	2170	1480	1930	2570	6880	6980
311	GEHA-Hi	PPO-FEE	2440	1630	1850	2620	7130	7130
444	SAMBA-Std	PPO-FEE	2290	1530	1880	2870	8530	8530
104	Blue Cross-Std	PPO-FEE	2690	1800	2230	2950	6800	6800
441	SAMBA-Hi	PPO-FEE	4740	3160	3480	4350	9160	9160

* These are the premiums after tax savings, offset by savings accounts for plans that offer them. If you have no or low health-care costs with these plans, it can result in actual saving to you, which we indicate with a negative number.

Persons Under 55: Postal Premiums (Category 1)

Self Plus One

Plan code	Plan name	Plan type	Published premium	Estimated yearly out-of-pocket costs, including premium and typical hospital, medical, drug, and dental bills near:				
				No costs*	Low use: $3,000 or less	Average cost	High use: $30,000 or more	Limit to you
DC Area Plans When You Use Preferred Providers								
E36	Kaiser-Std	HMO	3170	2110	2510	3260	5950	9110
B63	CareFirst HDHP	HDHP	3330	1320	3040	3510	6260	8720
T73	Kaiser-Basic	HMO	2750	1830	2610	3520	7260	9830
2G6	CareFirst-Std POS	HMO-POS	3790	2530	3470	3800	5500	7530
L93	UnitedHealthcare Choice Plus	PPO-FEE	2470	1650	3160	3870	7520	7650
JN6	Aetna Open Access Basic	HMO	3800	2540	3190	3950	6990	9390
V43	UnitedHealthcare HDHP	HDHP	3330	720	2920	3970	9010	9670
JP3	MD-IPA	HMO	3830	2550	3240	3990	7070	12550
LR3	UnitedHealthcare Choice	HMO	3570	2380	3200	4040	7530	12380
E33	Kaiser-Hi	HMO	5110	3410	3690	4150	5840	7910
F56	Aetna Value Plan	PPO-FEE	3570	2380	3230	4490	9530	9830
F53	Aetna HealthFund CDHP	CDHP	8710	3710	5840	6220	9650	13260
2G3	CareFirst-Hi	HMO	7400	4940	6210	6640	9010	9940
JN3	Aetna Open Access-Hi	HMO	16340	10900	11430	12030	14330	17750
National Plans When You Use Preferred Providers								
326	NALC CDHP	CDHP	2740	-540	1150	2480	7550	15060
343	GEHA HDHP	HDHP	2940	460	2340	3080	6170	11960
476	APWU CDHP	CDHP	3330	-140	2160	3380	8180	12860
N63	Aetna Direct CDHP	CDHP	3160	310	2710	3520	8150	8960
226	Aetna HealthFund HDHP	HDHP	3590	890	2940	3660	7170	9240
316	GEHA-Std	PPO-FEE	2790	1860	2620	3850	8510	9360
483	MHBP HDHP	HDHP	3430	530	3040	4050	8060	14330
383	Rural Carrier†	PPO-FEE	3550	2370	3540	4070	6870	6870
403	Foreign Service†	PPO-FEE	3830	2550	3630	4090	6560	9550
456	MHBP-Std	PPO-FEE	3660	2480	3600	4280	7420	14480
113	Blue Cross Basic	PPO	4110	2740	3450	4330	7820	13740
KM3	NALC Value Plan	PPO-FEE	2250	1340	3030	4390	9430	14740
323	NALC-Hi	PPO-FEE	4510	3040	3770	4450	7180	12040
473	APWU-Hi	PPO-FEE	4480	3020	4220	4860	7910	12020
423	Compass Rose†	PPO-FEE	5260	3510	4680	5100	7700	8980
416	MHBP Value Plan	PPO-FEE	3220	2190	4190	5100	9940	15390
313	GEHA-Hi	PPO-FEE	5920	3950	4660	5590	9020	10950
446	SAMBA-Std	PPO-FEE	5570	3720	4860	5950	10350	17720
106	Blue Cross-Std	PPO-FEE	6350	4230	5540	6290	9750	14230
443	SAMBA-Hi	PPO-FEE	10970	7320	8380	9300	13080	19320

† Plan is open only to specific groups.

Persons Under 55: Postal Premiums (Category 1)		Family of Two					
				Estimated yearly out-of-pocket costs, including premium and typical hospital, medical, drug, and dental bills near:			
Plan code	Plan name	Plan type	Published premium	No costs*	Low use: $3,000 or less	Average cost	High use: $30,000 or more	Limit to you
DC Area Plans When You Use Preferred Providers								
E35	Kaiser-Std	HMO	3170	2110	2510	3260	5950	9110
E32	Kaiser-Hi	HMO	4150	2770	3050	3510	5200	7270
T72	Kaiser-Basic	HMO	3020	2010	2790	3700	7440	10010
B62	CareFirst HDHP	HDHP	3950	1740	3460	3930	6680	9140
JN5	Aetna Open Access Basic	HMO	4140	2760	3410	4170	7210	9610
V42	UnitedHealthcare HDHP	HDHP	3870	1080	3280	4330	9370	10030
LR2	UnitedHealthcare Choice	HMO	4150	2770	3590	4430	7920	12770
F55	Aetna Value Plan	PPO-FEE	3640	2430	3280	4540	9580	9880
L92	UnitedHealthcare Choice Plus	PPO-FEE	3550	2370	3880	4590	8240	8370
2G5	CareFirst-Std POS	HMO-POS	5650	3770	4710	5040	6740	8770
F52	Aetna HealthFund CDHP	CDHP	7930	3190	5320	5700	9130	12740
JP2	MD-IPA	HMO	10030	6690	7380	8130	11210	16690
2G2	CareFirst-Hi	HMO	10250	6840	8110	8540	10910	11840
JN2	Aetna Open Access-Hi	HMO	15630	10430	10960	11560	13860	17280
National Plans When You Use Preferred Providers								
325	NALC CDHP	CDHP	2800	-490	1200	2530	7600	15110
342	GEHA HDHP	HDHP	3240	660	2540	3280	6370	12160
475	APWU CDHP	CDHP	3630	60	2360	3580	8380	13060
225	Aetna HealthFund HDHP	HDHP	3660	940	2990	3710	7220	9290
N62	Aetna Direct CDHP	CDHP	3630	620	3020	3830	8460	9270
315	GEHA-Std	PPO-FEE	3070	2050	2810	4040	8700	9550
402	Foreign Service†	PPO-FEE	3870	2580	3660	4120	6590	9580
382	Rural Carrier†	PPO-FEE	3620	2420	3590	4120	6920	6920
482	MHBP HDHP	HDHP	3600	640	3150	4160	8170	14440
322	NALC-Hi	PPO-FEE	4090	2770	3500	4180	6910	11770
455	MHBP-Std	PPO-FEE	3700	2510	3630	4310	7450	14510
112	Blue Cross Basic	PPO	4160	2770	3480	4360	7850	13770
KM2	NALC Value Plan	PPO-FEE	2300	1370	3060	4420	9460	14770
415	MHBP Value Plan	PPO-FEE	3280	2230	4230	5140	9980	15430
422	Compass Rose†	PPO-FEE	5930	3950	5120	5540	8140	9420
445	SAMBA-Std	PPO-FEE	5420	3610	4750	5840	10240	17610
472	APWU-Hi	PPO-FEE	5980	4030	5230	5870	8920	13030
312	GEHA-Hi	PPO-FEE	6440	4290	5000	5930	9360	11290
105	Blue Cross-Std	PPO-FEE	6510	4340	5650	6400	9860	14340
442	SAMBA-Hi	PPO-FEE	12160	8110	9170	10090	13870	20110

* These are the premiums after tax savings, offset by savings accounts for plans that offer them. If you have no or low health-care costs with these plans, it can result in actual saving to you, which we indicate with a negative number.

Persons Under 55: Postal Premiums (Category 1)		Family of Three					
				Estimated yearly out-of-pocket costs, including premium and typical hospital, medical, drug, and dental bills near:			
Plan code	Plan name	Plan type	Published premium	No costs*	Low use: $3,000 or less	Average cost	High use: $30,000 or more	Limit to you

Plan code	Plan name	Plan type	Published premium	No costs*	Low use: $3,000 or less	Average cost	High use: $30,000 or more	Limit to you
DC Area Plans When You Use Preferred Providers								
E35	Kaiser-Std	HMO	3170	2110	2510	3440	5950	9110
E32	Kaiser-Hi	HMO	4150	2770	3050	3630	5200	7270
T72	Kaiser-Basic	HMO	3020	2010	2790	3960	7440	10010
B62	CareFirst HDHP	HDHP	3950	1740	3460	4180	6680	9140
JN5	Aetna Open Access Basic	HMO	4140	2760	3410	4390	7210	9610
LR2	UnitedHealthcare Choice	HMO	4150	2770	3590	4670	7920	12770
V42	UnitedHealthcare HDHP	HDHP	3870	1080	3280	4730	9370	10030
F55	Aetna Value Plan	PPO-FEE	3640	2430	3280	4860	9580	9880
L92	UnitedHealthcare Choice Plus	PPO-FEE	3550	2370	3880	4860	8240	8370
2G5	CareFirst-Std POS	HMO-POS	5650	3770	4710	5170	6740	8770
F52	Aetna HealthFund CDHP	CDHP	7930	3190	5320	5990	9130	12740
JP2	MD-IPA	HMO	10030	6690	7380	8350	11210	16690
2G2	CareFirst-Hi	HMO	10250	6840	8110	8730	10910	11840
JN2	Aetna Open Access-Hi	HMO	15630	10430	10960	11730	13860	17280
National Plans When You Use Preferred Providers								
325	NALC CDHP	CDHP	2800	-490	1200	2960	7600	15110
342	GEHA HDHP	HDHP	3240	660	2540	3590	6370	12160
475	APWU CDHP	CDHP	3630	60	2360	4020	8380	13060
225	Aetna HealthFund HDHP	HDHP	3660	940	2990	4040	7220	9290
N62	Aetna Direct CDHP	CDHP	3630	620	3020	4200	8460	9270
382	Rural Carrier†	PPO-FEE	3620	2420	3590	4310	6920	6920
402	Foreign Service†	PPO-FEE	3870	2580	3660	4320	6590	9580
315	GEHA-Std	PPO-FEE	3070	2050	2810	4330	8700	9550
322	NALC-Hi	PPO-FEE	4090	2770	3500	4380	6910	11770
455	MHBP-Std	PPO-FEE	3700	2510	3630	4560	7450	14510
482	MHBP HDHP	HDHP	3600	640	3150	4560	8170	14440
112	Blue Cross Basic	PPO	4160	2770	3480	4610	7850	13770
KM2	NALC Value Plan	PPO-FEE	2300	1370	3060	4830	9460	14770
415	MHBP Value Plan	PPO-FEE	3280	2230	4230	5520	9980	15430
422	Compass Rose†	PPO-FEE	5930	3950	5120	5740	8140	9420
472	APWU-Hi	PPO-FEE	5980	4030	5230	6100	8920	13030
445	SAMBA-Std	PPO-FEE	5420	3610	4750	6150	10240	17610
312	GEHA-Hi	PPO-FEE	6440	4290	5000	6170	9360	11290
105	Blue Cross-Std	PPO-FEE	6510	4340	5650	6670	9860	14340
442	SAMBA-Hi	PPO-FEE	12160	8110	9170	10370	13870	20110

† Plan is open only to specific groups.

Persons Under 55: Postal Premiums (Category 1)			Family of Four				
				Estimated yearly out-of-pocket costs, including premium and typical hospital, medical, drug, and dental bills near:			
Plan code	Plan name	Plan type	Published premium	No costs*	Low use: $3,000 or less	Average cost	High use: $30,000 or more	Limit to you
DC Area Plans When You Use Preferred Providers								
E35	Kaiser-Std	HMO	3170	2110	2510	3630	5950	9110
E32	Kaiser-Hi	HMO	4150	2770	3050	3750	5200	7270
T72	Kaiser-Basic	HMO	3020	2010	2790	4200	7440	10010
B62	CareFirst HDHP	HDHP	3950	1740	3460	4400	6680	9140
JN5	Aetna Open Access Basic	HMO	4140	2760	3410	4590	7210	9610
LR2	UnitedHealthcare Choice	HMO	4150	2770	3590	4910	7920	12770
L92	UnitedHealthcare Choice Plus	PPO-FEE	3550	2370	3880	5100	8240	8370
V42	UnitedHealthcare HDHP	HDHP	3870	1080	3280	5110	9370	10030
F55	Aetna Value Plan	PPO-FEE	3640	2430	3280	5170	9580	9880
2G5	CareFirst-Std POS	HMO-POS	5650	3770	4710	5300	6740	8770
F52	Aetna HealthFund CDHP	CDHP	7930	3190	5320	6250	9130	12740
JP2	MD-IPA	HMO	10030	6690	7380	8550	11210	16690
2G2	CareFirst-Hi	HMO	10250	6840	8110	8900	10910	11840
JN2	Aetna Open Access-Hi	HMO	15630	10430	10960	11890	13860	17280
National Plans When You Use Preferred Providers								
325	NALC CDHP	CDHP	2800	-490	1200	3360	7600	15110
342	GEHA HDHP	HDHP	3240	660	2540	3870	6370	12160
225	Aetna HealthFund HDHP	HDHP	3660	940	2990	4340	7220	9290
475	APWU CDHP	CDHP	3630	60	2360	4420	8380	13060
382	Rural Carrier†	PPO-FEE	3620	2420	3590	4490	6920	6920
402	Foreign Service†	PPO-FEE	3870	2580	3660	4500	6590	9580
N62	Aetna Direct CDHP	CDHP	3630	620	3020	4550	8460	9270
322	NALC-Hi	PPO-FEE	4090	2770	3500	4580	6910	11770
315	GEHA-Std	PPO-FEE	3070	2050	2810	4620	8700	9550
455	MHBP-Std	PPO-FEE	3700	2510	3630	4780	7450	14510
112	Blue Cross Basic	PPO	4160	2770	3480	4850	7850	13770
482	MHBP HDHP	HDHP	3600	640	3150	4910	8170	14440
KM2	NALC Value Plan	PPO-FEE	2300	1370	3060	5220	9460	14770
415	MHBP Value Plan	PPO-FEE	3280	2230	4230	5870	9980	15430
422	Compass Rose†	PPO-FEE	5930	3950	5120	5930	8140	9420
472	APWU-Hi	PPO-FEE	5980	4030	5230	6310	8920	13030
312	GEHA-Hi	PPO-FEE	6440	4290	5000	6400	9360	11290
445	SAMBA-Std	PPO-FEE	5420	3610	4750	6450	10240	17610
105	Blue Cross-Std	PPO-FEE	6510	4340	5650	6920	9860	14340
442	SAMBA-Hi	PPO-FEE	12160	8110	9170	10630	13870	20110

* These are the premiums after tax savings, offset by savings accounts for plans that offer them. If you have no or low health-care costs with these plans, it can result in actual saving to you, which we indicate with a negative number.

Persons Under 55: Postal Premiums (Category 1)				Family of Five				
				Estimated yearly out-of-pocket costs, including premium and typical hospital, medical, drug, and dental bills near:				
Plan code	Plan name	Plan type	Published premium	No costs*	Low use: $3,000 or less	Average cost	High use: $30,000 or more	Limit to you
DC Area Plans When You Use Preferred Providers								
E35	Kaiser-Std	HMO	3170	2110	2510	3800	5950	9110
E32	Kaiser-Hi	HMO	4150	2770	3050	3860	5200	7270
T72	Kaiser-Basic	HMO	3020	2010	2790	4440	7440	10010
B62	CareFirst HDHP	HDHP	3950	1740	3460	4610	6680	9140
JN5	Aetna Open Access Basic	HMO	4140	2760	3410	4790	7210	9610
LR2	UnitedHealthcare Choice	HMO	4150	2770	3590	5130	7920	12770
L92	UnitedHealthcare Choice Plus	PPO-FEE	3550	2370	3880	5340	8240	8370
2G5	CareFirst-Std POS	HMO-POS	5650	3770	4710	5410	6740	8770
V42	UnitedHealthcare HDHP	HDHP	3870	1080	3280	5450	9370	10030
F55	Aetna Value Plan	PPO-FEE	3640	2430	3280	5470	9580	9880
F52	Aetna HealthFund CDHP	CDHP	7930	3190	5320	6490	9130	12740
JP2	MD-IPA	HMO	10030	6690	7380	8750	11210	16690
2G2	CareFirst-Hi	HMO	10250	6840	8110	9050	10910	11840
JN2	Aetna Open Access-Hi	HMO	15630	10430	10960	12050	13860	17280
National Plans When You Use Preferred Providers								
325	NALC CDHP	CDHP	2800	-490	1200	3740	7600	15110
342	GEHA HDHP	HDHP	3240	660	2540	4130	6370	12160
225	Aetna HealthFund HDHP	HDHP	3660	940	2990	4620	7220	9290
382	Rural Carrier[†]	PPO-FEE	3620	2420	3590	4660	6920	6920
402	Foreign Service[†]	PPO-FEE	3870	2580	3660	4670	6590	9580
322	NALC-Hi	PPO-FEE	4090	2770	3500	4760	6910	11770
475	APWU CDHP	CDHP	3630	60	2360	4780	8380	13060
N62	Aetna Direct CDHP	CDHP	3630	620	3020	4870	8460	9270
315	GEHA-Std	PPO-FEE	3070	2050	2810	4900	8700	9550
455	MHBP-Std	PPO-FEE	3700	2510	3630	5000	7450	14510
112	Blue Cross Basic	PPO	4160	2770	3480	5080	7850	13770
482	MHBP HDHP	HDHP	3600	640	3150	5230	8170	14440
KM2	NALC Value Plan	PPO-FEE	2300	1370	3060	5590	9460	14770
422	Compass Rose[†]	PPO-FEE	5930	3950	5120	6100	8140	9420
415	MHBP Value Plan	PPO-FEE	3280	2230	4230	6200	9980	15430
472	APWU-Hi	PPO-FEE	5980	4030	5230	6510	8920	13030
312	GEHA-Hi	PPO-FEE	6440	4290	5000	6620	9360	11290
445	SAMBA-Std	PPO-FEE	5420	3610	4750	6740	10240	17610
105	Blue Cross-Std	PPO-FEE	6510	4340	5650	7160	9860	14340
442	SAMBA-Hi	PPO-FEE	12160	8110	9170	10880	13870	20110

† Plan is open only to specific groups.

Persons Under 55: Postal Premiums (Category 2)				Self Only				
				Estimated yearly out-of-pocket costs, including premium and typical hospital, medical, drug, and dental bills near:				
Plan code	Plan name	Plan type	Published premium	No costs*	Low use: $3,000 or less	Average cost	High use: $30,000 or more	Limit to you
DC Area Plans When You Use Preferred Providers								
E34	Kaiser-Std	HMO	1260	840	910	1460	4340	4340
E31	Kaiser-Hi	HMO	1640	1100	1120	1500	3350	3350
B61	CareFirst HDHP	HDHP	1520	560	1070	1660	4420	5010
T71	Kaiser-Basic	HMO	1150	760	980	1660	4760	4760
V41	UnitedHealthcare HDHP	HDHP	1410	190	790	1750	5240	5240
L91	UnitedHealthcare Choice Plus	PPO-FEE	1150	770	1300	1870	3770	3770
JN4	Aetna Open Access Basic	HMO	1660	1110	1210	1900	5650	6110
LR1	UnitedHealthcare Choice	HMO	1510	1010	1200	1930	6010	6010
2G4	CareFirst-Std POS	HMO-POS	2030	1360	1800	2080	3860	3860
F54	Aetna Value Plan	PPO-FEE	1450	970	1220	2120	6270	6270
JP1	MD-IPA	HMO	2320	1550	1690	2360	6150	6550
F51	Aetna HealthFund CDHP	CDHP	3380	1200	1800	2520	6550	6550
2G1	CareFirst-Hi	HMO	3970	2650	3190	3550	5150	5150
JN1	Aetna Open Access-Hi	HMO	6950	4630	4700	5250	8120	8630
National Plans When You Use Preferred Providers								
324	NALC CDHP	CDHP	1160	-390	-30	1230	7410	7410
341	GEHA HDHP	HDHP	1250	80	580	1420	4890	5830
474	APWU CDHP	CDHP	1380	-240	410	1580	6260	6260
224	Aetna HealthFund HDHP	HDHP	1510	260	780	1640	5010	5010
N61	Aetna Direct CDHP	CDHP	1310	-20	680	1660	5880	5880
401	Foreign Service†	PPO-FEE	1430	950	1230	1780	4720	5950
481	MHBP HDHP	HDHP	1410	80	830	1890	5840	6980
314	GEHA-Std	PPO-FEE	1190	790	1020	1940	6790	6790
111	Blue Cross Basic	PPO	1590	1060	1180	1970	6270	6560
321	NALC-Hi	PPO-FEE	1720	1180	1400	2000	5150	7780
454	MHBP-Std	PPO-FEE	1450	1010	1290	2120	6960	7010
KM1	NALC Value Plan	PPO-FEE	950	570	940	2130	7270	7270
421	Compass Rose†	PPO-FEE	2060	1380	1690	2250	5320	6850
381	Rural Carrier†	PPO-FEE	1940	1290	1800	2320	5290	5290
414	MHBP Value Plan	PPO-FEE	1240	870	1340	2440	7470	7470
471	APWU-Hi	PPO-FEE	2090	1430	1880	2520	6830	6930
311	GEHA-Hi	PPO-FEE	2360	1580	1800	2570	7080	7080
444	SAMBA-Std	PPO-FEE	2210	1470	1820	2810	8470	8470
104	Blue Cross-Std	PPO-FEE	2610	1740	2170	2890	6740	6740
441	SAMBA-Hi	PPO-FEE	4660	3110	3430	4300	9110	9110

* These are the premiums after tax savings, offset by savings accounts for plans that offer them. If you have no or low health-care costs with these plans, it can result in actual saving to you, which we indicate with a negative number.

44

Persons Under 55: Postal Premiums (Category 2)		Self Plus One						
		Plan type	Published premium	Estimated yearly out-of-pocket costs, including premium and typical hospital, medical, drug, and dental bills near:				
Plan code	Plan name			No costs*	Low use: $3,000 or less	Average cost	High use: $30,000 or more	Limit to you
DC Area Plans When You Use Preferred Providers								
E36	Kaiser-Std	HMO	2890	1930	2330	3080	5770	8930
B63	CareFirst HDHP	HDHP	3040	1130	2850	3320	6070	8530
T73	Kaiser-Basic	HMO	2510	1670	2450	3360	7100	9670
2G6	CareFirst-Std POS	HMO-POS	3450	2300	3240	3570	5270	7300
JN6	Aetna Open Access Basic	HMO	3470	2310	2960	3720	6760	9160
L93	UnitedHealthcare Choice Plus	PPO-FEE	2250	1500	3010	3720	7370	7500
JP3	MD-IPA	HMO	3490	2330	3020	3770	6850	12330
V43	UnitedHealthcare HDHP	HDHP	3040	520	2720	3770	8810	9470
LR3	UnitedHealthcare Choice	HMO	3250	2170	2990	3830	7320	12170
E33	Kaiser-Hi	HMO	4750	3170	3450	3910	5600	7670
F56	Aetna Value Plan	PPO-FEE	3260	2170	3020	4280	9320	9620
F53	Aetna HealthFund CDHP	CDHP	8360	3470	5600	5980	9410	13020
2G3	CareFirst-Hi	HMO	7050	4700	5970	6400	8770	9700
JN3	Aetna Open Access-Hi	HMO	15990	10660	11190	11790	14090	17510
National Plans When You Use Preferred Providers								
326	NALC CDHP	CDHP	2500	-700	990	2320	7390	14900
343	GEHA HDHP	HDHP	2680	290	2170	2910	6000	11790
476	APWU CDHP	CDHP	3040	-340	1960	3180	7980	12660
N63	Aetna Direct CDHP	CDHP	2880	120	2520	3330	7960	8770
226	Aetna HealthFund HDHP	HDHP	3270	680	2730	3450	6960	9030
316	GEHA-Std	PPO-FEE	2550	1700	2460	3690	8350	9200
483	MHBP HDHP	HDHP	3130	330	2840	3850	7860	14130
383	Rural Carrier[†]	PPO-FEE	3240	2160	3330	3860	6660	6660
403	Foreign Service[†]	PPO-FEE	3490	2330	3410	3870	6340	9330
456	MHBP-Std	PPO-FEE	3340	2270	3390	4070	7210	14270
113	Blue Cross Basic	PPO	3760	2510	3220	4100	7590	13510
323	NALC-Hi	PPO-FEE	4150	2810	3540	4220	6950	11810
KM3	NALC Value Plan	PPO-FEE	2050	1200	2890	4250	9290	14600
473	APWU-Hi	PPO-FEE	4120	2780	3980	4620	7670	11780
423	Compass Rose[†]	PPO-FEE	4910	3270	4440	4860	7460	8740
416	MHBP Value Plan	PPO-FEE	2930	2000	4000	4910	9750	15200
313	GEHA-Hi	PPO-FEE	5560	3710	4420	5350	8780	10710
446	SAMBA-Std	PPO-FEE	5220	3480	4620	5710	10110	17480
106	Blue Cross-Std	PPO-FEE	5990	4000	5310	6060	9520	14000
443	SAMBA-Hi	PPO-FEE	10620	7080	8140	9060	12840	19080

† Plan is open only to specific groups.

Persons Under 55: Postal Premiums (Category 2)		**Family of Two**					
		Plan type	Published premium	*Estimated yearly out-of-pocket costs, including premium and typical hospital, medical, drug, and dental bills near:*			
Plan code	Plan name			No costs*	Low use: $3,000 or less	Average cost	High use: $30,000 or more	Limit to you
DC Area Plans When You Use Preferred Providers								
E35	Kaiser-Std	HMO	2890	1930	2330	3080	5770	8930
E32	Kaiser-Hi	HMO	3910	2610	2890	3350	5040	7110
T72	Kaiser-Basic	HMO	2750	1830	2610	3520	7260	9830
B62	CareFirst HDHP	HDHP	3610	1510	3230	3700	6450	8910
JN5	Aetna Open Access Basic	HMO	3890	2590	3240	4000	7040	9440
V42	UnitedHealthcare HDHP	HDHP	3530	850	3050	4100	9140	9800
LR2	UnitedHealthcare Choice	HMO	3930	2620	3440	4280	7770	12620
F55	Aetna Value Plan	PPO-FEE	3320	2220	3070	4330	9370	9670
L92	UnitedHealthcare Choice Plus	PPO-FEE	3230	2160	3670	4380	8030	8160
2G5	CareFirst-Std POS	HMO-POS	5460	3640	4580	4910	6610	8640
F52	Aetna HealthFund CDHP	CDHP	7740	3060	5190	5570	9000	12610
JP2	MD-IPA	HMO	9840	6560	7250	8000	11080	16560
2G2	CareFirst-Hi	HMO	10060	6710	7980	8410	10780	11710
JN2	Aetna Open Access-Hi	HMO	15440	10300	10830	11430	13730	17150
National Plans When You Use Preferred Providers								
325	NALC CDHP	CDHP	2560	-660	1030	2360	7430	14940
342	GEHA HDHP	HDHP	2950	470	2350	3090	6180	11970
475	APWU CDHP	CDHP	3310	-160	2140	3360	8160	12840
225	Aetna HealthFund HDHP	HDHP	3340	730	2780	3500	7010	9080
N62	Aetna Direct CDHP	CDHP	3310	410	2810	3620	8250	9060
315	GEHA-Std	PPO-FEE	2800	1870	2630	3860	8520	9370
402	Foreign Service†	PPO-FEE	3530	2350	3430	3890	6360	9350
382	Rural Carrier†	PPO-FEE	3310	2210	3380	3910	6710	6710
322	NALC-Hi	PPO-FEE	3730	2530	3260	3940	6670	11530
482	MHBP HDHP	HDHP	3280	430	2940	3950	7960	14230
455	MHBP-Std	PPO-FEE	3370	2290	3410	4090	7230	14290
112	Blue Cross Basic	PPO	3950	2640	3350	4230	7720	13640
KM2	NALC Value Plan	PPO-FEE	2100	1240	2930	4290	9330	14640
415	MHBP Value Plan	PPO-FEE	2990	2040	4040	4950	9790	15240
422	Compass Rose†	PPO-FEE	5740	3830	5000	5420	8020	9300
445	SAMBA-Std	PPO-FEE	5230	3490	4630	5720	10120	17490
472	APWU-Hi	PPO-FEE	5800	3900	5100	5740	8790	12900
312	GEHA-Hi	PPO-FEE	6250	4170	4880	5810	9240	11170
105	Blue Cross-Std	PPO-FEE	6320	4210	5520	6270	9730	14210
442	SAMBA-Hi	PPO-FEE	11970	7980	9040	9960	13740	19980

* These are the premiums after tax savings, offset by savings accounts for plans that offer them. If you have no or low health-care costs with these plans, it can result in actual saving to you, which we indicate with a negative number.

Persons Under 55: Postal Premiums (Category 2)		Plan type	Published premium	Family of Three — Estimated yearly out-of-pocket costs, including premium and typical hospital, medical, drug, and dental bills near:				
Plan code	Plan name			No costs*	Low use: $3,000 or less	Average cost	High use: $30,000 or more	Limit to you
DC Area Plans When You Use Preferred Providers								
E35	Kaiser-Std	HMO	2890	1930	2330	3260	5770	8930
E32	Kaiser-Hi	HMO	3910	2610	2890	3470	5040	7110
T72	Kaiser-Basic	HMO	2750	1830	2610	3780	7260	9830
B62	CareFirst HDHP	HDHP	3610	1510	3230	3950	6450	8910
JN5	Aetna Open Access Basic	HMO	3890	2590	3240	4220	7040	9440
V42	UnitedHealthcare HDHP	HDHP	3530	850	3050	4500	9140	9800
LR2	UnitedHealthcare Choice	HMO	3930	2620	3440	4520	7770	12620
F55	Aetna Value Plan	PPO-FEE	3320	2220	3070	4650	9370	9670
L92	UnitedHealthcare Choice Plus	PPO-FEE	3230	2160	3670	4650	8030	8160
2G5	CareFirst-Std POS	HMO-POS	5460	3640	4580	5040	6610	8640
F52	Aetna HealthFund CDHP	CDHP	7740	3060	5190	5860	9000	12610
JP2	MD-IPA	HMO	9840	6560	7250	8220	11080	16560
2G2	CareFirst-Hi	HMO	10060	6710	7980	8600	10780	11710
JN2	Aetna Open Access-Hi	HMO	15440	10300	10830	11600	13730	17150
National Plans When You Use Preferred Providers								
325	NALC CDHP	CDHP	2560	-660	1030	2790	7430	14940
342	GEHA HDHP	HDHP	2950	470	2350	3400	6180	11970
475	APWU CDHP	CDHP	3310	-160	2140	3800	8160	12840
225	Aetna HealthFund HDHP	HDHP	3340	730	2780	3830	7010	9080
N62	Aetna Direct CDHP	CDHP	3310	410	2810	3990	8250	9060
402	Foreign Service[†]	PPO-FEE	3530	2350	3430	4090	6360	9350
382	Rural Carrier[†]	PPO-FEE	3310	2210	3380	4100	6710	6710
322	NALC-Hi	PPO-FEE	3730	2530	3260	4140	6670	11530
315	GEHA-Std	PPO-FEE	2800	1870	2630	4150	8520	9370
455	MHBP-Std	PPO-FEE	3370	2290	3410	4340	7230	14290
482	MHBP HDHP	HDHP	3280	430	2940	4350	7960	14230
112	Blue Cross Basic	PPO	3950	2640	3350	4480	7720	13640
KM2	NALC Value Plan	PPO-FEE	2100	1240	2930	4700	9330	14640
415	MHBP Value Plan	PPO-FEE	2990	2040	4040	5330	9790	15240
422	Compass Rose[†]	PPO-FEE	5740	3830	5000	5620	8020	9300
472	APWU-Hi	PPO-FEE	5800	3900	5100	5970	8790	12900
445	SAMBA-Std	PPO-FEE	5230	3490	4630	6030	10120	17490
312	GEHA-Hi	PPO-FEE	6250	4170	4880	6050	9240	11170
105	Blue Cross-Std	PPO-FEE	6320	4210	5520	6540	9730	14210
442	SAMBA-Hi	PPO-FEE	11970	7980	9040	10240	13740	19980

† Plan is open only to specific groups.

Persons Under 55: Postal Premiums (Category 2)			Family of Four				
		Plan type	Published premium	**Estimated yearly out-of-pocket costs, including premium and typical hospital, medical, drug, and dental bills near:**			
Plan code	Plan name			No costs*	Low use: $3,000 or less	Average cost	High use: $30,000 or more	Limit to you

Plan code	Plan name	Plan type	Published premium	No costs*	Low use: $3,000 or less	Average cost	High use: $30,000 or more	Limit to you
DC Area Plans When You Use Preferred Providers								
E35	Kaiser-Std	HMO	2890	1930	2330	3450	5770	8930
E32	Kaiser-Hi	HMO	3910	2610	2890	3590	5040	7110
T72	Kaiser-Basic	HMO	2750	1830	2610	4020	7260	9830
B62	CareFirst HDHP	HDHP	3610	1510	3230	4170	6450	8910
JN5	Aetna Open Access Basic	HMO	3890	2590	3240	4420	7040	9440
LR2	UnitedHealthcare Choice	HMO	3930	2620	3440	4760	7770	12620
V42	UnitedHealthcare HDHP	HDHP	3530	850	3050	4880	9140	9800
L92	UnitedHealthcare Choice Plus	PPO-FEE	3230	2160	3670	4890	8030	8160
F55	Aetna Value Plan	PPO-FEE	3320	2220	3070	4960	9370	9670
2G5	CareFirst-Std POS	HMO-POS	5460	3640	4580	5170	6610	8640
F52	Aetna HealthFund CDHP	CDHP	7740	3060	5190	6120	9000	12610
JP2	MD-IPA	HMO	9840	6560	7250	8420	11080	16560
2G2	CareFirst-Hi	HMO	10060	6710	7980	8770	10780	11710
JN2	Aetna Open Access-Hi	HMO	15440	10300	10830	11760	13730	17150
National Plans When You Use Preferred Providers								
325	NALC CDHP	CDHP	2560	-660	1030	3190	7430	14940
342	GEHA HDHP	HDHP	2950	470	2350	3680	6180	11970
225	Aetna HealthFund HDHP	HDHP	3340	730	2780	4130	7010	9080
475	APWU CDHP	CDHP	3310	-160	2140	4200	8160	12840
402	Foreign Service†	PPO-FEE	3530	2350	3430	4270	6360	9350
382	Rural Carrier†	PPO-FEE	3310	2210	3380	4280	6710	6710
N62	Aetna Direct CDHP	CDHP	3310	410	2810	4340	8250	9060
322	NALC-Hi	PPO-FEE	3730	2530	3260	4340	6670	11530
315	GEHA-Std	PPO-FEE	2800	1870	2630	4440	8520	9370
455	MHBP-Std	PPO-FEE	3370	2290	3410	4560	7230	14290
482	MHBP HDHP	HDHP	3280	430	2940	4700	7960	14230
112	Blue Cross Basic	PPO	3950	2640	3350	4720	7720	13640
KM2	NALC Value Plan	PPO-FEE	2100	1240	2930	5090	9330	14640
415	MHBP Value Plan	PPO-FEE	2990	2040	4040	5680	9790	15240
422	Compass Rose†	PPO-FEE	5740	3830	5000	5810	8020	9300
472	APWU-Hi	PPO-FEE	5800	3900	5100	6180	8790	12900
312	GEHA-Hi	PPO-FEE	6250	4170	4880	6280	9240	11170
445	SAMBA-Std	PPO-FEE	5230	3490	4630	6330	10120	17490
105	Blue Cross-Std	PPO-FEE	6320	4210	5520	6790	9730	14210
442	SAMBA-Hi	PPO-FEE	11970	7980	9040	10500	13740	19980

* These are the premiums after tax savings, offset by savings accounts for plans that offer them. If you have no or low health-care costs with these plans, it can result in actual saving to you, which we indicate with a negative number.

Persons Under 55: Postal Premiums (Category 2)		Family of Five						
				Estimated yearly out-of-pocket costs, including premium and typical hospital, medical, drug, and dental bills near:				
		Plan type	Published premium	No costs*	Low use: $3,000 or less	Average cost	High use: $30,000 or more	Limit to you
Plan code	Plan name							
DC Area Plans When You Use Preferred Providers								
E35	Kaiser-Std	HMO	2890	1930	2330	3620	5770	8930
E32	Kaiser-Hi	HMO	3910	2610	2890	3700	5040	7110
T72	Kaiser-Basic	HMO	2750	1830	2610	4260	7260	9830
B62	CareFirst HDHP	HDHP	3610	1510	3230	4380	6450	8910
JN5	Aetna Open Access Basic	HMO	3890	2590	3240	4620	7040	9440
LR2	UnitedHealthcare Choice	HMO	3930	2620	3440	4980	7770	12620
L92	UnitedHealthcare Choice Plus	PPO-FEE	3230	2160	3670	5130	8030	8160
V42	UnitedHealthcare HDHP	HDHP	3530	850	3050	5220	9140	9800
F55	Aetna Value Plan	PPO-FEE	3320	2220	3070	5260	9370	9670
2G5	CareFirst-Std POS	HMO-POS	5460	3640	4580	5280	6610	8640
F52	Aetna HealthFund CDHP	CDHP	7740	3060	5190	6360	9000	12610
JP2	MD-IPA	HMO	9840	6560	7250	8620	11080	16560
2G2	CareFirst-Hi	HMO	10060	6710	7980	8920	10780	11710
JN2	Aetna Open Access-Hi	HMO	15440	10300	10830	11920	13730	17150
National Plans When You Use Preferred Providers								
325	NALC CDHP	CDHP	2560	-660	1030	3570	7430	14940
342	GEHA HDHP	HDHP	2950	470	2350	3940	6180	11970
225	Aetna HealthFund HDHP	HDHP	3340	730	2780	4410	7010	9080
402	Foreign Service†	PPO-FEE	3530	2350	3430	4440	6360	9350
382	Rural Carrier†	PPO-FEE	3310	2210	3380	4450	6710	6710
322	NALC-Hi	PPO-FEE	3730	2530	3260	4520	6670	11530
475	APWU CDHP	CDHP	3310	-160	2140	4560	8160	12840
N62	Aetna Direct CDHP	CDHP	3310	410	2810	4660	8250	9060
315	GEHA-Std	PPO-FEE	2800	1870	2630	4720	8520	9370
455	MHBP-Std	PPO-FEE	3370	2290	3410	4780	7230	14290
112	Blue Cross Basic	PPO	3950	2640	3350	4950	7720	13640
482	MHBP HDHP	HDHP	3280	430	2940	5020	7960	14230
KM2	NALC Value Plan	PPO-FEE	2100	1240	2930	5460	9330	14640
422	Compass Rose†	PPO-FEE	5740	3830	5000	5980	8020	9300
415	MHBP Value Plan	PPO-FEE	2990	2040	4040	6010	9790	15240
472	APWU-Hi	PPO-FEE	5800	3900	5100	6380	8790	12900
312	GEHA-Hi	PPO-FEE	6250	4170	4880	6500	9240	11170
445	SAMBA-Std	PPO-FEE	5230	3490	4630	6620	10120	17490
105	Blue Cross-Std	PPO-FEE	6320	4210	5520	7030	9730	14210
442	SAMBA-Hi	PPO-FEE	11970	7980	9040	10750	13740	19980

† Plan is open only to specific groups.

Persons 55 to 64: GS Premiums		Self Only					
				Estimated yearly out-of-pocket costs, including premium and typical hospital, medical, drug, and dental bills near:			
		Plan type	Published premium	No costs*	Low use: $3,000 or less	Average cost	High use: $30,000 or more	Limit to you
Plan code	Plan name	Plan type	Published premium	No costs*	Low use: $3,000 or less	Average cost	High use: $30,000 or more	Limit to you
DC Area Plans When You Use Preferred Providers								
E31	Kaiser-Hi	HMO	1980	1320	1340	1980	3570	3570
E34	Kaiser-Std	HMO	1510	1010	1080	2020	4510	4510
T71	Kaiser-Basic	HMO	1380	920	1140	2320	4920	4920
B61	CareFirst HDHP	HDHP	1830	770	1280	2340	4630	5220
L91	UnitedHealthcare Choice Plus	PPO-FEE	1390	930	1460	2470	3930	3930
2G4	CareFirst-Std POS	HMO-POS	2360	1580	2020	2570	4080	4080
JN4	Aetna Open Access Basic	HMO	1990	1330	1430	2620	5870	6330
V41	UnitedHealthcare HDHP	HDHP	1700	380	980	2640	5430	5430
LR1	UnitedHealthcare Choice	HMO	1820	1220	1410	2680	6220	6220
F54	Aetna Value Plan	PPO-FEE	1750	1170	1420	2970	6470	6470
JP1	MD-IPA	HMO	2650	1770	1910	3080	6370	6770
F51	Aetna HealthFund CDHP	CDHP	3710	1430	2030	3330	6780	6780
2G1	CareFirst-Hi	HMO	4300	2870	3410	4090	5370	5370
JN1	Aetna Open Access-Hi	HMO	7280	4850	4920	5870	8340	8850
National Plans When You Use Preferred Providers								
341	GEHA HDHP	HDHP	1500	250	750	2220	5060	6000
324	NALC CDHP	CDHP	1390	-240	120	2270	7560	7560
401	Foreign Service[†]	PPO-FEE	1720	1150	1430	2410	4920	6150
224	Aetna HealthFund HDHP	HDHP	1820	470	990	2480	5220	5220
N61	Aetna Direct CDHP	CDHP	1580	160	860	2590	6060	6060
474	APWU CDHP	CDHP	1660	-60	590	2610	6440	6440
321	NALC-Hi	PPO-FEE	2050	1400	1620	2690	5370	8000
111	Blue Cross Basic	PPO	1920	1280	1400	2760	6490	6780
314	GEHA-Std	PPO-FEE	1430	950	1180	2770	6950	6950
481	MHBP HDHP	HDHP	1700	280	1030	2880	6040	7180
421	Compass Rose[†]	PPO-FEE	2390	1600	1910	2920	5540	7070
454	MHBP-Std	PPO-FEE	1750	1210	1490	2950	7160	7210
381	Rural Carrier[†]	PPO-FEE	2270	1510	2020	2970	5510	5510
KM1	NALC Value Plan	PPO-FEE	1140	700	1070	3100	7400	7400
471	APWU-Hi	PPO-FEE	2420	1650	2100	3270	7050	7150
311	GEHA-Hi	PPO-FEE	2690	1800	2020	3370	7300	7300
414	MHBP Value Plan	PPO-FEE	1490	1040	1510	3420	7640	7640
104	Blue Cross-Std	PPO-FEE	2940	1960	2390	3670	6960	6960
444	SAMBA-Std	PPO-FEE	2540	1690	2040	3770	8690	8690
441	SAMBA-Hi	PPO-FEE	4990	3330	3650	5180	9330	9330

* These are the premiums after tax savings, offset by savings accounts for plans that offer them. If you have no or low health-care costs with these plans, it can result in actual saving to you, which we indicate with a negative number.

| Persons 55 to 64: GS Premiums | | | | Self Plus One | | | | |
| | | | | Estimated yearly out-of-pocket costs, including premium and typical hospital, medical, drug, and dental bills near: | | | | |
Plan code	Plan name	Plan type	Published premium	No costs*	Low use: $3,000 or less	Average cost	High use: $30,000 or more	Limit to you
DC Area Plans When You Use Preferred Providers								
E36	Kaiser-Std	HMO	3480	2320	2720	4270	6160	9320
2G6	CareFirst-Std POS	HMO-POS	4160	2780	3720	4590	5750	7780
B63	CareFirst HDHP	HDHP	3660	1540	3260	4690	6480	8940
T73	Kaiser-Basic	HMO	3020	2010	2790	4760	7440	10010
E33	Kaiser-Hi	HMO	5460	3640	3920	4890	6070	8140
L93	UnitedHealthcare Choice Plus	PPO-FEE	2710	1810	3320	5050	7680	7810
JN6	Aetna Open Access Basic	HMO	4180	2790	3440	5090	7240	9640
JP3	MD-IPA	HMO	4210	2810	3500	5170	7330	12810
LR3	UnitedHealthcare Choice	HMO	3920	2620	3440	5310	7770	12620
V43	UnitedHealthcare HDHP	HDHP	3660	940	3140	5730	9230	9890
F56	Aetna Value Plan	PPO-FEE	3930	2620	3470	6000	9770	10070
2G3	CareFirst-Hi	HMO	7760	5170	6440	7590	9240	10170
F53	Aetna HealthFund CDHP	CDHP	9070	3950	6080	7600	9890	13500
JN3	Aetna Open Access-Hi	HMO	16700	11140	11670	13000	14570	17990
National Plans When You Use Preferred Providers								
326	NALC CDHP	CDHP	3010	-350	1340	4420	7740	15250
343	GEHA HDHP	HDHP	3230	660	2540	4480	6370	12160
383	Rural Carrier†	PPO-FEE	3910	2600	3770	5040	7100	7100
403	Foreign Service†	PPO-FEE	4210	2810	3890	5150	6820	9810
N63	Aetna Direct CDHP	CDHP	3470	520	2920	5160	8360	9170
226	Aetna HealthFund HDHP	HDHP	3940	1130	3180	5170	7410	9480
316	GEHA-Std	PPO-FEE	3070	2050	2810	5240	8700	9550
476	APWU CDHP	CDHP	3660	80	2380	5320	8400	13080
456	MHBP-Std	PPO-FEE	4020	2720	3840	5530	7660	14720
323	NALC-Hi	PPO-FEE	4860	3280	4010	5540	7420	12280
113	Blue Cross Basic	PPO	4470	2980	3690	5620	8060	13980
483	MHBP HDHP	HDHP	3770	760	3270	5770	8290	14560
473	APWU-Hi	PPO-FEE	4830	3260	4460	6040	8150	12260
423	Compass Rose†	PPO-FEE	5620	3750	4920	6130	7940	9220
KM3	NALC Value Plan	PPO-FEE	2470	1490	3180	6220	9580	14890
313	GEHA-Hi	PPO-FEE	6270	4180	4890	6800	9250	11180
416	MHBP Value Plan	PPO-FEE	3530	2400	4400	6870	10150	15600
446	SAMBA-Std	PPO-FEE	5930	3960	5100	7520	10590	17960
106	Blue Cross-Std	PPO-FEE	6700	4470	5780	7640	9990	14470
443	SAMBA-Hi	PPO-FEE	11330	7560	8620	10700	13320	19560

† Plan is open only to specific groups.

Persons 55 to 64: GS Premiums				Family of Two				
				Estimated yearly out-of-pocket costs, including premium and typical hospital, medical, drug, and dental bills near:				
Plan code	Plan name	Plan type	Published premium	No costs*	Low use: $3,000 or less	Average cost	High use: $30,000 or more	Limit to you
DC Area Plans When You Use Preferred Providers								
E35	Kaiser-Std	HMO	3480	2320	2720	4270	6160	9320
E32	Kaiser-Hi	HMO	4660	3110	3390	4360	5540	7610
T72	Kaiser-Basic	HMO	3310	2210	2990	4960	7640	10210
B62	CareFirst HDHP	HDHP	4350	2000	3720	5150	6940	9400
JN5	Aetna Open Access Basic	HMO	4640	3100	3750	5400	7550	9950
LR2	UnitedHealthcare Choice	HMO	4680	3120	3940	5810	8270	13120
L92	UnitedHealthcare Choice Plus	PPO-FEE	3900	2600	4110	5840	8470	8600
2G5	CareFirst-Std POS	HMO-POS	6220	4150	5090	5960	7120	9150
F55	Aetna Value Plan	PPO-FEE	4000	2670	3520	6050	9820	10120
V42	UnitedHealthcare HDHP	HDHP	4250	1340	3540	6130	9630	10290
F52	Aetna HealthFund CDHP	CDHP	8490	3560	5690	7210	9500	13110
JP2	MD-IPA	HMO	10590	7060	7750	9420	11580	17060
2G2	CareFirst-Hi	HMO	10820	7220	8490	9640	11290	12220
JN2	Aetna Open Access-Hi	HMO	16200	10800	11330	12660	14230	17650
National Plans When You Use Preferred Providers								
325	NALC CDHP	CDHP	3080	-310	1380	4460	7780	15290
342	GEHA HDHP	HDHP	3560	870	2750	4690	6580	12370
382	Rural Carrier†	PPO-FEE	3980	2660	3830	5100	7160	7160
402	Foreign Service†	PPO-FEE	4250	2830	3910	5170	6840	9830
225	Aetna HealthFund HDHP	HDHP	4020	1180	3230	5220	7460	9530
322	NALC-Hi	PPO-FEE	4500	3030	3760	5290	7170	12030
315	GEHA-Std	PPO-FEE	3380	2250	3010	5440	8900	9750
N62	Aetna Direct CDHP	CDHP	3990	860	3260	5500	8700	9510
475	APWU CDHP	CDHP	3990	300	2600	5540	8620	13300
455	MHBP-Std	PPO-FEE	4060	2750	3870	5560	7690	14750
112	Blue Cross Basic	PPO	4710	3140	3850	5780	8220	14140
482	MHBP HDHP	HDHP	3960	880	3390	5890	8410	14680
KM2	NALC Value Plan	PPO-FEE	2530	1520	3210	6250	9610	14920
422	Compass Rose†	PPO-FEE	6490	4330	5500	6710	8520	9800
415	MHBP Value Plan	PPO-FEE	3600	2450	4450	6920	10200	15650
472	APWU-Hi	PPO-FEE	6550	4400	5600	7180	9290	13400
312	GEHA-Hi	PPO-FEE	7000	4670	5380	7290	9740	11670
445	SAMBA-Std	PPO-FEE	5980	3990	5130	7550	10620	17990
105	Blue Cross-Std	PPO-FEE	7070	4720	6030	7890	10240	14720
442	SAMBA-Hi	PPO-FEE	12720	8490	9550	11630	14250	20490

* These are the premiums after tax savings, offset by savings accounts for plans that offer them. If you have no or low health-care costs with these plans, it can result in actual saving to you, which we indicate with a negative number.

Persons 55 to 64: GS Premiums				Family of Three				
		Plan type	Published premium	Estimated yearly out-of-pocket costs, including premium and typical hospital, medical, drug, and dental bills near:				
Plan code	Plan name			No costs*	Low use: $3,000 or less	Average cost	High use: $30,000 or more	Limit to you
DC Area Plans When You Use Preferred Providers								
E35	Kaiser-Std	HMO	3480	2320	2720	4430	6160	9320
E32	Kaiser-Hi	HMO	4660	3110	3390	4470	5540	7610
T72	Kaiser-Basic	HMO	3310	2210	2990	5180	7640	10210
B62	CareFirst HDHP	HDHP	4350	2000	3720	5330	6940	9400
JN5	Aetna Open Access Basic	HMO	4640	3100	3750	5570	7550	9950
LR2	UnitedHealthcare Choice	HMO	4680	3120	3940	6010	8270	13120
L92	UnitedHealthcare Choice Plus	PPO-FEE	3900	2600	4110	6050	8470	8600
2G5	CareFirst-Std POS	HMO-POS	6220	4150	5090	6070	7120	9150
F55	Aetna Value Plan	PPO-FEE	4000	2670	3520	6330	9820	10120
V42	UnitedHealthcare HDHP	HDHP	4250	1340	3540	6420	9630	10290
F52	Aetna HealthFund CDHP	CDHP	8490	3560	5690	7420	9500	13110
JP2	MD-IPA	HMO	10590	7060	7750	9600	11580	17060
2G2	CareFirst-Hi	HMO	10820	7220	8490	9780	11290	12220
JN2	Aetna Open Access-Hi	HMO	16200	10800	11330	12800	14230	17650
National Plans When You Use Preferred Providers								
325	NALC CDHP	CDHP	3080	-310	1380	4790	7780	15290
342	GEHA HDHP	HDHP	3560	870	2750	4900	6580	12370
382	Rural Carrier†	PPO-FEE	3980	2660	3830	5250	7160	7160
402	Foreign Service†	PPO-FEE	4250	2830	3910	5320	6840	9830
225	Aetna HealthFund HDHP	HDHP	4020	1180	3230	5450	7460	9530
322	NALC-Hi	PPO-FEE	4500	3030	3760	5460	7170	12030
315	GEHA-Std	PPO-FEE	3380	2250	3010	5700	8900	9750
455	MHBP-Std	PPO-FEE	4060	2750	3870	5750	7690	14750
N62	Aetna Direct CDHP	CDHP	3990	860	3260	5770	8700	9510
475	APWU CDHP	CDHP	3990	300	2600	5840	8620	13300
112	Blue Cross Basic	PPO	4710	3140	3850	5990	8220	14140
482	MHBP HDHP	HDHP	3960	880	3390	6160	8410	14680
KM2	NALC Value Plan	PPO-FEE	2530	1520	3210	6570	9610	14920
422	Compass Rose†	PPO-FEE	6490	4330	5500	6860	8520	9800
415	MHBP Value Plan	PPO-FEE	3600	2450	4450	7210	10200	15650
472	APWU-Hi	PPO-FEE	6550	4400	5600	7360	9290	13400
312	GEHA-Hi	PPO-FEE	7000	4670	5380	7500	9740	11670
445	SAMBA-Std	PPO-FEE	5980	3990	5130	7810	10620	17990
105	Blue Cross-Std	PPO-FEE	7070	4720	6030	8100	10240	14720
442	SAMBA-Hi	PPO-FEE	12720	8490	9550	11860	14250	20490

† Plan is open only to specific groups.

Persons 55 to 64: Postal Premiums (Category 1)		Self Only						
				Estimated yearly out-of-pocket costs, including premium and typical hospital, medical, drug, and dental bills near:				
		Plan type	Published premium	No costs*	Low use: $3,000 or less	Average cost	High use: $30,000 or more	Limit to you
Plan code	Plan name							

DC Area Plans When You Use Preferred Providers

Plan code	Plan name	Plan type	Published premium	No costs*	Low use: $3,000 or less	Average cost	High use: $30,000 or more	Limit to you
E31	Kaiser-Hi	HMO	1800	1200	1220	1860	3450	3450
E34	Kaiser-Std	HMO	1380	920	990	1930	4420	4420
B61	CareFirst HDHP	HDHP	1660	660	1170	2230	4520	5110
T71	Kaiser-Basic	HMO	1260	840	1060	2240	4840	4840
L91	UnitedHealthcare Choice Plus	PPO-FEE	1260	840	1370	2380	3840	3840
2G4	CareFirst-Std POS	HMO-POS	2110	1410	1850	2400	3910	3910
JN4	Aetna Open Access Basic	HMO	1810	1210	1310	2500	5750	6210
V41	UnitedHealthcare HDHP	HDHP	1550	280	880	2540	5330	5330
LR1	UnitedHealthcare Choice	HMO	1660	1110	1300	2570	6110	6110
F54	Aetna Value Plan	PPO-FEE	1590	1060	1310	2860	6360	6360
JP1	MD-IPA	HMO	2400	1600	1740	2910	6200	6600
F51	Aetna HealthFund CDHP	CDHP	3460	1260	1860	3160	6610	6610
2G1	CareFirst-Hi	HMO	4050	2700	3240	3920	5200	5200
JN1	Aetna Open Access-Hi	HMO	7030	4690	4760	5710	8180	8690

National Plans When You Use Preferred Providers

Plan code	Plan name	Plan type	Published premium	No costs*	Low use: $3,000 or less	Average cost	High use: $30,000 or more	Limit to you
341	GEHA HDHP	HDHP	1370	160	660	2130	4970	5910
324	NALC CDHP	CDHP	1270	-320	40	2190	7480	7480
401	Foreign Service†	PPO-FEE	1560	1040	1320	2300	4810	6040
224	Aetna HealthFund HDHP	HDHP	1660	360	880	2370	5110	5110
N61	Aetna Direct CDHP	CDHP	1440	60	760	2490	5960	5960
474	APWU CDHP	CDHP	1510	-160	490	2510	6340	6340
321	NALC-Hi	PPO-FEE	1820	1250	1470	2540	5220	7850
111	Blue Cross Basic	PPO	1740	1160	1280	2640	6370	6660
381	Rural Carrier†	PPO-FEE	1800	1200	1710	2660	5200	5200
314	GEHA-Std	PPO-FEE	1300	870	1100	2690	6870	6870
421	Compass Rose†	PPO-FEE	2150	1430	1740	2750	5370	6900
481	MHBP HDHP	HDHP	1550	180	930	2780	5940	7080
454	MHBP-Std	PPO-FEE	1590	1100	1380	2840	7050	7100
KM1	NALC Value Plan	PPO-FEE	1040	630	1000	3030	7330	7330
471	APWU-Hi	PPO-FEE	2170	1480	1930	3100	6880	6980
311	GEHA-Hi	PPO-FEE	2440	1630	1850	3200	7130	7130
414	MHBP Value Plan	PPO-FEE	1360	950	1420	3330	7550	7550
104	Blue Cross-Std	PPO-FEE	2690	1800	2230	3510	6800	6800
444	SAMBA-Std	PPO-FEE	2290	1530	1880	3610	8530	8530
441	SAMBA-Hi	PPO-FEE	4740	3160	3480	5010	9160	9160

* These are the premiums after tax savings, offset by savings accounts for plans that offer them. If you have no or low health-care costs with these plans, it can result in actual saving to you, which we indicate with a negative number.

Persons 55 to 64: Postal Premiums (Category 1)				Self Plus One				
		Plan type	Published premium	Estimated yearly out-of-pocket costs, including premium and typical hospital, medical, drug, and dental bills near:				
Plan code	Plan name			No costs*	Low use: $3,000 or less	Average cost	High use: $30,000 or more	Limit to you
DC Area Plans When You Use Preferred Providers								
E36	Kaiser-Std	HMO	3170	2110	2510	4060	5950	9110
2G6	CareFirst-Std POS	HMO-POS	3790	2530	3470	4340	5500	7530
B63	CareFirst HDHP	HDHP	3330	1320	3040	4470	6260	8720
T73	Kaiser-Basic	HMO	2750	1830	2610	4580	7260	9830
E33	Kaiser-Hi	HMO	5110	3410	3690	4660	5840	7910
JN6	Aetna Open Access Basic	HMO	3800	2540	3190	4840	6990	9390
L93	UnitedHealthcare Choice Plus	PPO-FEE	2470	1650	3160	4890	7520	7650
JP3	MD-IPA	HMO	3830	2550	3240	4910	7070	12550
LR3	UnitedHealthcare Choice	HMO	3570	2380	3200	5070	7530	12380
V43	UnitedHealthcare HDHP	HDHP	3330	720	2920	5510	9010	9670
F56	Aetna Value Plan	PPO-FEE	3570	2380	3230	5760	9530	9830
F53	Aetna HealthFund CDHP	CDHP	8710	3710	5840	7360	9650	13260
2G3	CareFirst-Hi	HMO	7400	4940	6210	7360	9010	9940
JN3	Aetna Open Access-Hi	HMO	16340	10900	11430	12760	14330	17750
National Plans When You Use Preferred Providers								
326	NALC CDHP	CDHP	2740	-540	1150	4230	7550	15060
343	GEHA HDHP	HDHP	2940	460	2340	4280	6170	11960
383	Rural Carrier†	PPO-FEE	3550	2370	3540	4810	6870	6870
403	Foreign Service†	PPO-FEE	3830	2550	3630	4890	6560	9550
226	Aetna HealthFund HDHP	HDHP	3590	890	2940	4930	7170	9240
N63	Aetna Direct CDHP	CDHP	3160	310	2710	4950	8150	8960
316	GEHA-Std	PPO-FEE	2790	1860	2620	5050	8510	9360
476	APWU CDHP	CDHP	3330	-140	2160	5100	8180	12860
456	MHBP-Std	PPO-FEE	3660	2480	3600	5290	7420	14480
323	NALC-Hi	PPO-FEE	4510	3040	3770	5300	7180	12040
113	Blue Cross Basic	PPO	4110	2740	3450	5380	7820	13740
483	MHBP HDHP	HDHP	3430	530	3040	5540	8060	14330
473	APWU-Hi	PPO-FEE	4480	3020	4220	5800	7910	12020
423	Compass Rose†	PPO-FEE	5260	3510	4680	5890	7700	8980
KM3	NALC Value Plan	PPO-FEE	2250	1340	3030	6070	9430	14740
313	GEHA-Hi	PPO-FEE	5920	3950	4660	6570	9020	10950
416	MHBP Value Plan	PPO-FEE	3220	2190	4190	6660	9940	15390
446	SAMBA-Std	PPO-FEE	5570	3720	4860	7280	10350	17720
106	Blue Cross-Std	PPO-FEE	6350	4230	5540	7400	9750	14230
443	SAMBA-Hi	PPO-FEE	10970	7320	8380	10460	13080	19320

† Plan is open only to specific groups.

Persons 55 to 64: Postal Premiums (Category 1)		Family of Two					
				Estimated yearly out-of-pocket costs, including premium and typical hospital, medical, drug, and dental bills near:			
Plan code	Plan name	Plan type	Published premium	No costs*	Low use: $3,000 or less	Average cost	High use: $30,000 or more	Limit to you
DC Area Plans When You Use Preferred Providers								
E32	Kaiser-Hi	HMO	4150	2770	3050	4020	5200	7270
E35	Kaiser-Std	HMO	3170	2110	2510	4060	5950	9110
T72	Kaiser-Basic	HMO	3020	2010	2790	4760	7440	10010
B62	CareFirst HDHP	HDHP	3950	1740	3460	4890	6680	9140
JN5	Aetna Open Access Basic	HMO	4140	2760	3410	5060	7210	9610
LR2	UnitedHealthcare Choice	HMO	4150	2770	3590	5460	7920	12770
2G5	CareFirst-Std POS	HMO-POS	5650	3770	4710	5580	6740	8770
L92	UnitedHealthcare Choice Plus	PPO-FEE	3550	2370	3880	5610	8240	8370
F55	Aetna Value Plan	PPO-FEE	3640	2430	3280	5810	9580	9880
V42	UnitedHealthcare HDHP	HDHP	3870	1080	3280	5870	9370	10030
F52	Aetna HealthFund CDHP	CDHP	7930	3190	5320	6840	9130	12740
JP2	MD-IPA	HMO	10030	6690	7380	9050	11210	16690
2G2	CareFirst-Hi	HMO	10250	6840	8110	9260	10910	11840
JN2	Aetna Open Access-Hi	HMO	15630	10430	10960	12290	13860	17280
National Plans When You Use Preferred Providers								
325	NALC CDHP	CDHP	2800	-490	1200	4280	7600	15110
342	GEHA HDHP	HDHP	3240	660	2540	4480	6370	12160
382	Rural Carrier†	PPO-FEE	3620	2420	3590	4860	6920	6920
402	Foreign Service†	PPO-FEE	3870	2580	3660	4920	6590	9580
225	Aetna HealthFund HDHP	HDHP	3660	940	2990	4980	7220	9290
322	NALC-Hi	PPO-FEE	4090	2770	3500	5030	6910	11770
315	GEHA-Std	PPO-FEE	3070	2050	2810	5240	8700	9550
N62	Aetna Direct CDHP	CDHP	3630	620	3020	5260	8460	9270
475	APWU CDHP	CDHP	3630	60	2360	5300	8380	13060
455	MHBP-Std	PPO-FEE	3700	2510	3630	5320	7450	14510
112	Blue Cross Basic	PPO	4160	2770	3480	5410	7850	13770
482	MHBP HDHP	HDHP	3600	640	3150	5650	8170	14440
KM2	NALC Value Plan	PPO-FEE	2300	1370	3060	6100	9460	14770
422	Compass Rose†	PPO-FEE	5930	3950	5120	6330	8140	9420
415	MHBP Value Plan	PPO-FEE	3280	2230	4230	6700	9980	15430
472	APWU-Hi	PPO-FEE	5980	4030	5230	6810	8920	13030
312	GEHA-Hi	PPO-FEE	6440	4290	5000	6910	9360	11290
445	SAMBA-Std	PPO-FEE	5420	3610	4750	7170	10240	17610
105	Blue Cross-Std	PPO-FEE	6510	4340	5650	7510	9860	14340
442	SAMBA-Hi	PPO-FEE	12160	8110	9170	11250	13870	20110

* These are the premiums after tax savings, offset by savings accounts for plans that offer them. If you have no or low health-care costs with these plans, it can result in actual saving to you, which we indicate with a negative number.

Persons 55 to 64: Postal Premiums (Category 1)		Family of Three				
			Estimated yearly out-of-pocket costs, including premium and typical hospital, medical, drug, and dental bills near:			
		Plan type	Published premium	No costs*	Low use: $3,000 or less	Average cost	High use: $30,000 or more	Limit to you

Plan code	Plan name	Plan type	Published premium	No costs*	Low use: $3,000 or less	Average cost	High use: $30,000 or more	Limit to you
DC Area Plans When You Use Preferred Providers								
E32	Kaiser-Hi	HMO	4150	2770	3050	4130	5200	7270
E35	Kaiser-Std	HMO	3170	2110	2510	4220	5950	9110
T72	Kaiser-Basic	HMO	3020	2010	2790	4980	7440	10010
B62	CareFirst HDHP	HDHP	3950	1740	3460	5070	6680	9140
JN5	Aetna Open Access Basic	HMO	4140	2760	3410	5230	7210	9610
LR2	UnitedHealthcare Choice	HMO	4150	2770	3590	5660	7920	12770
2G5	CareFirst-Std POS	HMO-POS	5650	3770	4710	5690	6740	8770
L92	UnitedHealthcare Choice Plus	PPO-FEE	3550	2370	3880	5820	8240	8370
F55	Aetna Value Plan	PPO-FEE	3640	2430	3280	6090	9580	9880
V42	UnitedHealthcare HDHP	HDHP	3870	1080	3280	6160	9370	10030
F52	Aetna HealthFund CDHP	CDHP	7930	3190	5320	7050	9130	12740
JP2	MD-IPA	HMO	10030	6690	7380	9230	11210	16690
2G2	CareFirst-Hi	HMO	10250	6840	8110	9400	10910	11840
JN2	Aetna Open Access-Hi	HMO	15630	10430	10960	12430	13860	17280
National Plans When You Use Preferred Providers								
325	NALC CDHP	CDHP	2800	-490	1200	4610	7600	15110
342	GEHA HDHP	HDHP	3240	660	2540	4690	6370	12160
382	Rural Carrier[†]	PPO-FEE	3620	2420	3590	5010	6920	6920
402	Foreign Service[†]	PPO-FEE	3870	2580	3660	5070	6590	9580
322	NALC-Hi	PPO-FEE	4090	2770	3500	5200	6910	11770
225	Aetna HealthFund HDHP	HDHP	3660	940	2990	5210	7220	9290
315	GEHA-Std	PPO-FEE	3070	2050	2810	5500	8700	9550
455	MHBP-Std	PPO-FEE	3700	2510	3630	5510	7450	14510
N62	Aetna Direct CDHP	CDHP	3630	620	3020	5530	8460	9270
475	APWU CDHP	CDHP	3630	60	2360	5600	8380	13060
112	Blue Cross Basic	PPO	4160	2770	3480	5620	7850	13770
482	MHBP HDHP	HDHP	3600	640	3150	5920	8170	14440
KM2	NALC Value Plan	PPO-FEE	2300	1370	3060	6420	9460	14770
422	Compass Rose[†]	PPO-FEE	5930	3950	5120	6480	8140	9420
472	APWU-Hi	PPO-FEE	5980	4030	5230	6990	8920	13030
415	MHBP Value Plan	PPO-FEE	3280	2230	4230	6990	9980	15430
312	GEHA-Hi	PPO-FEE	6440	4290	5000	7120	9360	11290
445	SAMBA-Std	PPO-FEE	5420	3610	4750	7430	10240	17610
105	Blue Cross-Std	PPO-FEE	6510	4340	5650	7720	9860	14340
442	SAMBA-Hi	PPO-FEE	12160	8110	9170	11480	13870	20110

† Plan is open only to specific groups.

Persons 55 to 64: Postal Premiums (Category 2)		Self Only					
		Plan type	Published premium	Estimated yearly out-of-pocket costs, including premium and typical hospital, medical, drug, and dental bills near:			
Plan code	Plan name			No costs*	Low use: $3,000 or less	Average cost	High use: $30,000 or more	Limit to you

Plan code	Plan name	Plan type	Published premium	No costs*	Low use: $3,000 or less	Average cost	High use: $30,000 or more	Limit to you
DC Area Plans When You Use Preferred Providers								
E31	Kaiser-Hi	HMO	1640	1100	1120	1760	3350	3350
E34	Kaiser-Std	HMO	1260	840	910	1850	4340	4340
B61	CareFirst HDHP	HDHP	1520	560	1070	2130	4420	5010
T71	Kaiser-Basic	HMO	1150	760	980	2160	4760	4760
L91	UnitedHealthcare Choice Plus	PPO-FEE	1150	770	1300	2310	3770	3770
2G4	CareFirst-Std POS	HMO-POS	2030	1360	1800	2350	3860	3860
JN4	Aetna Open Access Basic	HMO	1660	1110	1210	2400	5650	6110
V41	UnitedHealthcare HDHP	HDHP	1410	190	790	2450	5240	5240
LR1	UnitedHealthcare Choice	HMO	1510	1010	1200	2470	6010	6010
F54	Aetna Value Plan	PPO-FEE	1450	970	1220	2770	6270	6270
JP1	MD-IPA	HMO	2320	1550	1690	2860	6150	6550
F51	Aetna HealthFund CDHP	CDHP	3380	1200	1800	3100	6550	6550
2G1	CareFirst-Hi	HMO	3970	2650	3190	3870	5150	5150
JN1	Aetna Open Access-Hi	HMO	6950	4630	4700	5650	8120	8630
National Plans When You Use Preferred Providers								
341	GEHA HDHP	HDHP	1250	80	580	2050	4890	5830
324	NALC CDHP	CDHP	1160	-390	-30	2120	7410	7410
401	Foreign Service†	PPO-FEE	1430	950	1230	2210	4720	5950
224	Aetna HealthFund HDHP	HDHP	1510	260	780	2270	5010	5010
N61	Aetna Direct CDHP	CDHP	1310	-20	680	2410	5880	5880
474	APWU CDHP	CDHP	1380	-240	410	2430	6260	6260
321	NALC-Hi	PPO-FEE	1720	1180	1400	2470	5150	7780
111	Blue Cross Basic	PPO	1590	1060	1180	2540	6270	6560
314	GEHA-Std	PPO-FEE	1190	790	1020	2610	6790	6790
481	MHBP HDHP	HDHP	1410	80	830	2680	5840	6980
421	Compass Rose†	PPO-FEE	2060	1380	1690	2700	5320	6850
454	MHBP-Std	PPO-FEE	1450	1010	1290	2750	6960	7010
381	Rural Carrier†	PPO-FEE	1940	1290	1800	2750	5290	5290
KM1	NALC Value Plan	PPO-FEE	950	570	940	2970	7270	7270
471	APWU-Hi	PPO-FEE	2090	1430	1880	3050	6830	6930
311	GEHA-Hi	PPO-FEE	2360	1580	1800	3150	7080	7080
414	MHBP Value Plan	PPO-FEE	1240	870	1340	3250	7470	7470
104	Blue Cross-Std	PPO-FEE	2610	1740	2170	3450	6740	6740
444	SAMBA-Std	PPO-FEE	2210	1470	1820	3550	8470	8470
441	SAMBA-Hi	PPO-FEE	4660	3110	3430	4960	9110	9110

* These are the premiums after tax savings, offset by savings accounts for plans that offer them. If you have no or low health-care costs with these plans, it can result in actual saving to you, which we indicate with a negative number.

Persons 55 to 64: Postal Premiums (Category 2)		Self Plus One						
		Plan type	Published premium	Estimated yearly out-of-pocket costs, including premium and typical hospital, medical, drug, and dental bills near:				
Plan code	Plan name			No costs*	Low use: $3,000 or less	Average cost	High use: $30,000 or more	Limit to you
DC Area Plans When You Use Preferred Providers								
E36	Kaiser-Std	HMO	2890	1930	2330	3880	5770	8930
2G6	CareFirst-Std POS	HMO-POS	3450	2300	3240	4110	5270	7300
B63	CareFirst HDHP	HDHP	3040	1130	2850	4280	6070	8530
E33	Kaiser-Hi	HMO	4750	3170	3450	4420	5600	7670
T73	Kaiser-Basic	HMO	2510	1670	2450	4420	7100	9670
JN6	Aetna Open Access Basic	HMO	3470	2310	2960	4610	6760	9160
JP3	MD-IPA	HMO	3490	2330	3020	4690	6850	12330
L93	UnitedHealthcare Choice Plus	PPO-FEE	2250	1500	3010	4740	7370	7500
LR3	UnitedHealthcare Choice	HMO	3250	2170	2990	4860	7320	12170
V43	UnitedHealthcare HDHP	HDHP	3040	520	2720	5310	8810	9470
F56	Aetna Value Plan	PPO-FEE	3260	2170	3020	5550	9320	9620
F53	Aetna HealthFund CDHP	CDHP	8360	3470	5600	7120	9410	13020
2G3	CareFirst-Hi	HMO	7050	4700	5970	7120	8770	9700
JN3	Aetna Open Access-Hi	HMO	15990	10660	11190	12520	14090	17510
National Plans When You Use Preferred Providers								
326	NALC CDHP	CDHP	2500	-700	990	4070	7390	14900
343	GEHA HDHP	HDHP	2680	290	2170	4110	6000	11790
383	Rural Carrier†	PPO-FEE	3240	2160	3330	4600	6660	6660
403	Foreign Service†	PPO-FEE	3490	2330	3410	4670	6340	9330
226	Aetna HealthFund HDHP	HDHP	3270	680	2730	4720	6960	9030
N63	Aetna Direct CDHP	CDHP	2880	120	2520	4760	7960	8770
316	GEHA-Std	PPO-FEE	2550	1700	2460	4890	8350	9200
476	APWU CDHP	CDHP	3040	-340	1960	4900	7980	12660
323	NALC-Hi	PPO-FEE	4150	2810	3540	5070	6950	11810
456	MHBP-Std	PPO-FEE	3340	2270	3390	5080	7210	14270
113	Blue Cross Basic	PPO	3760	2510	3220	5150	7590	13510
483	MHBP HDHP	HDHP	3130	330	2840	5340	7860	14130
473	APWU-Hi	PPO-FEE	4120	2780	3980	5560	7670	11780
423	Compass Rose†	PPO-FEE	4910	3270	4440	5650	7460	8740
KM3	NALC Value Plan	PPO-FEE	2050	1200	2890	5930	9290	14600
313	GEHA-Hi	PPO-FEE	5560	3710	4420	6330	8780	10710
416	MHBP Value Plan	PPO-FEE	2930	2000	4000	6470	9750	15200
446	SAMBA-Std	PPO-FEE	5220	3480	4620	7040	10110	17480
106	Blue Cross-Std	PPO-FEE	5990	4000	5310	7170	9520	14000
443	SAMBA-Hi	PPO-FEE	10620	7080	8140	10220	12840	19080

† Plan is open only to specific groups.

Persons 55 to 64: Postal Premiums (Category 2)		Family of Two						
				Estimated yearly out-of-pocket costs, including premium and typical hospital, medical, drug, and dental bills near:				
		Plan type	Published premium	No costs*	Low use: $3,000 or less	Average cost	High use: $30,000 or more	Limit to you
Plan code	Plan name							
DC Area Plans When You Use Preferred Providers								
E32	Kaiser-Hi	HMO	3910	2610	2890	3860	5040	7110
E35	Kaiser-Std	HMO	2890	1930	2330	3880	5770	8930
T72	Kaiser-Basic	HMO	2750	1830	2610	4580	7260	9830
B62	CareFirst HDHP	HDHP	3610	1510	3230	4660	6450	8910
JN5	Aetna Open Access Basic	HMO	3890	2590	3240	4890	7040	9440
LR2	UnitedHealthcare Choice	HMO	3930	2620	3440	5310	7770	12620
L92	UnitedHealthcare Choice Plus	PPO-FEE	3230	2160	3670	5400	8030	8160
2G5	CareFirst-Std POS	HMO-POS	5460	3640	4580	5450	6610	8640
F55	Aetna Value Plan	PPO-FEE	3320	2220	3070	5600	9370	9670
V42	UnitedHealthcare HDHP	HDHP	3530	850	3050	5640	9140	9800
F52	Aetna HealthFund CDHP	CDHP	7740	3060	5190	6710	9000	12610
JP2	MD-IPA	HMO	9840	6560	7250	8920	11080	16560
2G2	CareFirst-Hi	HMO	10060	6710	7980	9130	10780	11710
JN2	Aetna Open Access-Hi	HMO	15440	10300	10830	12160	13730	17150
National Plans When You Use Preferred Providers								
325	NALC CDHP	CDHP	2560	-660	1030	4110	7430	14940
342	GEHA HDHP	HDHP	2950	470	2350	4290	6180	11970
382	Rural Carrier†	PPO-FEE	3310	2210	3380	4650	6710	6710
402	Foreign Service†	PPO-FEE	3530	2350	3430	4690	6360	9350
225	Aetna HealthFund HDHP	HDHP	3340	730	2780	4770	7010	9080
322	NALC-Hi	PPO-FEE	3730	2530	3260	4790	6670	11530
N62	Aetna Direct CDHP	CDHP	3310	410	2810	5050	8250	9060
315	GEHA-Std	PPO-FEE	2800	1870	2630	5060	8520	9370
475	APWU CDHP	CDHP	3310	-160	2140	5080	8160	12840
455	MHBP-Std	PPO-FEE	3370	2290	3410	5100	7230	14290
112	Blue Cross Basic	PPO	3950	2640	3350	5280	7720	13640
482	MHBP HDHP	HDHP	3280	430	2940	5440	7960	14230
KM2	NALC Value Plan	PPO-FEE	2100	1240	2930	5970	9330	14640
422	Compass Rose†	PPO-FEE	5740	3830	5000	6210	8020	9300
415	MHBP Value Plan	PPO-FEE	2990	2040	4040	6510	9790	15240
472	APWU-Hi	PPO-FEE	5800	3900	5100	6680	8790	12900
312	GEHA-Hi	PPO-FEE	6250	4170	4880	6790	9240	11170
445	SAMBA-Std	PPO-FEE	5230	3490	4630	7050	10120	17490
105	Blue Cross-Std	PPO-FEE	6320	4210	5520	7380	9730	14210
442	SAMBA-Hi	PPO-FEE	11970	7980	9040	11120	13740	19980

* These are the premiums after tax savings, offset by savings accounts for plans that offer them. If you have no or low health-care costs with these plans, it can result in actual saving to you, which we indicate with a negative number.

60

Persons 55 to 64: Postal Premiums (Category 2)		Family of Three						
				Estimated yearly out-of-pocket costs, including premium and typical hospital, medical, drug, and dental bills near:				
		Plan type	Published premium	No costs*	Low use: $3,000 or less	Average cost	High use: $30,000 or more	Limit to you
Plan code	Plan name							
DC Area Plans When You Use Preferred Providers								
E32	Kaiser-Hi	HMO	3910	2610	2890	3970	5040	7110
E35	Kaiser-Std	HMO	2890	1930	2330	4040	5770	8930
T72	Kaiser-Basic	HMO	2750	1830	2610	4800	7260	9830
B62	CareFirst HDHP	HDHP	3610	1510	3230	4840	6450	8910
JN5	Aetna Open Access Basic	HMO	3890	2590	3240	5060	7040	9440
LR2	UnitedHealthcare Choice	HMO	3930	2620	3440	5510	7770	12620
2G5	CareFirst-Std POS	HMO-POS	5460	3640	4580	5560	6610	8640
L92	UnitedHealthcare Choice Plus	PPO-FEE	3230	2160	3670	5610	8030	8160
F55	Aetna Value Plan	PPO-FEE	3320	2220	3070	5880	9370	9670
V42	UnitedHealthcare HDHP	HDHP	3530	850	3050	5930	9140	9800
F52	Aetna HealthFund CDHP	CDHP	7740	3060	5190	6920	9000	12610
JP2	MD-IPA	HMO	9840	6560	7250	9100	11080	16560
2G2	CareFirst-Hi	HMO	10060	6710	7980	9270	10780	11710
JN2	Aetna Open Access-Hi	HMO	15440	10300	10830	12300	13730	17150
National Plans When You Use Preferred Providers								
325	NALC CDHP	CDHP	2560	-660	1030	4440	7430	14940
342	GEHA HDHP	HDHP	2950	470	2350	4500	6180	11970
382	Rural Carrier[†]	PPO-FEE	3310	2210	3380	4800	6710	6710
402	Foreign Service[†]	PPO-FEE	3530	2350	3430	4840	6360	9350
322	NALC-Hi	PPO-FEE	3730	2530	3260	4960	6670	11530
225	Aetna HealthFund HDHP	HDHP	3340	730	2780	5000	7010	9080
455	MHBP-Std	PPO-FEE	3370	2290	3410	5290	7230	14290
N62	Aetna Direct CDHP	CDHP	3310	410	2810	5320	8250	9060
315	GEHA-Std	PPO-FEE	2800	1870	2630	5320	8520	9370
475	APWU CDHP	CDHP	3310	-160	2140	5380	8160	12840
112	Blue Cross Basic	PPO	3950	2640	3350	5490	7720	13640
482	MHBP HDHP	HDHP	3280	430	2940	5710	7960	14230
KM2	NALC Value Plan	PPO-FEE	2100	1240	2930	6290	9330	14640
422	Compass Rose[†]	PPO-FEE	5740	3830	5000	6360	8020	9300
415	MHBP Value Plan	PPO-FEE	2990	2040	4040	6800	9790	15240
472	APWU-Hi	PPO-FEE	5800	3900	5100	6860	8790	12900
312	GEHA-Hi	PPO-FEE	6250	4170	4880	7000	9240	11170
445	SAMBA-Std	PPO-FEE	5230	3490	4630	7310	10120	17490
105	Blue Cross-Std	PPO-FEE	6320	4210	5520	7590	9730	14210
442	SAMBA-Hi	PPO-FEE	11970	7980	9040	11350	13740	19980

[†] Plan is open only to specific groups.

Half-Time Employees Under 55: GS Premiums		Self Only						
		Plan type	Published premium	Estimated yearly out-of-pocket costs, including premium and typical hospital, medical, drug, and dental bills near:				
Plan code	Plan name			No costs*	Low use: $3,000 or less	Average cost	High use: $30,000 or more	Limit to you
DC Area Plans When You Use Preferred Providers								
E34	Kaiser-Std	HMO	3790	2530	2600	3150	6030	6030
T71	Kaiser-Basic	HMO	3450	2300	2520	3200	6300	6300
L91	UnitedHealthcare Choice Plus	PPO-FEE	3470	2320	2850	3420	5320	5320
V41	UnitedHealthcare HDHP	HDHP	4250	2090	2690	3650	7140	7140
B61	CareFirst HDHP	HDHP	4570	2600	3110	3700	6460	7050
E31	Kaiser-Hi	HMO	4950	3300	3320	3700	5550	5550
LR1	UnitedHealthcare Choice	HMO	4560	3040	3230	3960	8040	8040
F54	Aetna Value Plan	PPO-FEE	4370	2920	3170	4070	8220	8220
JN4	Aetna Open Access Basic	HMO	4970	3320	3420	4110	7860	8320
2G4	CareFirst-Std POS	HMO-POS	5340	3560	4000	4280	6060	6060
JP1	MD-IPA	HMO	5630	3760	3900	4570	8360	8760
F51	Aetna HealthFund CDHP	CDHP	6690	3410	4010	4730	8760	8760
2G1	CareFirst-Hi	HMO	7280	4860	5400	5760	7360	7360
JN1	Aetna Open Access-Hi	HMO	10260	6840	6910	7460	10330	10840
National Plans When You Use Preferred Providers								
324	NALC CDHP	CDHP	3480	1160	1520	2780	8960	8960
341	GEHA HDHP	HDHP	3760	1760	2260	3100	6570	7510
KM1	NALC Value Plan	PPO-FEE	2860	1840	2210	3400	8540	8540
N61	Aetna Direct CDHP	CDHP	3960	1740	2440	3420	7640	7640
474	APWU CDHP	CDHP	4160	1610	2260	3430	8110	8110
314	GEHA-Std	PPO-FEE	3570	2380	2610	3530	8380	8380
224	Aetna HealthFund HDHP	HDHP	4560	2290	2810	3670	7040	7040
401	Foreign Service†	PPO-FEE	4290	2860	3140	3690	6630	7860
481	MHBP HDHP	HDHP	4260	1980	2730	3790	7740	8880
454	MHBP-Std	PPO-FEE	4370	2960	3240	4070	8910	8960
414	MHBP Value Plan	PPO-FEE	3730	2530	3000	4100	9130	9130
111	Blue Cross Basic	PPO	4790	3200	3320	4110	8410	8700
321	NALC-Hi	PPO-FEE	5030	3390	3610	4210	7360	9990
421	Compass Rose†	PPO-FEE	5380	3590	3900	4460	7530	9060
381	Rural Carrier†	PPO-FEE	5250	3500	4010	4530	7500	7500
471	APWU-Hi	PPO-FEE	5400	3640	4090	4730	9040	9140
311	GEHA-Hi	PPO-FEE	5670	3780	4000	4770	9280	9280
444	SAMBA-Std	PPO-FEE	5520	3680	4030	5020	10680	10680
104	Blue Cross-Std	PPO-FEE	5920	3950	4380	5100	8950	8950
441	SAMBA-Hi	PPO-FEE	7970	5320	5640	6510	11320	11320

* These are the premiums after tax savings, offset by savings accounts for plans that offer them. If you have no or low health-care costs with these plans, it can result in actual saving to you, which we indicate with a negative number.

62

Half-Time Employees Under 55: GS Premiums			Self Plus One				
			Estimated yearly out-of-pocket costs, including premium and typical hospital, medical, drug, and dental bills near:				
		Plan type	Published premium	No costs*	Low use: $3,000 or less	Average cost	High use: $30,000 or more	Limit to you
Plan code	Plan name	Plan type	Published premium	No costs*	Low use: $3,000 or less	Average cost	High use: $30,000 or more	Limit to you

Plan code	Plan name	Plan type	Published premium	No costs*	Low use: $3,000 or less	Average cost	High use: $30,000 or more	Limit to you
DC Area Plans When You Use Preferred Providers								
T73	Kaiser-Basic	HMO	7550	5030	5810	6720	10460	13030
L93	UnitedHealthcare Choice Plus	PPO-FEE	6790	4530	6040	6750	10400	10530
E36	Kaiser-Std	HMO	8710	5810	6210	6960	9650	12810
B63	CareFirst HDHP	HDHP	9150	5200	6920	7390	10140	12600
V43	UnitedHealthcare HDHP	HDHP	9140	4600	6800	7850	12890	13550
LR3	UnitedHealthcare Choice	HMO	9800	6540	7360	8200	11690	16540
2G6	CareFirst-Std POS	HMO-POS	10400	6940	7880	8210	9910	11940
JN6	Aetna Open Access Basic	HMO	10450	6970	7620	8380	11420	13820
JP3	MD-IPA	HMO	10510	7010	7700	8450	11530	17010
E33	Kaiser-Hi	HMO	11840	7900	8180	8640	10330	12400
F56	Aetna Value Plan	PPO-FEE	9820	6550	7400	8660	13700	14000
F53	Aetna HealthFund CDHP	CDHP	15450	8210	10340	10720	14150	17760
2G3	CareFirst-Hi	HMO	14140	9430	10700	11130	13500	14430
JN3	Aetna Open Access-Hi	HMO	23080	15400	15930	16530	18830	22250
National Plans When You Use Preferred Providers								
326	NALC CDHP	CDHP	7530	2660	4350	5680	10750	18260
343	GEHA HDHP	HDHP	8080	3890	5770	6510	9600	15390
KM3	NALC Value Plan	PPO-FEE	6180	3960	5650	7010	12050	17360
316	GEHA-Std	PPO-FEE	7680	5120	5880	7110	11770	12620
N63	Aetna Direct CDHP	CDHP	8680	3990	6390	7200	11830	12640
476	APWU CDHP	CDHP	9150	3740	6040	7260	12060	16740
226	Aetna HealthFund HDHP	HDHP	9850	5070	7120	7840	11350	13420
483	MHBP HDHP	HDHP	9420	4530	7040	8050	12060	18330
383	Rural Carrier[†]	PPO-FEE	9760	6510	7680	8210	11010	11010
403	Foreign Service[†]	PPO-FEE	10520	7010	8090	8550	11020	14010
456	MHBP-Std	PPO-FEE	10060	6750	7870	8550	11690	18750
113	Blue Cross Basic	PPO	10850	7240	7950	8830	12320	18240
416	MHBP Value Plan	PPO-FEE	8830	5930	7930	8840	13680	19130
323	NALC-Hi	PPO-FEE	11250	7540	8270	8950	11680	16540
473	APWU-Hi	PPO-FEE	11210	7510	8710	9350	12400	16510
423	Compass Rose[†]	PPO-FEE	12000	8000	9170	9590	12190	13470
313	GEHA-Hi	PPO-FEE	12650	8440	9150	10080	13510	15440
446	SAMBA-Std	PPO-FEE	12310	8210	9350	10440	14840	22210
106	Blue Cross-Std	PPO-FEE	13090	8730	10040	10790	14250	18730
443	SAMBA-Hi	PPO-FEE	17710	11810	12870	13790	17570	23810

† Plan is open only to specific groups.

Half-Time Employees Under 55: GS Premiums		Family of Three					
		Plan type	Published premium	Estimated yearly out-of-pocket costs, including premium and typical hospital, medical, drug, and dental bills near:			
Plan code	Plan name			No costs*	Low use: $3,000 or less	Average cost	High use: $30,000 or more	Limit to you

Plan code	Plan name	Plan type	Published premium	No costs*	Low use: $3,000 or less	Average cost	High use: $30,000 or more	Limit to you
DC Area Plans When You Use Preferred Providers								
E35	Kaiser-Std	HMO	8710	5810	6210	7140	9650	12810
T72	Kaiser-Basic	HMO	8280	5530	6310	7480	10960	13530
E32	Kaiser-Hi	HMO	11450	7630	7910	8490	10060	12130
B62	CareFirst HDHP	HDHP	10870	6350	8070	8790	11290	13750
L92	UnitedHealthcare Choice Plus	PPO-FEE	9740	6500	8010	8990	12370	12500
F55	Aetna Value Plan	PPO-FEE	10010	6680	7530	9110	13830	14130
V42	UnitedHealthcare HDHP	HDHP	10630	5590	7790	9240	13880	14540
JN5	Aetna Open Access Basic	HMO	11420	7620	8270	9250	12070	14470
LR2	UnitedHealthcare Choice	HMO	11460	7640	8460	9540	12790	17640
2G5	CareFirst-Std POS	HMO-POS	13000	8670	9610	10070	11640	13670
F52	Aetna HealthFund CDHP	CDHP	15270	8090	10220	10890	14030	17640
JP2	MD-IPA	HMO	17370	11590	12280	13250	16110	21590
2G2	CareFirst-Hi	HMO	17600	11740	13010	13630	15810	16740
JN2	Aetna Open Access-Hi	HMO	22980	15330	15860	16630	18760	22180
National Plans When You Use Preferred Providers								
325	NALC CDHP	CDHP	7700	2770	4460	6220	10860	18370
342	GEHA HDHP	HDHP	8890	4430	6310	7360	10140	15930
KM2	NALC Value Plan	PPO-FEE	6320	4050	5740	7510	12140	17450
315	GEHA-Std	PPO-FEE	8450	5630	6390	7910	12280	13130
475	APWU CDHP	CDHP	9980	4290	6590	8250	12610	17290
225	Aetna HealthFund HDHP	HDHP	10050	5200	7250	8300	11480	13550
N62	Aetna Direct CDHP	CDHP	9980	4860	7260	8440	12700	13510
382	Rural Carrier†	PPO-FEE	9960	6640	7810	8530	11140	11140
482	MHBP HDHP	HDHP	9890	4840	7350	8760	12370	18640
402	Foreign Service†	PPO-FEE	10620	7080	8160	8820	11090	14080
455	MHBP-Std	PPO-FEE	10150	6810	7930	8860	11750	18810
322	NALC-Hi	PPO-FEE	11240	7530	8260	9140	11670	16530
415	MHBP Value Plan	PPO-FEE	9010	6050	8050	9340	13800	19250
112	Blue Cross Basic	PPO	11490	7660	8370	9500	12740	18660
422	Compass Rose†	PPO-FEE	13270	8850	10020	10640	13040	14320
472	APWU-Hi	PPO-FEE	13330	8930	10130	11000	13820	17930
445	SAMBA-Std	PPO-FEE	12760	8510	9650	11050	15140	22510
312	GEHA-Hi	PPO-FEE	13780	9190	9900	11070	14260	16190
105	Blue Cross-Std	PPO-FEE	13850	9240	10550	11570	14760	19240
442	SAMBA-Hi	PPO-FEE	19500	13010	14070	15270	18770	25010

* These are the premiums after tax savings, offset by savings accounts for plans that offer them. If you have no or low health-care costs with these plans, it can result in actual saving to you, which we indicate with a negative number.

64

Four-Fifths-Time Employees Under 55: GS Premiums		Self Only					
		Plan type	Published premium	Estimated yearly out-of-pocket costs, including premium and typical hospital, medical, drug, and dental bills near:			
Plan code	Plan name			No costs*	Low use: $3,000 or less	Average cost	High use: $30,000 or more	Limit to you

Plan code	Plan name	Plan type	Published premium	No costs*	Low use: $3,000 or less	Average cost	High use: $30,000 or more	Limit to you
DC Area Plans When You Use Preferred Providers								
E34	Kaiser-Std	HMO	2420	1620	2490	3040	5920	5920
T71	Kaiser-Basic	HMO	2210	1470	2430	3110	6210	6210
L91	UnitedHealthcare Choice Plus	PPO-FEE	2220	1480	2750	3320	5220	5220
E31	Kaiser-Hi	HMO	3170	2110	3190	3570	5420	5420
LR1	UnitedHealthcare Choice	HMO	2920	1950	3110	3840	7920	7920
F54	Aetna Value Plan	PPO-FEE	2800	1870	3050	3950	8100	8100
JN4	Aetna Open Access Basic	HMO	3190	2120	3290	3980	7730	8190
B61	CareFirst HDHP	HDHP	2930	1500	3440	4030	6790	7380
2G4	CareFirst-Std POS	HMO-POS	3550	2370	3990	4270	6050	6050
V41	UnitedHealthcare HDHP	HDHP	2720	1070	3320	4280	7770	7770
JP1	MD-IPA	HMO	3840	2560	3980	4650	8440	8840
F51	Aetna HealthFund CDHP	CDHP	4900	2220	5500	6220	10250	10250
2G1	CareFirst-Hi	HMO	5490	3660	6030	6390	7990	7990
JN1	Aetna Open Access-Hi	HMO	8470	5650	8540	9090	11960	12470
National Plans When You Use Preferred Providers								
KM1	NALC Value Plan	PPO-FEE	1830	1160	2200	3390	8530	8530
314	GEHA-Std	PPO-FEE	2290	1520	2520	3440	8290	8290
401	Foreign Service†	PPO-FEE	2750	1830	3030	3580	6520	7750
341	GEHA HDHP	HDHP	2410	850	2910	3750	7220	8160
324	NALC CDHP	CDHP	2230	320	2590	3850	10030	10030
454	MHBP-Std	PPO-FEE	2800	1910	3080	3910	8750	8800
414	MHBP Value Plan	PPO-FEE	2390	1630	2860	3960	8990	8990
111	Blue Cross Basic	PPO	3070	2050	3190	3980	8280	8570
321	NALC-Hi	PPO-FEE	3240	2200	3460	4060	7210	9840
N61	Aetna Direct CDHP	CDHP	2530	790	3230	4210	8430	8430
224	Aetna HealthFund HDHP	HDHP	2920	1190	3440	4300	7670	7670
421	Compass Rose†	PPO-FEE	3590	2390	3900	4460	7530	9060
474	APWU CDHP	CDHP	2660	610	3310	4480	9160	9160
381	Rural Carrier†	PPO-FEE	3460	2310	3970	4490	7460	7460
481	MHBP HDHP	HDHP	2730	960	3480	4540	8490	9630
471	APWU-Hi	PPO-FEE	3610	2440	4060	4700	9010	9110
311	GEHA-Hi	PPO-FEE	3880	2590	4100	4870	9380	9380
444	SAMBA-Std	PPO-FEE	3730	2490	4080	5070	10730	10730
104	Blue Cross-Std	PPO-FEE	4130	2760	4560	5280	9130	9130
441	SAMBA-Hi	PPO-FEE	6180	4120	6500	7370	12180	12180

† Plan is open only to specific groups.

Four-Fifths-Time Employees Under 55: GS Premiums				Self Plus One				
				Estimated yearly out-of-pocket costs, including premium and typical hospital, medical, drug, and dental bills near:				
Plan code	Plan name	Plan type	Published premium	No costs*	Low use: $3,000 or less	Average cost	High use: $30,000 or more	Limit to you
DC Area Plans When You Use Preferred Providers								
E36	Kaiser-Std	HMO	5580	3720	4120	4870	7560	10720
T73	Kaiser-Basic	HMO	4830	3220	4000	4910	8650	11220
L93	UnitedHealthcare Choice Plus	PPO-FEE	4340	2900	4410	5120	8770	8900
B63	CareFirst HDHP	HDHP	5850	3000	4720	5190	7940	10400
V43	UnitedHealthcare HDHP	HDHP	5850	2400	4600	5650	10690	11350
2G6	CareFirst-Std POS	HMO-POS	6660	4440	5380	5710	7410	9440
LR3	UnitedHealthcare Choice	HMO	6270	4190	5010	5850	9340	14190
JN6	Aetna Open Access Basic	HMO	6690	4460	5110	5870	8910	11310
JP3	MD-IPA	HMO	6730	4490	5180	5930	9010	14490
E33	Kaiser-Hi	HMO	8010	5340	5620	6080	7770	9840
F56	Aetna Value Plan	PPO-FEE	6280	4190	5040	6300	11340	11640
F53	Aetna HealthFund CDHP	CDHP	11620	5650	7780	8160	11590	15200
2G3	CareFirst-Hi	HMO	10310	6880	8150	8580	10950	11880
JN3	Aetna Open Access-Hi	HMO	19250	12840	13370	13970	16270	19690
National Plans When You Use Preferred Providers								
326	NALC CDHP	CDHP	4820	850	2540	3870	8940	16450
343	GEHA HDHP	HDHP	5170	1950	3830	4570	7660	13450
476	APWU CDHP	CDHP	5850	1540	3840	5060	9860	14540
N63	Aetna Direct CDHP	CDHP	5550	1900	4300	5110	9740	10550
316	GEHA-Std	PPO-FEE	4910	3280	4040	5270	9930	10780
226	Aetna HealthFund HDHP	HDHP	6310	2710	4760	5480	8990	11060
KM3	NALC Value Plan	PPO-FEE	3960	2470	4160	5520	10560	15870
483	MHBP HDHP	HDHP	6030	2260	4770	5780	9790	16060
383	Rural Carrier†	PPO-FEE	6250	4170	5340	5870	8670	8670
403	Foreign Service†	PPO-FEE	6730	4490	5570	6030	8500	11490
456	MHBP-Std	PPO-FEE	6440	4330	5450	6130	9270	16330
113	Blue Cross Basic	PPO	7020	4680	5390	6270	9760	15680
323	NALC-Hi	PPO-FEE	7420	4980	5710	6390	9120	13980
416	MHBP Value Plan	PPO-FEE	5650	3810	5810	6720	11560	17010
473	APWU-Hi	PPO-FEE	7380	4960	6160	6800	9850	13960
423	Compass Rose†	PPO-FEE	8170	5450	6620	7040	9640	10920
313	GEHA-Hi	PPO-FEE	8820	5890	6600	7530	10960	12890
446	SAMBA-Std	PPO-FEE	8480	5660	6800	7890	12290	19660
106	Blue Cross-Std	PPO-FEE	9260	6170	7480	8230	11690	16170
443	SAMBA-Hi	PPO-FEE	13880	9260	10320	11240	15020	21260

* These are the premiums after tax savings, offset by savings accounts for plans that offer them. If you have no or low health-care costs with these plans, it can result in actual saving to you, which we indicate with a negative number.

Four-Fifths-Time Employees Under 55: GS Premiums		Family of Three					
				Estimated yearly out-of-pocket costs, including premium and typical hospital, medical, drug, and dental bills near:			
		Plan type	Published premium	No costs*	Low use: $3,000 or less	Average cost	High use: $30,000 or more	Limit to you
Plan code	Plan name	Plan type	Published premium	No costs*	Low use: $3,000 or less	Average cost	High use: $30,000 or more	Limit to you
DC Area Plans When You Use Preferred Providers								
E35	Kaiser-Std	HMO	5580	3720	4120	5050	7560	10720
T72	Kaiser-Basic	HMO	5300	3540	4320	5490	8970	11540
E32	Kaiser-Hi	HMO	7380	4920	5200	5780	7350	9420
B62	CareFirst HDHP	HDHP	6950	3740	5460	6180	8680	11140
JN5	Aetna Open Access Basic	HMO	7350	4910	5560	6540	9360	11760
L92	UnitedHealthcare Choice Plus	PPO-FEE	6240	4160	5670	6650	10030	10160
V42	UnitedHealthcare HDHP	HDHP	6800	3040	5240	6690	11330	11990
F55	Aetna Value Plan	PPO-FEE	6410	4270	5120	6700	11420	11720
LR2	UnitedHealthcare Choice	HMO	7390	4930	5750	6830	10080	14930
2G5	CareFirst-Std POS	HMO-POS	8930	5950	6890	7350	8920	10950
F52	Aetna HealthFund CDHP	CDHP	11200	5370	7500	8170	11310	14920
JP2	MD-IPA	HMO	13300	8870	9560	10530	13390	18870
2G2	CareFirst-Hi	HMO	13530	9020	10290	10910	13090	14020
JN2	Aetna Open Access-Hi	HMO	18910	12610	13140	13910	16040	19460
National Plans When You Use Preferred Providers								
325	NALC CDHP	CDHP	4930	920	2610	4370	9010	16520
342	GEHA HDHP	HDHP	5690	2300	4180	5230	8010	13800
475	APWU CDHP	CDHP	6390	1900	4200	5860	10220	14900
225	Aetna HealthFund HDHP	HDHP	6430	2790	4840	5890	9070	11140
315	GEHA-Std	PPO-FEE	5400	3610	4370	5890	10260	11110
KM2	NALC Value Plan	PPO-FEE	4050	2530	4220	5990	10620	15930
N62	Aetna Direct CDHP	CDHP	6390	2460	4860	6040	10300	11110
382	Rural Carrier†	PPO-FEE	6370	4250	5420	6140	8750	8750
402	Foreign Service†	PPO-FEE	6800	4530	5610	6270	8540	11530
482	MHBP HDHP	HDHP	6330	2470	4980	6390	10000	16270
455	MHBP-Std	PPO-FEE	6500	4380	5500	6430	9320	16380
322	NALC-Hi	PPO-FEE	7190	4830	5560	6440	8970	13830
112	Blue Cross Basic	PPO	7420	4950	5660	6790	10030	15950
415	MHBP Value Plan	PPO-FEE	5770	3890	5890	7180	11640	17090
422	Compass Rose†	PPO-FEE	9200	6140	7310	7930	10330	11610
472	APWU-Hi	PPO-FEE	9260	6210	7410	8280	11100	15210
445	SAMBA-Std	PPO-FEE	8700	5800	6940	8340	12430	19800
312	GEHA-Hi	PPO-FEE	9710	6480	7190	8360	11550	13480
105	Blue Cross-Std	PPO-FEE	9780	6530	7840	8860	12050	16530
442	SAMBA-Hi	PPO-FEE	15440	10300	11360	12560	16060	22300

† Plan is open only to specific groups.

| Persons Under 55 Who Pay Full Premiums | | | | Self Only | | | | |
| | | | | Estimated yearly out-of-pocket costs, including premium and typical hospital, medical, drug, and dental bills near: | | | | |
Plan code	Plan name	Plan type	Published premium	No costs*	Low use: $3,000 or less	Average cost	High use: $30,000 or more	Limit to you
DC Area Plans When You Use Preferred Providers								
T71	Kaiser-Basic	HMO	5520	5520	5740	6420	9520	9520
L91	UnitedHealthcare Choice Plus	PPO-FEE	5560	5560	6090	6660	8560	8560
E34	Kaiser-Std	HMO	6060	6060	6130	6680	9560	9560
V41	UnitedHealthcare HDHP	HDHP	6800	6050	6650	7610	11100	11100
B61	CareFirst HDHP	HDHP	7320	6870	7380	7970	10730	11320
F54	Aetna Value Plan	PPO-FEE	7000	7000	7250	8150	12300	12300
LR1	UnitedHealthcare Choice	HMO	7300	7300	7490	8220	12300	12300
E31	Kaiser-Hi	HMO	7920	7920	7940	8320	10170	10170
JN4	Aetna Open Access Basic	HMO	7950	7950	8050	8740	12490	12950
2G4	CareFirst-Std POS	HMO-POS	8320	8320	8760	9040	10820	10820
JP1	MD-IPA	HMO	8610	8610	8750	9420	13210	13610
F51	Aetna HealthFund CDHP	CDHP	9670	8620	9220	9940	13970	13970
2G1	CareFirst-Hi	HMO	10260	10260	10800	11160	12760	12760
JN1	Aetna Open Access-Hi	HMO	13240	13240	13310	13860	16730	17240
National Plans When You Use Preferred Providers								
324	NALC CDHP	CDHP	5570	4370	4730	5990	12170	12170
KM1	NALC Value Plan	PPO-FEE	4570	4470	4840	6030	11170	11170
341	GEHA HDHP	HDHP	6020	5270	5770	6610	10080	11020
314	GEHA-Std	PPO-FEE	5710	5710	5940	6860	11710	11710
N61	Aetna Direct CDHP	CDHP	6330	5430	6130	7110	11330	11330
474	APWU CDHP	CDHP	6650	5450	6100	7270	11950	11950
414	MHBP Value Plan	PPO-FEE	5960	5960	6430	7530	12560	12560
401	Foreign Service†	PPO-FEE	6870	6870	7150	7700	10640	11870
481	MHBP HDHP	HDHP	6810	5910	6660	7720	11670	12810
224	Aetna HealthFund HDHP	HDHP	7290	6540	7060	7920	11290	11290
454	MHBP-Std	PPO-FEE	6990	6990	7270	8100	12940	12990
111	Blue Cross Basic	PPO	7670	7670	7790	8580	12880	13170
321	NALC-Hi	PPO-FEE	8010	8010	8230	8830	11980	14610
421	Compass Rose†	PPO-FEE	8360	8360	8670	9230	12300	13830
381	Rural Carrier†	PPO-FEE	8230	8230	8740	9260	12230	12230
471	APWU-Hi	PPO-FEE	8380	8380	8830	9470	13780	13880
311	GEHA-Hi	PPO-FEE	8650	8650	8870	9640	14150	14150
444	SAMBA-Std	PPO-FEE	8500	8500	8850	9840	15500	15500
104	Blue Cross-Std	PPO-FEE	8900	8900	9330	10050	13900	13900
441	SAMBA-Hi	PPO-FEE	10950	10950	11270	12140	16950	16950

* These are the premiums after tax savings, offset by savings accounts for plans that offer them. If you have no or low health-care costs with these plans, it can result in actual saving to you, which we indicate with a negative number.

Persons Under 55 Who Pay Full Premiums		Self Plus One						
				Estimated yearly out-of-pocket costs, including premium and typical hospital, medical, drug, and dental bills near:				
Plan code	Plan name	Plan type	Published premium	No costs*	Low use: $3,000 or less	Average cost	High use: $30,000 or more	Limit to you
DC Area Plans When You Use Preferred Providers								
L93	UnitedHealthcare Choice Plus	PPO-FEE	10860	10860	12370	13080	16730	16860
T73	Kaiser-Basic	HMO	12070	12070	12850	13760	17500	20070
E36	Kaiser-Std	HMO	13940	13940	14340	15090	17780	20940
B63	CareFirst HDHP	HDHP	14630	13730	15450	15920	18670	21130
F56	Aetna Value Plan	PPO-FEE	15710	15710	16560	17820	22860	23160
2G6	CareFirst-Std POS	HMO-POS	16650	16650	17590	17920	19620	21650
JN6	Aetna Open Access Basic	HMO	16720	16720	17370	18130	21170	23570
JP3	MD-IPA	HMO	16820	16820	17510	18260	21340	26820
V43	UnitedHealthcare HDHP	HDHP	17010	15510	17710	18760	23800	24460
E33	Kaiser-Hi	HMO	18230	18230	18510	18970	20660	22730
LR3	UnitedHealthcare Choice	HMO	18240	18240	19060	19900	23390	28240
2G3	CareFirst-Hi	HMO	20520	20520	21790	22220	24590	25520
F53	Aetna HealthFund CDHP	CDHP	21830	19730	21860	22240	25670	29280
JN3	Aetna Open Access-Hi	HMO	29460	29460	29990	30590	32890	36310
National Plans When You Use Preferred Providers								
326	NALC CDHP	CDHP	12050	9650	11340	12670	17740	25250
KM3	NALC Value Plan	PPO-FEE	9890	9690	11380	12740	17780	23090
343	GEHA HDHP	HDHP	12930	11430	13310	14050	17140	22930
316	GEHA-Std	PPO-FEE	12280	12280	13040	14270	18930	19780
N63	Aetna Direct CDHP	CDHP	13890	12090	14490	15300	19930	20740
476	APWU CDHP	CDHP	14640	12240	14540	15760	20560	25240
483	MHBP HDHP	HDHP	15080	13280	15790	16800	20810	27080
226	Aetna HealthFund HDHP	HDHP	15760	14260	16310	17030	20540	22610
416	MHBP Value Plan	PPO-FEE	14130	14130	16130	17040	21880	27330
383	Rural Carrier†	PPO-FEE	15620	15620	16790	17320	20120	20120
456	MHBP-Std	PPO-FEE	16090	16090	17210	17890	21030	28090
403	Foreign Service†	PPO-FEE	16830	16830	17910	18370	20840	23830
113	Blue Cross Basic	PPO	17230	17230	17940	18820	22310	28230
323	NALC-Hi	PPO-FEE	17630	17630	18360	19040	21770	26630
473	APWU-Hi	PPO-FEE	17600	17600	18800	19440	22490	26600
423	Compass Rose†	PPO-FEE	18380	18380	19550	19970	22570	23850
313	GEHA-Hi	PPO-FEE	19040	19040	19750	20680	24110	26040
446	SAMBA-Std	PPO-FEE	18700	18700	19840	20930	25330	32700
106	Blue Cross-Std	PPO-FEE	19470	19470	20780	21530	24990	29470
443	SAMBA-Hi	PPO-FEE	24090	24090	25150	26070	29850	36090

† Plan is open only to specific groups.

Persons Under 55 Who Pay Full Premiums		Family of Three					
				Estimated yearly out-of-pocket costs, including premium and typical hospital, medical, drug, and dental bills near:			
		Plan type	Published premium	No costs*	Low use: $3,000 or less	Average cost	High use: $30,000 or more	Limit to you
Plan code	Plan name						

Plan code	Plan name	Plan type	Published premium	No costs*	Low use: $3,000 or less	Average cost	High use: $30,000 or more	Limit to you
DC Area Plans When You Use Preferred Providers								
T72	Kaiser-Basic	HMO	13250	13250	14030	15200	18680	21250
E35	Kaiser-Std	HMO	13940	13940	14340	15270	17780	20940
L92	UnitedHealthcare Choice Plus	PPO-FEE	15590	15590	17100	18080	21460	21590
F55	Aetna Value Plan	PPO-FEE	16020	16020	16870	18450	23170	23470
B62	CareFirst HDHP	HDHP	17380	16480	18200	18920	21420	23880
E32	Kaiser-Hi	HMO	18230	18230	18510	19090	20660	22730
V42	UnitedHealthcare HDHP	HDHP	17010	15510	17710	19160	23800	24460
JN5	Aetna Open Access Basic	HMO	18200	18200	18850	19830	22650	25050
LR2	UnitedHealthcare Choice	HMO	18240	18240	19060	20140	23390	28240
2G5	CareFirst-Std POS	HMO-POS	19780	19780	20720	21180	22750	24780
F52	Aetna HealthFund CDHP	CDHP	22050	19950	22080	22750	25890	29500
JP2	MD-IPA	HMO	24150	24150	24840	25810	28670	34150
2G2	CareFirst-Hi	HMO	24380	24380	25650	26270	28450	29380
JN2	Aetna Open Access-Hi	HMO	29760	29760	30290	31060	33190	36610
National Plans When You Use Preferred Providers								
KM2	NALC Value Plan	PPO-FEE	10110	9910	11600	13370	18000	23310
325	NALC CDHP	CDHP	12320	9920	11610	13370	18010	25520
342	GEHA HDHP	HDHP	14230	12730	14610	15660	18440	24230
315	GEHA-Std	PPO-FEE	13510	13510	14270	15790	20160	21010
475	APWU CDHP	CDHP	15970	13570	15870	17530	21890	26570
225	Aetna HealthFund HDHP	HDHP	16080	14580	16630	17680	20860	22930
415	MHBP Value Plan	PPO-FEE	14410	14410	16410	17700	22160	27610
N62	Aetna Direct CDHP	CDHP	15970	14170	16570	17750	22010	22820
382	Rural Carrier†	PPO-FEE	15930	15930	17100	17820	20430	20430
482	MHBP HDHP	HDHP	15830	14030	16540	17950	21560	27830
455	MHBP-Std	PPO-FEE	16240	16240	17360	18290	21180	28240
402	Foreign Service†	PPO-FEE	16990	16990	18070	18730	21000	23990
322	NALC-Hi	PPO-FEE	17980	17980	18710	19590	22120	26980
112	Blue Cross Basic	PPO	18270	18270	18980	20110	23350	29270
422	Compass Rose†	PPO-FEE	20050	20050	21220	21840	24240	25520
445	SAMBA-Std	PPO-FEE	19550	19550	20690	22090	26180	33550
472	APWU-Hi	PPO-FEE	20110	20110	21310	22180	25000	29110
312	GEHA-Hi	PPO-FEE	20560	20560	21270	22440	25630	27560
105	Blue Cross-Std	PPO-FEE	20630	20630	21940	22960	26150	30630
442	SAMBA-Hi	PPO-FEE	26290	26290	27350	28550	32050	38290

* These are the premiums after tax savings, offset by savings accounts for plans that offer them. If you have no or low health-care costs with these plans, it can result in actual saving to you, which we indicate with a negative number.

(Continued from page 31)
Deductible plans that give you a savings account as large or larger than the premium. With double coverage you will probably not ever reach the high deductible and will realize this saving in most circumstances. In other words, these plans really are almost "free" if they supplement other coverage from your spouse.

Part-Time Employees

Many career Federal employees work part-time schedules. In these cases, most government agencies do not pay the regular share of the premium. Instead, employees receive a *pro rata* amount based on their work schedules. For example, an employee scheduled to work 40 hours per biweekly pay period receives only one half of the regular government contribution and must pay the regular employee contribution plus the extra one half, or about two thirds of the total premium cost for the plan. There are many possible part-time schedules. We present comparisons on the basis of 50 percent and 80 percent of the regular work schedule. Almost all part-time employees are reasonably close to one of these scenarios. (A few agencies, including the Postal Service and the FDIC, give part-time employees the same rates as full-time employees.)

Persons Who Pay Full Premiums

The FEHBP also provides coverage for former spouses, former employees, children turning age 26, and others. In each of these cases, the covered enrollee must pay the full premium without government contribution. This often results, nonetheless, in a better price than is available for non-group insurance purchased individually, which is the only other insurance available to many.

Persons eligible for continuing coverage for as long as needed include:

- Those **former spouses** who have a qualifying court order and meet other conditions. They may enroll in any plan on the same basis as employees and annuitants, except for premiums.
- **Temporary employees** who have worked for one full year also may enroll on the same basis as employees, except for premium cost. (Such employees should switch to permanent employment if at all possible to reduce premium costs by three-fourths.)

Time-limited coverage is also available for several categories of persons. They pay a small surcharge—two percent of the premium—and are eligible only for a limited time:

- **Employees separating from Federal service** for any reason may continue their coverage for 18 months.
- **Children reaching age 26** are, unless severely handicapped, no longer eligible for coverage under their parents' family plan. They may obtain coverage in their own name for 36 months.

- **Former spouses without a qualifying court order** also may enroll for 36 months.

For all purposes except premium contribution, tax shelter, and time limit, a temporary enrollee is treated like a regular enrollee. For example, there is no disqualification for preexisting conditions. There is a 60-day time limit for applying after the qualifying event, but once enrolled a person may switch plans in the next Open Season just like any employee or annuitant. At the end of the temporary period, these persons may switch to a "conversion" plan that is not part of the FEHB program and is sold at individual rather than group rates. However, the costs and coverages of these conversion plans are generally far worse than one can get by shopping on the private market. Some young adults will not have a parent with a family plan, or will become ineligible for family coverage upon reaching age 26. **You can usually (but not always) get better deals from marketplace exchange plans than you would from paying full premiums for the regular FEHBP plans, but must pay careful attention because bronze and silver plans have much higher deductibles and other cost-sharing than FEHBP plans.**

For persons who pay full premiums, we compare plans based on paying both the government and employee share. Although some of these persons must pay a two percent surcharge, we have omitted this factor to avoid the need for extra tables. Under any of the less-costly plans, the surcharge would be under $100 per year for singles and $200 per year for families. These tables do not include premium tax savings because persons who are not current employees are not eligible for this benefit. Of particular importance to former spouses turning age 65, joining Medicare Parts A and B, suspending FEHB enrollment, and enrolling in a Medicare Advantage plan will reduce premium costs by two thirds or more, and provide benefits very nearly as good as those in FEHB plans.

Chapter 4

Cost Comparisons and Advice for Annuitants

As explained in Chapter 2 "Comparing Plan Costs," we rate and compare health plans based on their likely cost to you, taking into account your pay system, employment or retirement status, family size, age, health status, location, and other factors. A key element of our ratings are estimates of likely out-of-pocket costs under each plan, based on actuarial estimates of the size and likelihood of low, average, and high spending for families of different sizes and ages. Our ratings also reflect varying premium levels and tax situations faced by different eligibility groups. For example, unlike employee annuitants do not obtain "Premium Conversion" tax advantages.

Online *Guide* users see a summary cost comparison table for their group, and then have the option to look at tables providing more detailed cost comparisons. Readers of the printed *Guide* see both summary and detailed cost information for their comparison group for all national plans and local plans available in the DC area.

All of these comparisons take into account not only premiums and potential health care costs, but also plan features such as Health Savings Accounts, personal accounts, and Wellness benefits that involve cash rewards. We also include dental benefits and premiums, both for dental benefits built into some health plans and for the costs and benefits of standalone dental plans. For annuitants, our estimates and comparisons also take into account both Medicare benefits and Medicare premiums, depending on choices about Medicare enrollment. In summary, we provide a comprehensive set of financial comparisons that allow users to make "apple to apple" comparisons of costs for both premiums and likely health care expenses under each plan and across all plans for which they are eligible.

Very importantly, our comparisons take into account that a few plans provide both a Medicare "wraparound" and a fund that will pay part of the Medicare Part B premium. The two national plans that provide a complete wraparound for hospital and doctor costs and also fund Part B costs are Aetna Direct (funding offsets up to $900 of Part B premium) and, starting in 2018, Blue Cross Basic Option (funding offsets $600 of Part B premium).

All of our calculations should be considered approximations that will be broadly accurate in the great majority of situations but that cannot provide precise predictions that cover every possible situation. What our calculations also do, therefore, is take into account the risks of ruinously high health care costs from an unexpected illness or accident, and compare the maximum out-of-pocket and premium costs under each plan.

Using the Cost Comparison Tables for Annuitants

We provide rating comparisons for self-only, self plus one, and families of two for annuitants in the print Guide, and additionally for families of sizes three through five online. Comparisons include:

- **Annuitants without Medicare**.
- **Annuitants with Medicare Parts A and B who pay regular premium rates**. These tables include not only the FEHB premium, but also the Part B Medicare premium.
- **Annuitants with Medicare Parts A and B who pay higher "income-tested" rates** (online only).
- **Annuitants who have only Part A of Medicare**, the hospital benefit. You can compare these with the preceding ratings to see how much you gain, or in most cases lose, by paying the Part B premium.

There are many comparisons, but **only one cost comparison table applies to your current situation**. Of course, your situation may

You Can Keep Flexibility Only at a Price

The best two arguments for paying the Medicare Part B premium are to preserve your choices over time, as both the FEHBP and Medicare evolve, and to get you low costs for providers who are not in your plan network. However, this choice is costly.

change if your family changes or if you change your Medicare decisions—and you can compare tables to see those differences. For example, if you are trying to decide whether to enroll in Medicare Part B or not, you can compare plans with or without this option—but be careful to read our advice on this decision, since there are important advantages to Part B enrollment that for most annuitants outweigh its premium costs.

By looking at the different columns in a table, you can find how you will come out under each plan if your expenses range from none to the maximum you could pay in a year. Very importantly for those with Medicare Part B, the "Published premium" column, as well as following columns, includes both FEHB and Part B premiums. These columns also credit you with the savings you gain from a Health Savings Account (HSA) or personal health care account or Health Reimbursement Arrangement (HRA) in plans that give you these benefits (annuitants get the HSA amount as an HRA contribution, as explained in Chapter 8 on "Plan Types and Flexibility"). Personal care accounts and HRAs are the equivalent of a reduction in premium. If you don't spend that account at the end of the year you will have a bank balance in that amount that carries over to the next year. Therefore, the "No costs" column includes your yearly premium adjusted, as pertinent, for the Medicare Part B Premium, HRA account, and any membership dues. These will be

your only out-of-pocket costs if you have no medical bills. We rank the plans in order of average cost to emphasize the importance of each plan's treatment of "average" expenses for a family of a particular size and type.

You begin by making profile choices to find the table that relates to families of your age, premium category, and size. Unless you know something to the contrary, you should expect average expenses in the coming year. The plans that are likely to cost families the least have the lowest dollar figures in this column. But do not choose the highest-ranked plan until you consider whether there is some reason the average column does not apply to you or your family.

In your cost table you will notice that differences among closely ranked plans are often very small. Differences of $100 or less are not important. A different mix of bills from those we use to compare plans could overcome these. Differences of several hundred dollars or more, however, reflect significant variations in how expensively the plans handle most cases.

Notice that most of the higher-ranked plans will save you money in every situation—whether your expenses are high or low—compared to the plans ranked lower in each group on your comparison. You can also see that many HMOs and CDHP and HDHP plans will save you hundreds of dollars compared to most national PPO plans, but that many will not.

Preferred Providers and Annuitants Over Age 65

We rate plan costs based on the assumption that you will always or almost always want to use preferred providers, also known as "staying in the network". However, network problems largely disappear if you have Medicare Parts A and B, since most of the national plans waive doctor and hospital cost-sharing whether you obtain care in or out of the network. Even in HMOs that don't waive these costs, you can use Medicare to go out of network. Therefore, **for retirees who participate in Medicare Parts A and B preferred provider**

(Text continues on page 85)

| Annuitants 55 to 64 Without Medicare | | | | Self Only | | | | |
| | | | | Estimated yearly out-of-pocket costs, including premium and typical hospital, medical, drug, and dental bills near: | | | | |
Plan code	Plan name	Plan type	Published premium	No costs*	Low use: $3,000 or less	Average cost	High use: $30,000 or more	Limit to you
DC Area Plans When You Use Preferred Providers								
E34	Kaiser-Std	HMO	1510	1510	1580	2520	5010	5010
E31	Kaiser-Hi	HMO	1980	1980	2000	2640	4230	4230
T71	Kaiser-Basic	HMO	1380	1380	1600	2780	5380	5380
L91	UnitedHealthcare Choice Plus	PPO-FEE	1390	1390	1920	2930	4390	4390
B61	CareFirst HDHP	HDHP	1830	1380	1890	2950	5240	5830
V41	UnitedHealthcare HDHP	HDHP	1700	950	1550	3210	6000	6000
JN4	Aetna Open Access Basic	HMO	1990	1990	2090	3280	6530	6990
LR1	UnitedHealthcare Choice	HMO	1820	1820	2010	3280	6820	6820
2G4	CareFirst-Std POS	HMO-POS	2360	2360	2800	3350	4860	4860
F54	Aetna Value Plan	PPO-FEE	1750	1750	2000	3550	7050	7050
JP1	MD-IPA	HMO	2650	2650	2790	3960	7250	7650
F51	Aetna HealthFund CDHP	CDHP	3710	2660	3260	4560	8010	8010
2G1	CareFirst-Hi	HMO	4300	4300	4840	5520	6800	6800
JN1	Aetna Open Access-Hi	HMO	7280	7280	7350	8300	10770	11280
National Plans When You Use Preferred Providers								
324	NALC CDHP	CDHP	1390	190	550	2700	7990	7990
341	GEHA HDHP	HDHP	1500	750	1250	2720	5560	6500
401	Foreign Service[†]	PPO-FEE	1720	1720	2000	2980	5490	6720
224	Aetna HealthFund HDHP	HDHP	1820	1070	1590	3080	5820	5820
N61	Aetna Direct CDHP	CDHP	1580	680	1380	3110	6580	6580
474	APWU CDHP	CDHP	1660	460	1110	3130	6960	6960
314	GEHA-Std	PPO-FEE	1430	1430	1660	3250	7430	7430
321	NALC-Hi	PPO-FEE	2050	2050	2270	3340	6020	8650
111	Blue Cross Basic	PPO	1920	1920	2040	3400	7130	7420
481	MHBP HDHP	HDHP	1700	800	1550	3400	6560	7700
KM1	NALC Value Plan	PPO-FEE	1140	1040	1410	3440	7740	7740
454	MHBP-Std	PPO-FEE	1750	1750	2030	3490	7700	7750
421	Compass Rose[†]	PPO-FEE	2390	2390	2700	3710	6330	7860
381	Rural Carrier[†]	PPO-FEE	2270	2270	2780	3730	6270	6270
414	MHBP Value Plan	PPO-FEE	1490	1490	1960	3870	8090	8090
471	APWU-Hi	PPO-FEE	2420	2420	2870	4040	7820	7920
311	GEHA-Hi	PPO-FEE	2690	2690	2910	4260	8190	8190
444	SAMBA-Std	PPO-FEE	2540	2540	2890	4620	9540	9540
104	Blue Cross-Std	PPO-FEE	2940	2940	3370	4650	7940	7940
441	SAMBA-Hi	PPO-FEE	4990	4990	5310	6840	10990	10990

* These are the premiums after tax savings, offset by savings accounts for plans that offer them. If you have no or low health-care costs with these plans, it can result in actual saving to you, which we indicate with a negative number.

Annuitants 55 to 64 Without Medicare				Self Plus One				
		Plan type	Published premium	Estimated yearly out-of-pocket costs, including premium and typical hospital, medical, drug, and dental bills near:				
Plan code	Plan name			No costs*	Low use: $3,000 or less	Average cost	High use: $30,000 or more	Limit to you
DC Area Plans When You Use Preferred Providers								
E36	Kaiser-Std	HMO	3480	3480	3880	5430	7320	10480
T73	Kaiser-Basic	HMO	3020	3020	3800	5770	8450	11020
B63	CareFirst HDHP	HDHP	3660	2760	4480	5910	7700	10160
L93	UnitedHealthcare Choice Plus	PPO-FEE	2710	2710	4220	5950	8580	8710
2G6	CareFirst-Std POS	HMO-POS	4160	4160	5100	5970	7130	9160
JN6	Aetna Open Access Basic	HMO	4180	4180	4830	6480	8630	11030
JP3	MD-IPA	HMO	4210	4210	4900	6570	8730	14210
LR3	UnitedHealthcare Choice	HMO	3920	3920	4740	6610	9070	13920
E33	Kaiser-Hi	HMO	5460	5460	5740	6710	7890	9960
V43	UnitedHealthcare HDHP	HDHP	3660	2160	4360	6950	10450	11110
F56	Aetna Value Plan	PPO-FEE	3930	3930	4780	7310	11080	11380
2G3	CareFirst-Hi	HMO	7760	7760	9030	10180	11830	12760
F53	Aetna HealthFund CDHP	CDHP	9070	6970	9100	10620	12910	16520
JN3	Aetna Open Access-Hi	HMO	16700	16700	17230	18560	20130	23550
National Plans When You Use Preferred Providers								
326	NALC CDHP	CDHP	3010	610	2300	5380	8700	16210
343	GEHA HDHP	HDHP	3230	1730	3610	5550	7440	13230
316	GEHA-Std	PPO-FEE	3070	3070	3830	6260	9720	10570
N63	Aetna Direct CDHP	CDHP	3470	1670	4070	6310	9510	10320
383	Rural Carrier†	PPO-FEE	3910	3910	5080	6350	8410	8410
226	Aetna HealthFund HDHP	HDHP	3940	2440	4490	6480	8720	10790
476	APWU CDHP	CDHP	3660	1260	3560	6500	9580	14260
403	Foreign Service†	PPO-FEE	4210	4210	5290	6550	8220	11210
456	MHBP-Std	PPO-FEE	4020	4020	5140	6830	8960	16020
483	MHBP HDHP	HDHP	3770	1970	4480	6980	9500	15770
KM3	NALC Value Plan	PPO-FEE	2470	2270	3960	7000	10360	15670
113	Blue Cross Basic	PPO	4470	4470	5180	7110	9550	15470
323	NALC-Hi	PPO-FEE	4860	4860	5590	7120	9000	13860
473	APWU-Hi	PPO-FEE	4830	4830	6030	7610	9720	13830
423	Compass Rose†	PPO-FEE	5620	5620	6790	8000	9810	11090
416	MHBP Value Plan	PPO-FEE	3530	3530	5530	8000	11280	16730
313	GEHA-Hi	PPO-FEE	6270	6270	6980	8890	11340	13270
446	SAMBA-Std	PPO-FEE	5930	5930	7070	9490	12560	19930
106	Blue Cross-Std	PPO-FEE	6700	6700	8010	9870	12220	16700
443	SAMBA-Hi	PPO-FEE	11330	11330	12390	14470	17090	23330

† Plan is open only to specific groups.

Annuitants 55 to 64 Without Medicare				Family of Two				
				Estimated yearly out-of-pocket costs, including premium and typical hospital, medical, drug, and dental bills near:				
		Plan type	Published premium	No costs*	Low use: $3,000 or less	Average cost	High use: $30,000 or more	Limit to you
Plan code	Plan name							
DC Area Plans When You Use Preferred Providers								
E35	Kaiser-Std	HMO	3480	3480	3880	5430	7320	10480
E32	Kaiser-Hi	HMO	4660	4660	4940	5910	7090	9160
T72	Kaiser-Basic	HMO	3310	3310	4090	6060	8740	11310
B62	CareFirst HDHP	HDHP	4350	3450	5170	6600	8390	10850
JN5	Aetna Open Access Basic	HMO	4640	4640	5290	6940	9090	11490
L92	UnitedHealthcare Choice Plus	PPO-FEE	3900	3900	5410	7140	9770	9900
LR2	UnitedHealthcare Choice	HMO	4680	4680	5500	7370	9830	14680
F55	Aetna Value Plan	PPO-FEE	4000	4000	4850	7380	11150	11450
V42	UnitedHealthcare HDHP	HDHP	4250	2750	4950	7540	11040	11700
2G5	CareFirst-Std POS	HMO-POS	6220	6220	7160	8030	9190	11220
F52	Aetna HealthFund CDHP	CDHP	8490	6390	8520	10040	12330	15940
JP2	MD-IPA	HMO	10590	10590	11280	12950	15110	20590
2G2	CareFirst-Hi	HMO	10820	10820	12090	13240	14890	15820
JN2	Aetna Open Access-Hi	HMO	16200	16200	16730	18060	19630	23050
National Plans When You Use Preferred Providers								
325	NALC CDHP	CDHP	3080	680	2370	5450	8770	16280
342	GEHA HDHP	HDHP	3560	2060	3940	5880	7770	13560
382	Rural Carrier[†]	PPO-FEE	3980	3980	5150	6420	8480	8480
225	Aetna HealthFund HDHP	HDHP	4020	2520	4570	6560	8800	10870
315	GEHA-Std	PPO-FEE	3380	3380	4140	6570	10030	10880
402	Foreign Service[†]	PPO-FEE	4250	4250	5330	6590	8260	11250
322	NALC-Hi	PPO-FEE	4500	4500	5230	6760	8640	13500
N62	Aetna Direct CDHP	CDHP	3990	2190	4590	6830	10030	10840
475	APWU CDHP	CDHP	3990	1590	3890	6830	9910	14590
455	MHBP-Std	PPO-FEE	4060	4060	5180	6870	9000	16060
KM2	NALC Value Plan	PPO-FEE	2530	2330	4020	7060	10420	15730
482	MHBP HDHP	HDHP	3960	2160	4670	7170	9690	15960
112	Blue Cross Basic	PPO	4710	4710	5420	7350	9790	15710
415	MHBP Value Plan	PPO-FEE	3600	3600	5600	8070	11350	16800
422	Compass Rose[†]	PPO-FEE	6490	6490	7660	8870	10680	11960
472	APWU-Hi	PPO-FEE	6550	6550	7750	9330	11440	15550
445	SAMBA-Std	PPO-FEE	5980	5980	7120	9540	12610	19980
312	GEHA-Hi	PPO-FEE	7000	7000	7710	9620	12070	14000
105	Blue Cross-Std	PPO-FEE	7070	7070	8380	10240	12590	17070
442	SAMBA-Hi	PPO-FEE	12720	12720	13780	15860	18480	24720

* These are the premiums after tax savings, offset by savings accounts for plans that offer them. If you have no or low health-care costs with these plans, it can result in actual saving to you, which we indicate with a negative number.

Annuitants 65 and Older with Medicare Parts A & B		Self Only						
		Plan type	Published premium	Estimated yearly out-of-pocket costs, including premium and typical hospital, medical, drug, and dental bills near:				
Plan code	Plan name			No costs*	Low use: $3,000 or less	Average cost	High use: $30,000 or more	Limit to you
DC Area Plans When You Use Preferred Providers								
B61	CareFirst HDHP	HDHP	3440	2990	2990	3410	4170	9440
E34	Kaiser-Std	HMO	3120	3120	3170	4050	5700	6620
E31	Kaiser-Hi	HMO	3590	3590	3590	4140	5020	5840
2G4	CareFirst-Std POS	HMO-POS	3970	3970	3970	4380	5120	6470
T71	Kaiser-Basic	HMO	2990	2990	3200	4530	6990	6990
L91	UnitedHealthcare Choice Plus	PPO-FEE	3000	3000	3530	4770	6000	6000
LR1	UnitedHealthcare Choice	HMO	3430	3430	3570	5140	8050	8430
V41	UnitedHealthcare HDHP	HDHP	3310	2560	3160	5190	7610	7610
JN4	Aetna Open Access Basic	HMO	3600	3600	3700	5240	8140	8600
JP1	MD-IPA	HMO	4260	4260	4530	5260	6340	9260
F54	Aetna Value Plan	PPO-FEE	3360	3360	3610	5450	8660	8660
F51	Aetna HealthFund CDHP	CDHP	5320	4270	4870	6320	8860	9620
2G1	CareFirst-Hi	HMO	5910	5910	5980	6550	7360	8410
JN1	Aetna Open Access-Hi	HMO	8880	8880	8950	10170	12370	12880
National Plans When You Use Preferred Providers								
N61	Aetna Direct CDHP	CDHP	3190	2290	2450	3380	4570	8190
481	MHBP HDHP	HDHP	3310	2410	2670	3690	5090	9310
111	Blue Cross Basic	PPO	3520	2920	2990	3880	5160	8420
401	Foreign Service†	PPO-FEE	3330	3330	3410	4250	5460	8330
454	MHBP-Std	PPO-FEE	3360	3360	3430	4340	5540	9360
381	Rural Carrier†	PPO-FEE	3880	3880	3880	4380	4930	7880
314	GEHA-Std	PPO-FEE	3040	3040	3160	4440	6410	9040
324	NALC CDHP	CDHP	3000	1800	2160	4460	7540	9600
321	NALC-Hi	PPO-FEE	3660	3660	3750	4500	5460	10260
341	GEHA HDHP	HDHP	3110	2360	2860	4580	6630	8110
421	Compass Rose†	PPO-FEE	4000	4000	4110	4760	5620	9470
224	Aetna HealthFund HDHP	HDHP	3430	2680	3200	4970	7360	7430
471	APWU-Hi	PPO-FEE	4030	4030	4180	5000	6210	9530
474	APWU CDHP	CDHP	3270	2070	2720	5080	8250	8570
KM1	NALC Value Plan	PPO-FEE	2750	2650	3020	5280	8390	9350
311	GEHA-Hi	PPO-FEE	4300	4300	4400	5380	6780	9800
444	SAMBA-Std	PPO-FEE	4150	4150	4370	5570	7300	11150
104	Blue Cross-Std	PPO-FEE	4550	4550	4670	5640	6930	9550
414	MHBP Value Plan	PPO-FEE	3100	3100	3570	5860	9700	9700
441	SAMBA-Hi	PPO-FEE	6600	6600	6800	7920	9480	12600

† Plan is open only to specific groups.

Annuitants 65 and Older with Medicare Parts A & B		Self Plus One					
				Estimated yearly out-of-pocket costs, including premium and typical hospital, medical, drug, and dental bills near:			
Plan code	Plan name	Plan type	Published premium	No costs*	Low use: $3,000 or less	Average cost	High use: $30,000 or more	Limit to you

Plan code	Plan name	Plan type	Published premium	No costs*	Low use: $3,000 or less	Average cost	High use: $30,000 or more	Limit to you
DC Area Plans When You Use Preferred Providers								
B63	CareFirst HDHP	HDHP	6870	5970	5970	6600	6900	18870
2G6	CareFirst-Std POS	HMO-POS	7380	7380	7380	7940	8230	12380
E36	Kaiser-Std	HMO	6700	6700	6970	8290	9180	13700
T73	Kaiser-Basic	HMO	6230	6230	6940	8900	10350	14230
JP3	MD-IPA	HMO	7420	7420	8160	9120	9680	17420
L93	UnitedHealthcare Choice Plus	PPO-FEE	5930	5930	7400	9460	11080	11930
E33	Kaiser-Hi	HMO	8680	8680	8810	9630	10090	13180
LR3	UnitedHealthcare Choice	HMO	7140	7140	7860	10120	11690	17140
JN6	Aetna Open Access Basic	HMO	7390	7390	8040	10210	11840	14240
V43	UnitedHealthcare HDHP	HDHP	6870	5370	7570	10830	13060	14320
F56	Aetna Value Plan	PPO-FEE	7140	7140	7990	11090	13510	14590
2G3	CareFirst-Hi	HMO	10970	10970	11240	12050	12420	15970
F53	Aetna HealthFund CDHP	CDHP	12280	10180	12310	14120	15580	19730
JN3	Aetna Open Access-Hi	HMO	19910	19910	20440	22160	23340	26760
National Plans When You Use Preferred Providers								
N63	Aetna Direct CDHP	CDHP	6690	4890	5500	6600	7170	13540
483	MHBP HDHP	HDHP	6990	5190	5990	7220	7920	18990
383	Rural Carrier†	PPO-FEE	7120	7120	7230	7770	8000	11620
113	Blue Cross Basic	PPO	7680	6480	6860	8020	8670	17480
316	GEHA-Std	PPO-FEE	6290	6290	6670	8500	9510	13790
456	MHBP-Std	PPO-FEE	7240	7240	7570	8690	9270	19240
403	Foreign Service†	PPO-FEE	7420	7420	7840	8940	9550	14420
326	NALC CDHP	CDHP	6230	3830	5520	9100	11200	19430
343	GEHA HDHP	HDHP	6450	4950	6830	9230	10480	16450
323	NALC-Hi	PPO-FEE	8080	8080	8450	9410	9840	17080
473	APWU-Hi	PPO-FEE	8050	8050	8500	9630	10230	17050
423	Compass Rose†	PPO-FEE	8830	8830	9230	10060	10450	14300
226	Aetna HealthFund HDHP	HDHP	7160	5660	7710	10150	11580	14010
476	APWU CDHP	CDHP	6880	4480	6780	10290	12260	17480
KM3	NALC Value Plan	PPO-FEE	5690	5490	7180	10770	12860	18890
313	GEHA-Hi	PPO-FEE	9490	9490	9840	11120	11820	16490
446	SAMBA-Std	PPO-FEE	9150	9150	9850	11400	12280	23150
106	Blue Cross-Std	PPO-FEE	9920	9920	10430	11610	12250	19920
416	MHBP Value Plan	PPO-FEE	6750	6750	8750	11810	14020	19950
443	SAMBA-Hi	PPO-FEE	14540	14540	15200	16610	17390	26540

* These are the premiums after tax savings, offset by savings accounts for plans that offer them. If you have no or low health-care costs with these plans, it can result in actual saving to you, which we indicate with a negative number.

Annuitants 65 and Older with Medicare Parts A & B		Family of Two						
				Estimated yearly out-of-pocket costs, including premium and typical hospital, medical, drug, and dental bills near:				
		Plan type	Published premium	No costs*	Low use: $3,000 or less	Average cost	High use: $30,000 or more	Limit to you
Plan code	Plan name							
DC Area Plans When You Use Preferred Providers								
B62	CareFirst HDHP	HDHP	7560	6660	6660	7290	7590	19560
E35	Kaiser-Std	HMO	6700	6700	6970	8290	9180	13700
E32	Kaiser-Hi	HMO	7880	7880	8010	8830	9290	12380
T72	Kaiser-Basic	HMO	6530	6530	7240	9200	10650	14530
2G5	CareFirst-Std POS	HMO-POS	9430	9430	9430	9990	10280	14430
L92	UnitedHealthcare Choice Plus	PPO-FEE	7110	7110	8580	10640	12260	13110
JN5	Aetna Open Access Basic	HMO	7860	7860	8510	10680	12310	14710
LR2	UnitedHealthcare Choice	HMO	7890	7890	8610	10870	12440	17890
F55	Aetna Value Plan	PPO-FEE	7220	7220	8070	11170	13590	14670
V42	UnitedHealthcare HDHP	HDHP	7470	5970	8170	11430	13660	14920
F52	Aetna HealthFund CDHP	CDHP	11710	9610	11740	13550	15010	19160
2G2	CareFirst-Hi	HMO	14030	14030	14300	15110	15480	19030
JP2	MD-IPA	HMO	13810	13810	14550	15510	16070	23810
JN2	Aetna Open Access-Hi	HMO	19410	19410	19940	21660	22840	26260
National Plans When You Use Preferred Providers								
N62	Aetna Direct CDHP	CDHP	7210	5410	6020	7120	7690	14060
482	MHBP HDHP	HDHP	7170	5370	6170	7400	8100	19170
382	Rural Carrier†	PPO-FEE	7200	7200	7310	7850	8080	11700
112	Blue Cross Basic	PPO	7920	6720	7100	8260	8910	17720
455	MHBP-Std	PPO-FEE	7280	7280	7610	8730	9310	19280
315	GEHA-Std	PPO-FEE	6590	6590	6970	8800	9810	14090
402	Foreign Service†	PPO-FEE	7460	7460	7880	8980	9590	14460
322	NALC-Hi	PPO-FEE	7710	7710	8080	9040	9470	16710
325	NALC CDHP	CDHP	6300	3900	5590	9170	11270	19500
342	GEHA HDHP	HDHP	6770	5270	7150	9550	10800	16770
225	Aetna HealthFund HDHP	HDHP	7240	5740	7790	10230	11660	14090
475	APWU CDHP	CDHP	7210	4810	7110	10620	12590	17810
KM2	NALC Value Plan	PPO-FEE	5740	5540	7230	10820	12910	18940
422	Compass Rose†	PPO-FEE	9710	9710	10110	10940	11330	15180
472	APWU-Hi	PPO-FEE	9770	9770	10220	11350	11950	18770
445	SAMBA-Std	PPO-FEE	9200	9200	9900	11450	12330	23200
312	GEHA-Hi	PPO-FEE	10220	10220	10570	11850	12550	17220
415	MHBP Value Plan	PPO-FEE	6820	6820	8820	11880	14090	20020
105	Blue Cross-Std	PPO-FEE	10290	10290	10800	11980	12620	20290
442	SAMBA-Hi	PPO-FEE	15940	15940	16600	18010	18790	27940

† Plan is open only to specific groups.

Annuitants 65 and Older with Medicare Part A Only		Self Only					
				Estimated yearly out-of-pocket costs, including premium and typical hospital, medical, drug, and dental bills near:			
		Plan type	Published premium	No costs*	Low use: $3,000 or less	Average cost	High use: $30,000 or more	Limit to you
Plan code	Plan name							
DC Area Plans When You Use Preferred Providers								
E34	Kaiser-Std	HMO	1510	1510	1580	2790	5010	5010
E31	Kaiser-Hi	HMO	1980	1980	2000	2820	4230	4230
T71	Kaiser-Basic	HMO	1380	1380	1600	3110	5380	5380
L91	UnitedHealthcare Choice Plus	PPO-FEE	1390	1390	1920	3190	4390	4390
B61	CareFirst HDHP	HDHP	1830	1380	1890	3240	5240	5830
2G4	CareFirst-Std POS	HMO-POS	2360	2360	2800	3520	4860	4860
V41	UnitedHealthcare HDHP	HDHP	1700	950	1550	3620	6000	6000
JN4	Aetna Open Access Basic	HMO	1990	1990	2090	3630	6530	6990
LR1	UnitedHealthcare Choice	HMO	1820	1820	2010	3650	6820	6820
F54	Aetna Value Plan	PPO-FEE	1750	1750	2000	3840	7050	7050
JP1	MD-IPA	HMO	2650	2650	2790	4300	7250	7650
F51	Aetna HealthFund CDHP	CDHP	3710	2660	3260	4750	7430	8010
2G1	CareFirst-Hi	HMO	4300	4300	4840	5710	6800	6800
JN1	Aetna Open Access-Hi	HMO	7280	7280	7350	8570	10770	11280
National Plans When You Use Preferred Providers								
324	NALC CDHP	CDHP	1390	190	550	2900	6170	7990
341	GEHA HDHP	HDHP	1500	750	1250	2990	5080	6500
401	Foreign Service[†]	PPO-FEE	1720	1720	2000	3260	5490	6720
224	Aetna HealthFund HDHP	HDHP	1820	1070	1590	3380	5820	5820
N61	Aetna Direct CDHP	CDHP	1580	680	1380	3410	6580	6580
474	APWU CDHP	CDHP	1660	460	1110	3510	6820	6960
314	GEHA-Std	PPO-FEE	1430	1430	1660	3610	7430	7430
321	NALC-Hi	PPO-FEE	2050	2050	2270	3640	6020	8650
454	MHBP-Std	PPO-FEE	1750	1750	2030	3700	6620	7750
111	Blue Cross Basic	PPO	1920	1920	2040	3720	6780	7420
KM1	NALC Value Plan	PPO-FEE	1140	1040	1410	3720	7020	7740
481	MHBP HDHP	HDHP	1700	800	1550	3850	6560	7700
421	Compass Rose[†]	PPO-FEE	2390	2390	2700	3940	6130	7860
381	Rural Carrier[†]	PPO-FEE	2270	2270	2780	4020	6270	6270
471	APWU-Hi	PPO-FEE	2420	2420	2870	4210	6860	7920
414	MHBP Value Plan	PPO-FEE	1490	1490	1960	4250	8090	8090
311	GEHA-Hi	PPO-FEE	2690	2690	2910	4490	7410	8190
444	SAMBA-Std	PPO-FEE	2540	2540	2890	4950	8970	9540
104	Blue Cross-Std	PPO-FEE	2940	2940	3370	4970	7940	7940
441	SAMBA-Hi	PPO-FEE	4990	4990	5310	7150	10570	10990

* These are the premiums after tax savings, offset by savings accounts for plans that offer them. If you have no or low health-care costs with these plans, it can result in actual saving to you, which we indicate with a negative number.

Annuitants 65 and Older with Medicare Part A Only		Self Plus One						
		Plan type	Published premium	Estimated yearly out-of-pocket costs, including premium and typical hospital, medical, drug, and dental bills near:				
Plan code	Plan name			No costs*	Low use: $3,000 or less	Average cost	High use: $30,000 or more	Limit to you
DC Area Plans When You Use Preferred Providers								
E36	Kaiser-Std	HMO	3480	3480	3880	5910	7320	10480
2G6	CareFirst-Std POS	HMO-POS	4160	4160	5100	6290	7130	9160
L93	UnitedHealthcare Choice Plus	PPO-FEE	2710	2710	4220	6340	8100	8710
B63	CareFirst HDHP	HDHP	3660	2760	4480	6410	7700	10160
T73	Kaiser-Basic	HMO	3020	3020	3800	6450	8450	11020
JN6	Aetna Open Access Basic	HMO	4180	4180	4830	7010	8630	11030
E33	Kaiser-Hi	HMO	5460	5460	5740	7010	7890	9960
JP3	MD-IPA	HMO	4210	4210	4900	7110	8730	14210
LR3	UnitedHealthcare Choice	HMO	3920	3920	4740	7220	9070	13920
V43	UnitedHealthcare HDHP	HDHP	3660	2160	4360	7810	10450	11110
F56	Aetna Value Plan	PPO-FEE	3930	3930	4780	7980	10600	11380
2G3	CareFirst-Hi	HMO	7760	7760	9030	10600	11830	12760
F53	Aetna HealthFund CDHP	CDHP	9070	6970	9100	11030	12550	16520
JN3	Aetna Open Access-Hi	HMO	16700	16700	17230	18970	20130	23550
National Plans When You Use Preferred Providers								
326	NALC CDHP	CDHP	3010	610	2300	5990	8220	16210
343	GEHA HDHP	HDHP	3230	1730	3610	6030	7320	13230
383	Rural Carrier†	PPO-FEE	3910	3910	5080	6800	8410	8410
N63	Aetna Direct CDHP	CDHP	3470	1670	4070	6880	9030	10320
316	GEHA-Std	PPO-FEE	3070	3070	3830	6900	9400	10570
226	Aetna HealthFund HDHP	HDHP	3940	2440	4490	6990	8480	10790
403	Foreign Service†	PPO-FEE	4210	4210	5290	7000	8220	11210
476	APWU CDHP	CDHP	3660	1260	3560	7140	9220	14260
456	MHBP-Std	PPO-FEE	4020	4020	5140	7390	8960	16020
113	Blue Cross Basic	PPO	4470	4470	5180	7520	9200	15470
323	NALC-Hi	PPO-FEE	4860	4860	5590	7620	9000	13860
KM3	NALC Value Plan	PPO-FEE	2470	2270	3960	7660	9880	15670
483	MHBP HDHP	HDHP	3770	1970	4480	7710	9500	15770
473	APWU-Hi	PPO-FEE	4830	4830	6030	8030	9480	13830
423	Compass Rose†	PPO-FEE	5620	5620	6790	8330	9610	11090
416	MHBP Value Plan	PPO-FEE	3530	3530	5530	8600	10800	16730
313	GEHA-Hi	PPO-FEE	6270	6270	6980	9390	11110	13270
106	Blue Cross-Std	PPO-FEE	6700	6700	8010	10250	11870	16700
446	SAMBA-Std	PPO-FEE	5930	5930	7070	10280	12560	19930
443	SAMBA-Hi	PPO-FEE	11330	11330	12390	15140	17090	23330

† Plan is open only to specific groups.

Annuitants 65 and Older with Medicare Part A Only		Family of Two					
				Estimated yearly out-of-pocket costs, including premium and typical hospital, medical, drug, and dental bills near:			
		Plan type	Published premium				
Plan code	Plan name			No costs*	Low use: $3,000 or less	Average cost	High use: $30,000 or more	Limit to you
DC Area Plans When You Use Preferred Providers							
E35	Kaiser-Std	HMO	3480	3480	3880	5910	7320	10480
E32	Kaiser-Hi	HMO	4660	4660	4940	6210	7090	9160
T72	Kaiser-Basic	HMO	3310	3310	4090	6740	8740	11310
B62	CareFirst HDHP	HDHP	4350	3450	5170	7100	8390	10850
JN5	Aetna Open Access Basic	HMO	4640	4640	5290	7470	9090	11490
L92	UnitedHealthcare Choice Plus	PPO-FEE	3900	3900	5410	7530	9290	9900
LR2	UnitedHealthcare Choice	HMO	4680	4680	5500	7980	9830	14680
F55	Aetna Value Plan	PPO-FEE	4000	4000	4850	8050	10670	11450
2G5	CareFirst-Std POS	HMO-POS	6220	6220	7160	8350	9190	11220
V42	UnitedHealthcare HDHP	HDHP	4250	2750	4950	8400	11040	11700
F52	Aetna HealthFund CDHP	CDHP	8490	6390	8520	10450	11970	15940
JP2	MD-IPA	HMO	10590	10590	11280	13490	15110	20590
2G2	CareFirst-Hi	HMO	10820	10820	12090	13660	14890	15820
JN2	Aetna Open Access-Hi	HMO	16200	16200	16730	18470	19630	23050
National Plans When You Use Preferred Providers							
325	NALC CDHP	CDHP	3080	680	2370	6060	8290	16280
342	GEHA HDHP	HDHP	3560	2060	3940	6360	7650	13560
382	Rural Carrier[†]	PPO-FEE	3980	3980	5150	6870	8480	8480
402	Foreign Service[†]	PPO-FEE	4250	4250	5330	7040	8260	11250
225	Aetna HealthFund HDHP	HDHP	4020	2520	4570	7070	8560	10870
315	GEHA-Std	PPO-FEE	3380	3380	4140	7210	9710	10880
322	NALC-Hi	PPO-FEE	4500	4500	5230	7260	8640	13500
N62	Aetna Direct CDHP	CDHP	3990	2190	4590	7400	9550	10840
455	MHBP-Std	PPO-FEE	4060	4060	5180	7430	9000	16060
475	APWU CDHP	CDHP	3990	1590	3890	7470	9550	14590
KM2	NALC Value Plan	PPO-FEE	2530	2330	4020	7720	9940	15730
112	Blue Cross Basic	PPO	4710	4710	5420	7760	9440	15710
482	MHBP HDHP	HDHP	3960	2160	4670	7900	9690	15960
415	MHBP Value Plan	PPO-FEE	3600	3600	5600	8670	10870	16800
422	Compass Rose[†]	PPO-FEE	6490	6490	7660	9200	10480	11960
472	APWU-Hi	PPO-FEE	6550	6550	7750	9750	11200	15550
312	GEHA-Hi	PPO-FEE	7000	7000	7710	10120	11840	14000
445	SAMBA-Std	PPO-FEE	5980	5980	7120	10330	12610	19980
105	Blue Cross-Std	PPO-FEE	7070	7070	8380	10620	12240	17070
442	SAMBA-Hi	PPO-FEE	12720	12720	13780	16530	18480	24720

* These are the premiums after tax savings, offset by savings accounts for plans that offer them. If you have no or low health-care costs with these plans, it can result in actual saving to you, which we indicate with a negative number.

(Continued from page 75)
restrictions largely disappear when enrolled in any plan. You can go to any hospital and almost any doctor without penalty. Moreover, persons over age 65 are by law guaranteed a Medicare rate and can use all doctors who have not opted out of Medicare without fearing very high charges, even while enrolled in plans that offer no reduced cost sharing for those with Part B of Medicare.

You should be aware, however, that there are many complexities. For example, some doctors do not accept new Medicare patients, even if the patients are in a plan whose network includes these doctors. Some doctors accept no insurance of any kind. And still others will accept new Medicare patients but do not "take assignment" and have their patients pay in full and submit Medicare claims. In such cases a 15% higher Medicare rate called the "limiting charge" may apply. The great majority of doctors do not present such problems, so your best option will often be to avoid those who do.

Savings for Couples Using Self Only Enrollments

For a husband and wife who are **both** Federal annuitants and who have no dependent children, it is possible to save on premium costs by enrolling separately as self only rather than together as self plus one. The premiums for two self enrollments are usually less than the self plus one premium. This option can be particularly valuable in cases where each spouse prefers a different plan, perhaps because no one plan covers both family physicians in its network.

Be cautious, however, because each person will have to meet a separate catastrophic limit rather than the single limit that applies to self plus one. Most plans do not increase your risk because they include individual limits of about half the amount of the overall self plus one or family limit. Moreover, while you are still technically subject to meeting two catastrophic limits if you both enroll self-only, the fee structure of most HMOs makes it almost impossible to reach those limits. Finally, if two Federal annuitants both have Medicare Parts A and B your risk exposure is low in all plans, and very low in plans that offer a Part B wrap-around. For these reasons, you are almost always safe with two self only enrollments. But do check the plan brochure's catastrophic limits carefully before making this decision.

However, couples in which one is a federal annuitant and the other still federally employed should almost never use two self only enrollments. It is always less expensive for the employed spouse to enroll in a self plus one or family option, and get about a one-third savings from Premium Conversion.

Savings for Couples or Single Parents with One Child Under Self Plus One Enrollment

Married couples with no children to cover, and single parents with one child to cover, can enroll as self plus one rather than as a family and, depending on the plan chosen, often save two or three hundred dollars a year in premium costs. Since the benefits of the plan are identical (or in a few cases even better) in the self plus one plan, this is a clear saving. You should use our comparison table for self plus one with adults of your age to make your initial plan comparison. **But before you make a final decision, check to make sure the premium for a family enrollment isn't lower for the plan you have chosen. And while you are at it, check our ratings to see other plans that offer even larger savings.**

In addition to the regular Open Season, where you can switch plans or enrollment category or both, OPM allows annuitants to switch "down" to from family to self plus one at any time during the year. This can only be used for the plan you are already enrolled in, not to switch plans, unless there is a "qualifying life event" such as death of family member or divorce.

Annuitants Without Medicare Part B

Older persons, on average, incur much higher expenses than do younger persons. Children's expenses average about $2,000 a year, and those of an adult below 55 years of age about $6,000 per year. Expenses for people age 65 and older average about $12,000 per year. Of course, most enrollees have much lower bills. The average cost is pulled up by a small fraction that has much higher bills, a fraction that rises sharply with age. To reflect these large differences, our cost tables for annuitants compare plans on the basis of expenses faced by older persons. We provide separate results for annuitants age 55 to 64, and over age 65, as their expense profiles are quite different. In either age group, the plans with better coverage tend to rank higher despite bigger premiums. In using our print comparisons a safe approach for couples in which only one member has Medicare coverage is to use the cost comparisons for retirees without Medicare (in the online Guide we provide specific estimates for these situations).

Once you reach age 65, a special rule applies whether or not you enroll in Medicare Part B. **It is illegal for doctors who have not opted out entirely from Medicare to charge patients covered by Medicare more than a "limiting charge." This restriction applies to all FEHB annuitants over age 65, whether or not they have Medicare.** Under this provision, you will not be exposed to high charges that neither Medicare nor your FEHB plan recognizes as reasonable. You do **not** have to sign up for Medicare Part B to get this guarantee. Therefore, unlike employees, if you are over 65 you can use non-preferred providers without fear of being charged substantially more than the plan will recognize as reasonable. You do, of course, have to pay higher deductibles and coinsurance if the provider is not in your plan's network.

Annuitants with Medicare Part A or Parts A and B

Obviously, if Medicare covers you, the rankings in our regular cost comparisons do not apply, since Medicare is "primary" for retirees and will pay most expenses. Therefore, we present tables for single persons and couples with either both Parts A and B of Medicare, or Part A only. Since couples can choose either self plus one or family enrollments, we provide comparisons for both. Although these tables are presented in terms of preferred providers, it is important to understand that the main advantage of preferred providers, guaranteed low rates, is available once you reach age 65 from almost any doctor you might use, whether or not you have Medicare Part B. The online *Guide* also presents a comparison for couples in which one spouse does not have Medicare and the other has both Parts A and B. Each comparison takes into account:

- Premium costs for the FEHB plan and, in the "both Part A and B" tables, for Medicare Part B (Part A has no premium for Federal annuitants who retired after 1983);
- Each plan's coverage for services, such as prescription drugs and dental care, that are not covered by Medicare Parts A and; and
- Elimination of all or most hospital and medical cost-sharing offered by many plans for Medicare Part A and B enrollees.

Should You Stay Enrolled in the FEHB Program After Age 65?

You could drop the FEHB once you enroll in Parts A and B. But this would be a bad decision. Medicare Part B requires you to pay 20 percent of the cost of doctors' fees, and deductibles, with no upper limit. The Medicare Part A hospital deductible is almost $1,400 and the Part B medical deductible is almost $200. To obtain Medicare coverage roughly comparable to FEHB plans you would have to pay a Part B premium of about $134 a month, or about $1,600 for the year (many pay more, as discussed below), and a Part D premium for drug coverage of about $40 a month and $480 for the year (there is a wide range of prescription drug premiums, some lower and some higher). The total premium cost for all three parts of Medicare is about $2,000 a person—higher than in many FEHB plans and with cost-sharing worse than most and no protection against catastrophically high expenses. You could improve your protection by enrolling in what are called "Medigap" plans, but only at the cost of paying another $2,000 a year in premium, the exact amount depending on the Medigap plan chosen. Therefore, if paying both FEHB and Medicare premiums presses you financially, and you are not sure which program to retain, **the FEHB program alone is a better bargain than Medicare alone, unless you are willing to enroll in a Medicare Advantage plan** (discussed below). And even then, you should never drop the FEHB program completely, but "suspend" enrollment with the option of rejoining in the next Open Season. Moreover, almost all Federal annuitants over age 65 have premium-free Medicare Part A, and in combination with almost all FEHB plans will never have to pay more than a few hundred dollars for hospital costs. Finally, FEHB plans, unlike Medicare (except in parts of Canada and Mexico), cover you if you travel or live abroad.

Should You Enroll in Part B After Age 65?

There are advantages to enrolling in Part B as a complement to an FEHB plan (technically, Medicare is "primary" and pays first). Almost all of the national plans waive their hospital and medical deductibles, copays, and coinsurance for members enrolled in both Medicare Part A (hospital) and Part B (medical). In effect, they "wrap around" Medicare. HMOs generally have only nominal deductibles or copayments and most of them do not provide such waivers. However, an increasing number do. For example, in the Washington, DC area CareFirst and M.D. IPA provide wraparound benefits to retirees with both parts of Medicare. In other parts of the nation, the Humana plans offer similar savings. With Medicare Parts A and B and most national Federal plans, you will have close to 100 percent coverage of almost all medical expenses (a few services are not covered by either program and would not get this coverage). Coverage for dental and prescription drug expenses will still differ depending on which plan you choose.

However, Medicare Part B will rarely save you nearly as much money as you spend on the Part B premium. This is because the cost sharing for physician visits and tests in almost all FEHB plans is already so low. And as we discuss below, for those who pay more for Part B than the normal premium, it is almost always a bad buy in purely financial terms.

By comparing tables for those with Part A only, versus those with Parts A and B, you will see that in most plans you are likely to spend several hundred dollars a year more for this combination than by retaining the FEHB plan alone. Simply put, Medicare Part B is of limited dollar value to someone already covered by a good health plan. **If you join an HMO, the Medicare premium gains you very little in dollar benefits. If you are willing to use preferred providers in national plans, or to join an HMO and use its network, you can usually save several hundred dollars per year or more—often a thousand dollars a year or more—by not joining, or dropping, Medicare Part B**. Even if you do not use preferred providers, you will do almost as well without Medicare Part B, because of the special rate ceiling discussed above.

Part B does have some important advantages. Perhaps most importantly, in almost all the plans that wrap around Part B, **enrollment in Part B gives you the freedom to go outside the plan's network** at **no cost**.

Even if you enroll in one of the plans that don't wrap around, you can use your Part B benefit to **go outside the plan's doctor network and pay only 20% of the Medicare allowed charge**. For example, for using a specialist at the Mayo Clinic, you could simply charge the visit to Part B without your HMO or PPO plan's permission,

Part B provides more generous benefits than most FEHB plans in a few categories, such as physical therapy and home health care, and it covers more of the costs of some injected specialty drugs, prostheses and durable medical equipment than many. Still, Medicare Part B rarely reduces overall costs enough to pay for the extra premium. For those plans that provide a wraparound, in almost all situations Part B will likely save you several hundred dollars a year and often as much as half the Part B premium—but rarely as much as the "for sure" premium expense.

Also importantly, Part B gives you the option of joining a Medicare Advantage plan—either PPO or HMO—through Medicare and suspending your FEHB enrollment and premium payment, as discussed below.

For everyone, enrollment in Part B gives you some "insurance" against the possibility that the Congress would enact some major adverse change to the FEHB program.

Finally, for many the value of "peace of mind" that you get from coverage under both programs exceeds the increase in premium costs.

There is an important innovation under way that reduces the cost of enrolling under both programs that will be attractive so many. The national Aetna Direct plan not only has a Medicare wraparound, but also lets you use your $900 a year per spouse personal care account to reimburse most of your Medicare Part B premium, or offset dental and other expenses not covered by FEHB plans or Medicare. This gives you the advantage of wraparound coverage at a significantly lower cost than you would otherwise pay. Since the plan also waives its deductible and other cost sharing if you have parts A and B, this plan winds up costing less with Medicare than without Medicare for those who pay normal Part B premiums. Likewise, the Blue Cross Basic plan now provides both a wraparound benefit and a $600 yearly reimbursement for each spouse with Part B. Most HDHP and CDHP plans, including the national Aetna, GEHA, and MHBP HDHP plans, and the CareFirst HDHP plan in the DC metro area, offer similar premium and/or personal account advantages, but not the wraparound benefit.

If you do decide to drop (or not start) Part B you can join it later. But there is a 10 percent a year penalty if you later decide to join or rejoin. As a financial matter, however many years you elect to do without Part B, you will be money ahead for approximately the first five or six years after joining or rejoining. After that, the penalty will outweigh your earlier savings (except for those who were once above, but now fall below, the income-tested premium). If you never join or rejoin, you will (on average) save annually roughly the amounts indicated in our tables showing costs with and without Parts B—generally about half the cost of the Part B premium, though this varies somewhat from plan to plan. Thus, either not joining or dropping Part B is not an irrevocable decision, and later rejoining Part need not be highly costly.

There are some circumstances to which the conclusions above do not apply:

- **Working employees over age 65** with Medicare Parts A and B coverage face a different situation. The special waivers of deductibles and coinsurance do not apply, because Medicare is by law the secondary rather than primary payer (except for firms with fewer than 20 employees). Your best choice is to stay in your preferred FEHB plan, and **postpone joining Medicare Part B until you actually retire. There is no penalty** for joining after age 65 if you were working and covered by employer insurance (subject to the same exception for small firms).
- **A few people over age 65 did not earn Medicare Part A and can join by paying** a very substantial premium—about $5,000 a year. We recommend strongly against this purchase. Almost all FEHB plans charge you at most a few hundred dollars for hospital admissions, far less than the Part A premium.

Income-Related Part B Premiums

Historically, the taxpayer has funded three-fourths of the Medicare Part B premium and the enrollee has paid only one fourth of the cost. Under current law, however, some higher income enrollees pay more than the traditional one-fourth share.

This only affects individuals with Adjusted Gross Income (AGI) of $85,000 or more, and married couples filing jointly with income of $170,000 or more. These thresholds are not adjusted for inflation. The actual calculation includes adding some forms of income, such as tax-exempt interest income, to AGI. In 2018 the Medicare Trustees project that the resulting annual Part B premium will be about $2,250 for individual AGI of $85,000 to $107,000; $3,210 for income of $107,000 to $160,000; $4,180 for income of $160,000 to $214,000; and $5,140 for income of more than $214,000. The corresponding amounts for married couples filing jointly are twice as high.

There are additional factors that may determine whether this affects you. For example, if you marry or divorce or suffer a casualty loss you may become exempt. If your income fluctuates from year to year you may be subject to the increase one year but not the next (generally, the calculation is based on your AGI two years previously). If you have just retired with previous income above these thresholds, it is very important to apply to the Social Security Administration to use your lower retirement income to reduce or eliminate the higher premium. The premium calculation is made based on your income two years ago, which for many is a much higher pre-retirement amount, unless you apply for an adjustment. The "bottom line" is that if your income is above these thresholds and likely to remain there, the case for enrolling in Medicare Part B becomes far weaker. Dropping Part B will not affect your continued premium-free enrollment in Part A. The sensible solution for many will be to drop out of Medicare Part B and rely on your FEHB plan. Why pay $2,250 or more annually for a Part B benefit that rarely results in reduced cost sharing of more than a third of that amount?

The Medicare Part B Premiums for 2018

Inflation has been so low in recent years that there was almost no cost of living increase for Social Security recipients in 2016 or 2017. Under a "hold harmless" provision in current law, most retirees receiving Social Security and paying for Part B by deduction from their Social Security benefit paid about the same premium in 2017 as they paid in 2015 and 2016. The problem this created was that the law also requires overall premiums to cover their share of program costs, which rise even when overall inflation does not. As a result, those who were not held harmless had to make up the difference and premiums for them were higher. For 2018 there will be a 2% increase in Social Security benefits and the dollar amounts involved will be large enough to allow increasing the Part B premium for those previously held harmless. The Medicare Trustees project that the regular Part B premium for 2018 will be about $134 a month, or about $1,610 for the year. This will apply to almost all Part B enrollees who are not in the income-related surcharge categories. We have used this estimated premium in our plan comparisons for those who are enrolled in both FEHB plans and Medicare Parts A and B. If the final decision on 2018 Part B premiums expected in November is different by a few dollars this will not affect the relative rankings of the plans or the cost differences among the plans.

Medicare Advantage

Almost a third of Medicare beneficiaries now enroll in a Medicare Advantage plan, rather than sticking with Original Medicare. Medicare Advantage (MA) is a program designed to be very similar in operation to the FEHB program. Retirees can choose from a wide range of PPO and HMO plans in an annual Open Season. These plans' premiums are paid mainly through the Medicare Part A and B payments (with some adjustments) that the government would otherwise have paid in direct benefits. The enrollees continue to pay their Part B premium. Almost all of these plans include prescription drug coverage and various improvements over the original Medicare structure. For example, most eliminate most of the hospital deductible. In some cases, these plans charge no extra premium for drug coverage and other benefits. Very importantly, all of these plans now provide protection against catastrophic costs. The MA program is thoroughly described in the *Medicare & You* brochure mailed to all Medicare participants. The Medicare web site at *www.medicare.gov* contains additional information and contains an MA plan comparison tool that includes many of the same features as the online *Guide*, with a comparison of total costs including both premium and out-of-pocket expenses.

This is important to Federal retirees because if you join an MA plan you are allowed to temporarily suspend your FEHB enrollment and stop paying two sets of premiums. Under this "suspend" option you pay only the Part B premium and sometimes an extra premium charge (usually only a few hundred dollars per year and often nothing at all) that the Medicare Advantage plan charges Medicare enrollees for additional benefits such as prescription drug coverage. You can later switch out of Medicare Advantage and rejoin the FEHB program as if you had never left during any future Open Season. This works equally well for a couple when both spouses are enrolled in Medicare, or if they are willing to pursue separate health insurance options.

Suspending your FEHB enrollment generates substantial savings because you will pay one premium instead of two. How much you will save depends on the precise benefits the MA plan offers to Medicare enrollees and whether or how much it charges in extra premium. Most MA plans are comparable to FEHB plans in hospital and medical benefits, but the prescription drug benefits will not be as good because the plans have a "coverage gap" where you are responsible for all or most drug costs until you reach a catastrophic limit. Assuming you join a plan with no extra premium, you would pay only the Part B premium, at a cost in 2018 of about $1,610 (for those who do not pay a higher income-tested premium).

Your Final Decision on Medicare Part B and the FEHB Program

Throughout our advice we have highlighted specific advantages and disadvantages of enrolling in Medicare Part B in addition to your FEHB enrollment. On the minus side, there is one large factor—paying two costly sets of premiums instead of one. For those who pay the higher part B income-tested premiums, this is a very considerable cost, between about $2,250 and $5,140 extra to join Part B, depending on exact income level. On the plus side there are several factors, including avoiding network restrictions, better coverage for a few services, and having the option to join Medicare Advantage plans and paying only one premium without losing FEHB eligibility.

By now, you should realize that you have many options, each with advantages and disadvantages. Taking into account dollar costs only, there are four good sets of options. One of these is to enroll in one of the better Medicare Advantage plans and suspend FEHB enrollment. A second option is to enroll in the Aetna Direct CDHP plan or the Blue Cross Basic plan. Your special account will pay towards the Part B premium (or in the Aetna Direct plan for drug or dental costs not otherwise covered), and you also get a Medicare wraparound. We note that two Kaiser plans, one in northern California and one in Oregon, will pay almost the entire Part B premium. These two plans only provide a partial wraparound, however. A third cost-saving choice is to enroll in an FEHB plan with rich benefits such as APWU, NALC, Kaiser, or many other HMOs, and drop Medicare Part B. As a fourth choice, you can enroll in a low-premium national plan like GEHA Standard option along with Part B and get a Medicare wraparound benefit, or join a low-premium HMO and use Part B to fill holes and get services outside the plan's network. Two of these good options involve keeping both Part B and the FEHB enrollment, but two let you pay only one premium. All of them vary in details that you can only assess after studying the brochure of one or two plans. All of them can provide most annuitants substantial annual savings.

What you should generally not do is stay in a high premium FEHB plan to get the Part B wraparound benefit when you can join a less costly FEHB plan with an equally good wraparound benefit. Of course, there are always cases where even the most expensive combination provides a benefit essential to you. And differences in prescription drug formularies or cost sharing can make a seemingly more expensive option actually a less expensive option. So there is no simple "one size fits all" answer. What you should do, regardless, is at least be aware of the dollar costs or gains of whatever decision you reach.

Medicare Part D

The Medicare Part D prescription drug program benefits millions of low-income elderly. It fills a major hole in Medicare that lasted fifty years. But it will rarely benefit those, like Federal retirees, who have good drug coverage from their former employer.

Few Federal retirees should join a Part D plan. A typical plan will cost four or five hundred dollars in premium and provide little improved benefit for most.

Also, there is no penalty for joining Part D at a later time if you have current "creditable" coverage. This test is met by all FEHB plans. There are three exceptions. First, a few Federal annuitants have incomes and liquid assets low enough to qualify for special help. For example, a divorced former spouse may receive so little in pension that he or she qualifies for low-income assistance (the income cutoff is approximately $18,000, depending on state of residence). In such a case, the annuitant may be able to reduce drug costs to almost nothing. You apply to the Social Security Administration to obtain an official decision. Second, the Part D benefit can offer savings to annuitants in plans with relatively weak prescription drug coverage, like GEHA Standard option. This GEHA plan only reimburses half the cost of name brand drugs. An enrollee with a name brand drug costing at retail $2,000 a year would be out of pocket $1,000 under GEHA. Many Part D plans would pay more of this cost for a premium of $500 a year or less, and GEHA would pay half the rest. Third, a Part D plan will let enrollees in High Deductible and Consumer-Driven plans such as Aetna Direct, NALC CDHP, or MHBP HDHP avoid using their personal account for routine drug expenses.

Unfortunately, the national plans are not offering extra benefits such as copay waivers to those who join Part D, unlike their improved coverage for those with Parts A or B. They simply promise to "consider" paying part of your Part D costs, whatever that means. And having two drug plans can involve a lot of paperwork. Hence, only if you can achieve substantial savings for your particular drugs is it worthwhile to join Part D. Also, before enrolling in Part D check whether or not you are subject to income-related premiums. The law now subjects Part D enrollees to the same income-tested levels as under Part B. If your adjusted gross income is $85,000 or more for single people, or $170,000 or more for couples, you would have to pay a premium surcharge for Part D.

Chapter 5

Cost Sharing

Health insurance plans never pay 100 percent of all health-related expenses. Every plan limits coverages in various ways. For example, no plan pays for elective cosmetic surgery. Most plans pay little or nothing towards expensive dental procedures. Almost all plans charge something—usually $20 to $40—for physician visits. Almost all plans charge much more for name brand drugs than for generic drugs. Many plans charge deductibles, either before reimbursing any expenses or before reimbursing particular categories of expenses, such as hospital or prescription drugs. These and other payment limitations are complicated and vary from plan to plan. Taken together, they dictate what you will pay out-of-pocket at various levels and mixes of health care expenses. We estimate these out-of-pocket costs for you using a complex computer model that takes into account all these various interactions, but in some cases you may want to focus on particular coverages and copayments of concern to you.

Deductibles, Copayments, and Coinsurance

You can use cost sharing details to assist you in choosing a plan by pinpointing strengths and weaknesses for cost items of particular concern to you. If you are especially concerned about a broad area of coverage, such as reimbursement for prescription drugs, copayment information can identify plans that are most acceptable to you for that feature, and be used together with the cost rankings to narrow your choice. Our comparisons of deductibles, coinsurance, and copays display many—but by no means all—of the cost sharing provisions taken into account in our overall cost comparisons. (In the printed *Guide,* we present a cost-sharing table for national plans and DC area local plans, but not for the local plans in other parts of the country that we are able to display online.)

In recent years prescription drug copayments have become increasingly complex. Plans require you to pay more for "name brand" drugs than for "generic" drugs. Name brand drugs, once past their patent protection period, are usually met with competition from generic drugs that the Food and Drug Administration has determined to be therapeutically identical. As a result, generic drugs tend to be much less expensive, and it is in the financial interest of both you and the plan that you select them. Most plans now use at least a six-tier reimbursement structure for prescription drugs: generic, preferred name brand, and non-formulary name brand at the local pharmacy for a one-month supply;

and the same three categories for a three-month supply by mail order (multi-thousand dollar "specialty drugs" are often yet another tier). Our overall cost comparisons reflect these differences, but if you have unusually high (or low) name brand drug costs, you can use our cost sharing tables to identify plans most likely to match your needs.

You should not rely primarily on cost sharing information to select a plan. Choosing a plan with the best rate for a particular benefit without taking into account its premium and all its other benefits would be a mistake. You could try to compare key factors two or three at a time, but this approach necessarily either omits other key factors or requires so many oversimplified comparisons as to become meaningless. For example, whether or not and how much a separate hospital deductible matters compared to premium dollars depends on a key unknown: your likelihood of one or more hospital stays. With few exceptions (e.g., routine visits and maintenance prescription drugs, and some planned operations if you avoid complications that lead to readmissions) you cannot forecast just what medical expenses of each type you will incur next year, and even if you could it is very complex to make all the interactive calculations involved. Furthermore, cost sharing can be and often is expressed in annual, monthly, biweekly, per dollar spent, and per service unit for different benefits in the same plan. It can be expressed as the dollar amount you pay, the dollar amount the plan pays, the percent you pay, or the percent the plan

Dealing with a Known High Expense

There is an exception to our general advice about focusing on overall plan costs, not just one benefit category. If you know for sure that you will need a particular expensive service, you should look for the answer to "Which plans pay best?" If several plans pay equally well, then you can choose whichever of these is an overall better buy.

pays. Converting all these disparate measures to the common metric of annual cost is essential to making comparisons. Otherwise, you are comparing apples to oranges—how much biweekly premium equals how many annual physician visit copayments or what coinsurance percent for name brand prescriptions? We not only handle these messy computations for you, but also use actuarial information on the probability of different kinds and amounts of costs. **Most importantly, you cannot sensibly compare plans based only or primarily on expenses you already expect—that misses the main purpose of insurance: to protect you against unknown and potentially devastating future expenses.**

Each of the table entries for costs of various types shows the dollar copayment or coinsurance percentage you must pay for bills of each type. In some cases a plan uses both methods of payment for the same benefit, or a different amount depending on which type of provider or prescription drug is involved. These

Cost Sharing for National Plans & DC Area Plans		Savings account for self ($)	Savings account for family ($)	Deductibles ($)			
Plan code	Plan name (Listed in alphabetical order within group)			Single	Family	Extra for drugs (self)	Extra for 2-day hospital stay
DC Area Plans When You Use Preferred Providers							
F51-3	Aetna HealthFund CDHP	$1,000	$2,000	$1,000	$2,000	None	None
JN1-3	Aetna Open Access-Hi	None	None	None	None	None	$300
JN4-6	Aetna Open Access Basic	None	None	None	None	None	$200
F54-6	Aetna Value Plan	None	None	$600	$1,200	None	None
B51-3	CareFirst HDHP*	$450	$900	$1,400	$2,800	None	$500
2G1-3	CareFirst-Hi*	None	None	$500	$1,000	None	$300
2G4-6	CareFirst-Std POS*	None	None	$500	$1,000	None	$300
T71-3	Kaiser Basic*	None	None	$100	$200	None	$750
E31-3	Kaiser-Hi*	None	None	None	None	None	$100
E34-6	Kaiser-Std*	None	None	None	None	None	$500
JP1-3	MD-IPA*	None	None	None	None	None	$300
LR1-3	UnitedHealthcare Choice	None	None	None	None	None	$300
L91-3	UnitedHealthcare Choice Plus	None	None	$500	$1,000	None	None
V41-3	UnitedHealthcare HDHP	$750	$1,500	$1,500	$3,000	None	$500
National Plans When You Use Preferred Providers							
N61-3	Aetna Direct CDHP*	$900	$1,800	$1,500	$3,000	None	None
224-6	Aetna HealthFund HDHP	$750	$1,500	$1,500	$3,000	None	None
474-6	APWU CDHP	$1,200	$2,400	$800	$1,600	None	None
471-3	APWU-Hi*	None	None	$350	$700	None	None
111-3	Blue Cross Basic*†	None†	None†	None	None	None	$350
104-6	Blue Cross-Std*	None	None	$350	$700	None	$350
421-3	Compass Rose*	None	None	$350	$700	None	$200
401-3	Foreign Service*	None	None	$300	$600	None	None
341-3	GEHA HDHP	$750	$1,500	$1,500	$3,000	None	None
311-3	GEHA-Hi*	None	None	$350	$700	None	$100
314-6	GEHA-Std*	None	None	$350	$700	None	None
481-3	MHBP HDHP	$900	$1,800	$2,000	$4,000	None	$150
414-6	MHBP Value	None	None	$500	$1,000	None	None
454-6	MHBP-Std*	None	None	$350	$700	None	$200
324-6	NALC CDHP	$1,200	$2,400	$2,000	$4,000	None	None
KM1-3	NALC Value	$100	$200	$2,000	$4,000	None	None
321-3	NALC-Hi*	None	None	$300	$600	None	$200
381-3	Rural Carrier*	None	None	$350	$700	$200	$100
441-3	SAMBA-Hi*	None	None	$300	$600	None	$200
444-6	SAMBA-Std*	None	None	$350	$700	None	$200

* If you have Medicare parts A and B, most or all deductibles and hospital and physician cost sharing are waived.

				Prescription drugs ($) or (%)			
Hospital room & board (%)	Other hospital inpatient (%)	Visit to Primary Care ($ or %)	Visit to Specialist ($ or %)	Generic local pharmacy	Name brand local pharmacy	Generic mail order 90 day	Name brand mail order 90 day
15%	15%	15%	15%	$10	$35	$20	$70
None	None	$15	$30	$3	$35	$6	$70
None	None	$20	$45	$5	$50	$10	$100
20%	20%	$25	$40	$10	30%	$20	30%
None	None	None	$35	None	$30	None	$60
None	None	$30	$40	None	$35	None	$70
None	None	None	$40	None	$35	None	$70
None	None	$30	$40	$10	$45	$24	$129
None	None	$10	$20	$7	$30	$15	$84
None	None	$20	$30	$10	$40	$24	$114
None	None	$25	$40	$7	$35	$21	$105
None	None	$25	$35	$10	$40	$25	$100
20%	20%	$25	$50	$10	$35	$25	$88
None	None	$15	$30	$10	$40	$25	$100
20%	20%	20%	20%	$5	30%	None	$60
10%	10%	10%	10%	$10	$35	$20	$70
15%	15%	15%	15%	25%	25%	25%	25%
10%	10%	$25	$25	$10	25%	$20	25%
None	None	$30	$40	$10	$50	NA	NA
None	None	$25	$35	20%	30%	$15	$95
None	None	$15	$25	$5	$35	$10	$70
None	None	10%	10%	$10	25%	$15	$60
5%	5%	5%	5%	25%	25%	25%	25%
None	10%	$20	$20	$10	25%	$20	25%
15%	15%	$15	$30	$10	50%	$20	50%
None	None	$15	$15	$10	30%	$20	$80
20%	20%	$30	$50	$10	45%	$30	45%
None	15%	$10-20	$30	$5	30%	$10	$80
20%	20%	$20	$20	$10	$40	$20	$80
20%	20%	$20	$20	$10	$40	$20	$80
None	None	$20	$20	20%	30%	$12	$65
None	None	$20	$20	30%	30%	$10	$30
None	15%	$25	$25	$10	30%	$15	30%
None	20%	$30	$30	$12	35%	$20	35%

You pay after deductible and after using savings account:

† For those who pay Medicare Part B premiums, Blue Cross pays a reimbursement of $600 per member.

amounts and percentages do not take into account deductibles, and can be very misleading. A plan that pays all expenses in excess of a deductible of $300 pays none of your bills in a year when your costs are less than $300, and only half in a year in which your costs reach $600.

In most cases, our entries are the same as those given in the plan brochures. Unfortunately, the reimbursement structure for many plans is so complicated that there is no simple way to present or compare these payments, even organized by type of expense. For example, some plans vary your hospital copayment based on how many days you stay as a patient, and while some use dollar copayments others use percentage coinsurance. Therefore, unless you are quite confident as to a high level of spending in a particular category, and are willing to compare several plan brochures carefully, do not rely on cost sharing details to inform your decision.

The High Deductible and Consumer-Driven plans' copayments are particularly subject to confusion because they change by expenditure level. You start the year with a savings account you can use for any physician, dental, drug, or other expense. In addition, just as in all other plans you get complete coverage of a physical exam that will cost hundreds of dollars. Your copayment for these expenses is zero. If and when you exhaust the savings account, you pay a substantial deductible. After that, you pay a small proportion of hospital and physician costs until you reach the catastrophic limit. Your coinsurance ranges from zero, to 100 percent, to 10 or 15 percent and, once you reach the catastrophic limit, back to zero. The purpose of this is to give you incentives for careful decisions on medical spending. However, these plans' designs make it very difficult to estimate your costs.

Non-Preferred Providers

You face far higher costs if you use non-preferred providers. Plans not only charge you more for deductibles, copayments, and coinsurance, but also require you to pay the entire cost above the rate the plan sets as its allowance for a particular procedure. In general, we advise you to stay with preferred providers whenever possible. Remember that these alternative cost-sharing provisions are valid ONLY if the non-preferred provider accepts the plan's allowance. In most cases this will not be true unless you bargain, and the plan will likely pay less than half the bill. Half is better than nothing, but you should plan your health care to stay in network wherever possible. There is almost always a wide range of high quality preferred providers in network.

Chapter 6

Coverage Features

Using the *Guide*'s cost comparisons, you should first select several plans for which your costs are likely to be relatively low. The second step in selecting a plan is to focus on any special needs or circumstances that the cost tables do not fully reflect. The third step is to consider how important it is to you to retain a particular doctor(s) and, if necessary, to find out whether your doctor belongs to particular plans. The best way to do this is simply to call the doctor's office and ask. You can also go to the plan's Web site, or get a provider list at a health fair, but those provider lists are sometimes out of date. You can reverse the order of these steps, but it never makes sense to pay an extra $1,000 in premium if the most you will spend on a particular physician or service is a few hundred dollars. You should save the "for sure" premium cost and if necessary pay for a particular visit directly, without using your insurance.

Even if you know you are going to use a particular service, you can enroll in a plan that costs less overall but doesn't necessary have a particularly good benefit in that area. Use the savings to establish a Flexible Spending Account and focus that spending on that special need. Flexible Spending Accounts give employees (but not retirees) a way to reduce foreseeable costs substantially. If you anticipate, for example, having substantial dental or talk therapy expenses even after your coverage by health or dental insurance, you can set aside up to $2,600 in a health care FSA account ($5,200 for a couple) and that income will not be subject of Federal and State income taxes, or to Social Security taxes. For most, this has the effect of reducing the amount you actually pay by about one third. You estimate your likely spending and set up this account during the same Open Season used for selecting health plans. An FSA is perfect way to get about a one-third discount on a benefit for which your plan restricts coverage. FSA accounts are no longer "use or lose" and you can carry over up to $500 into the next without penalty.

Still, it is best to choose the low-cost plan that best covers an expense you can predict. Our Coverage Features analysis and tables focus on benefit categories that vary widely across plans, such as non-network psychiatric care. Online our tables show Coverage Features for all plans in the program, nationwide. In the printed *Guide*, we present these detailed tables only for national plans and DC area local plans, and very selectively for plans in other States in the "Cost and Coverage Features of Local Plans" table at the end of the "Key Tips and Final Plan Selection" section.

We have worded the comparison headings to allow standard entries, such as "Yes," "Some," or "No." A "Yes" always means broader coverage and a "No" always means narrower coverage. However, even though a number of plans are rated "Yes," this does not mean that the benefits are identical. You need to compare brochures.

Very importantly, if you know that you will need some specific and expensive type of care, whether or not it is in our tables, and whether or not the brochure seems clear, it is always a sensible strategy to talk to at least one potential provider and ask the simple question "Which plans pay best for the care I need?" You can also talk to a plan representative, but the information you get is not always reliable and carries no guarantee. The actual providers (or their office staff) know which plans pay best in the real world. Explore especially carefully if the service is near some boundary of coverage. For example, some hospitals provide regular hospital care, skilled nursing care, and custodial care in the same facility. You need to be sure that whichever level of service you get will be billed and paid under a category paid by your plan.

Nursing Care

There are four kinds of nursing care: skilled care while in a hospital, skilled care in a special "extended" or "skilled" care facility, care in your own home provided by visiting nurses, and "custodial" care either in your own home or in a "nursing home." No health insurance plan will pay for custodial care, the kind where your principal needs are to be fed, bathed, and clothed and where you need help with ordinary life tasks rather than to recover. At the other extreme, all plans pay for necessary care by nurses while you are in the hospital. Similarly, all plans cover some form of home health care, usually with at least 90 days or visits.

Plans differ in their coverage of care in an "extended" or "skilled" nursing care facility. Most national plans offer no coverage; but a few cover 60 or 90 days per confinement, usually at the same cost to you as hospital treatment. Most HMOs, however, cover skilled nursing care, usually 90 or 100 days.

We did not reflect the value of skilled care in a facility in our cost tables. Since very few younger persons ever need such care, the plan rankings would not have changed much if we had taken into account the statistical probabilities. Virtually all retirees over age 65 have a substantial Medicare Part A benefit for skilled nursing care. Accordingly, they will rarely if ever need any FEHB plan benefit for this care.

Nonetheless, stays in skilled nursing care facilities cost about half as much as in hospitals. This is one of the potentially substantial expenses to which some plans leave you exposed. If you think you are likely to need more than a month of this care, we recommend careful attention to brochure language in relation to your particular needs. Remember, moreover, that these stays are subject to plan approval and must involve rehabilitative needs, not simply help with daily living.

For custodial care, either in your own home or a nursing home, OPM sponsors a Long Term Care insurance program, separate from the FEHB program. This program pays for long term care services if you can't take care of yourself because of an extended illness, such as Alzheimer's disease. The program covers both institutional and home care. Premiums are substantial, and there is no government contribution. You can find out more about it at *www.opm.gov/insure/ltc*. Similar insurance can be purchased individually from the same companies that underwrite the OPM program. If your retirement income and assets are relatively low, and you otherwise cannot afford needed custodial care, you can ultimately rely on the Federal/State Medicaid program.

Value of Outpatient Mental Benefits

OPM has long required that plans pay the same benefits for physician visits or hospital stays whether due to either physical or mental illness. This requirement is called "parity," and, at face value, seems to eliminate any distinction between physical and mental health benefits. It represented a significant advance in covering clinically necessary hospital stays for mental illness. In 2010 the government issued regulations requiring all employer-sponsored health plans to meet an even stricter version of parity. Under these regulations, plans are no longer allowed even to charge separate deductibles for physical and mental health or substance abuse services. In theory, all FEHB plans will now pay for unlimited mental health services without even such a small difference in cost sharing.

The catch is that all plans select the providers for their networks, and will rarely if ever use providers whose practices emphasize weekly sessions of "talk therapy." Nor will plans reimburse full costs for services provided by a psychiatrist of your choosing. Instead, they provide a limited number of plan-affiliated psychiatrists, and often rely mainly on the services of clinical psychologists, clinical social workers, and other non-M.D. staff.

Few of the HMO plans offer any mental health services outside of the plan network, or outside of pre-approved treatment plans. The major exceptions are the HMOs with an Opt-Out or "Point of Service" provision. In contrast, all of the national fee-for-service plans except Blue Cross Basic offer a relatively unconstrained out-of-network benefit, as do Consumer-Driven and High Deductible plans. If you expect to use an out of network provider, consider setting up a Flexible Spending Account during Open Season.

Other Coverage Features

Most plans limit reimbursement for most of the following services. Current employees can cover any of them through a Flexible Spending Account.

- *Dental care*—We indicate which health insurance plans pay for routine and accidental dental expenses, and show the better benefits with a "Yes." Our separate chapter on "Dental, Vision and Hearing" provides dollar ratings of these plans along with the standalone dental plans (we have even more detailed comparisons online). Those standalone plans charge a premium, but offer stronger benefits. Nonetheless, our ratings show that for most people joining an FEHB plan with modest dental benefits is a low-cost option.

Coverage Features of National Plans and D.C. Area Plans

Plan code	Plan name (Listed in alphabetical order within group)	Pays for (in most cases only if medically necessary):				
		Day limit in skilled nursing facility	Maximum non-network mental out-patient	Routine dental care	Dental accident	Adult vision care
DC Area Plans When You Use Preferred Providers						
F51-3	Aetna HealthFund CDHP	60	Unlim	Yes	Some	Exam
JN1-3	Aetna Open Access-Hi	60	None	Some	No	Yes
JN4-6	Aetna Open Access Basic	60	None	Some	No	Yes
F54-6	Aetna Value Plan	60	Unlim	No	No	Yes
B61-3	CareFirst HDHP	Unlim	Unlim	Yes	Yes	Exam
2G1-3	CareFirst-Hi	Unlim	None	Yes	Yes	Exam
2G4-6	CareFirst-Std POS	Unlim	Unlim	Yes	Yes	Exam
T71-3	Kaiser Basic	100	None	No	Yes	Exam
E31-3	Kaiser-Hi	100	None	Yes	Yes	Exam
E34-6	Kaiser-Std	100	None	Yes	Yes	Exam
JP1-3	MD-IPA	60	None	Yes	Yes	Yes
LR1-3	UnitedHealthcare Choice	60	None	Some	Yes	Exam
L91-3	UnitedHealthcare Choice Plus	60	Unlim	Some	Yes	Exam
V41-3	UnitedHealthcare HDHP	60	Unlim	Some	Yes	Exam
National Plans When You Use Preferred Providers						
N61-3	Aetna Direct CDHP	60	Unlim	No	Yes	Exam
224-6	Aetna HealthFund HDHP	60	Unlim	Yes	Some	Exam
474-6	APWU CDHP	0	Unlim	Yes	Yes	Some
471-3	APWU-Hi	0	Unlim	Yes	Yes	No
111-3	Blue Cross Basic	0	None	Some	Yes	No
104-6	Blue Cross-Std	0	Unlim	Yes	Yes	No
421-3	Compass Rose	90	Unlim	Yes	Yes	Exam
401-3	Foreign Service	90	Unlim	Some	Yes	No
341-3	GEHA HDHP	14	Unlim	Yes	Yes	Yes
311-3	GEHA-Hi	14	Unlim	Yes	Yes	No
314-6	GEHA-Std	14	Unlim	Yes	Yes	No
481-3	MHBP HDHP	28	Unlim	No	Yes	No
414-6	MHBP Value	28	Unlim	No	Yes	No
454-6	MHBP-Std	28	Unlim	No	Yes	No
324-6	NALC CDHP	0	Unlim	Yes	Some	No
KM1-3	NALC Value	0	Unlim	Yes	Some	No
321-3	NALC-Hi	0	Unlim	Yes	Some	No
381-3	Rural Carrier	60	Unlim	Yes	Yes	No
441-3	SAMBA-Hi	45	Unlim	No	Yes	No
444-6	SAMBA-Std	30	Unlim	No	Yes	No

Note: Your savings accounts in CDHP and HDHP plans, or your FSA account, pay for ALL of these benefits, in addition to what the plans pay.

Chiropractic	Acupuncture	Hearing aids	Infertility treatment	Prostheses (artificial limbs)	Diabetic supplies	Durable medical equipment	Nurse advice by phone

Pays for (in most cases only if medically necessary):

Chiropractic	Acupuncture	Hearing aids	Infertility treatment	Prostheses (artificial limbs)	Diabetic supplies	Durable medical equipment	Nurse advice by phone
Yes	No	No	Some	Yes	Some	Yes	800-556-1555
Some	No	Yes	Little	Yes	Yes	Yes	800-556-1555
Some	No	Yes	Little	Yes	Yes	Yes	800-556-1555
No	Little	No	Some	Yes	Some	Yes	800-556-1555
Some	Some	Yes	Little	Yes	Yes	Yes	800-535-9700
Some	Some	Yes	Some	Yes	Yes	Yes	800-535-9700
Some	Some	Yes	Little	Yes	Yes	Yes	800-535-9700
Some	Some	Child	Little	Yes	Yes	Some	703-359-7878
Yes	Yes	Child	Little	Yes	Yes	Some	703-359-7878
Some	Some	Child	Little	Yes	Yes	Some	703-359-7878
Some	Some	Child	Yes	Some	Yes	Some	888-887-4114
Some	Some	No	Some	Yes	Yes	Yes	888-887-4114
Some	Some	Child	Some	Yes	Yes	Yes	888-887-4114
Yes	Some	Yes	Some	Yes	Yes	Yes	888-887-4114
No	No	Some	Some	Yes	Some	Yes	800-556-1555
No	No	No	Some	Yes	Some	Yes	800-556-1555
Some	Yes	Yes	Some	Yes	Yes	Yes	800-582-1314
Some	Yes	Yes	Some	Yes	Yes	Yes	888-993-0333
Some	Some	Yes	Some	Some	Yes	Some	888-258-3432
Some	Yes	Yes	Some	Yes	Yes	Yes	888-258-3432
Yes	Yes	Yes	Some	Yes	Yes	Yes	None
Yes	Yes	Yes	Some	Yes	Yes	Yes	855-482-5750
Some	Yes	No	Little	Yes	Some	Yes	888-257-4342
Some	Yes	Yes	Little	Yes	Yes	Yes	888-257-4342
Some	Yes	Some	Little	Yes	Yes	Yes	888-257-4342
Yes	Yes	Some	Little	Yes	Yes	Yes	800-694-9901
Yes	Yes	Some	Little	Yes	Yes	Yes	800-410-7778
Yes	Yes	Yes	Little	Yes	Yes	Yes	800-410-7778
Some	Some	Some	Some	Yes	Yes	Yes	877-220-6252
Some	Some	Some	Some	Yes	Yes	Yes	877-220-6252
Some	Some	Some	Some	Yes	Yes	Yes	877-220-6252
Yes	Yes	Some	Some	Yes	Yes	Yes	800-638-8432
Yes	Yes	Some	Little	Yes	Yes	Yes	800-887-9735
Some	Yes	Some	Little	Yes	Yes	Yes	800-887-9735

- *Vision care*—All plans pay for medically necessary care of your eyes, such as cataract surgery. No national plans pay for eyeglasses or contact lenses, although several of them have arranged for discounts at some chains. A few pay for examinations to determine the prescription you need. Among HMOs, many pay just for an "Exam," and some for most of the cost of glasses or contact lenses ("Yes" in our tables). You may want to join one of the vision plans described in our chapter on "Dental, Vision and Hearing," but a combination of prudent shopping and Flexible Spending Account will often match the value of the standalone vision plans.
- *Chiropractic services*—Most national plans and some HMO plans reimburse some chiropractic services. The medical establishment has traditionally viewed chiropractors unfavorably because chiropractors are not trained as medical doctors. However, chiropractic services have been proven useful in treating some problems of the muscles, back, and joints.
- *Acupuncture*—Another non-traditional treatment that an increasing number of plans reimburse, often for a dozen or more visits.
- *Hearing aids*—Most plans pay for diagnostic hearing tests performed by a physician or audiologist, and all pay for medically necessary treatment for hearing problems. At OPM urging, most plans now pay for hearing aids for both adults and children, and others for hearing aids for children only. In our table, a "Yes" indicates both a relatively generous allowance, and coverage of both children and adults. The "Dental, Vision and Hearing" chapter provides detailed comparisons.
- *Infertility treatment*—Very few plans pay for the costs of in vitro fertilization or for the most advanced and expensive infertility treatments such as assisted reproductive technology procedures. However, many plans pay for fertility drugs or for treatments such as artificial insemination. Generosity varies so you should compare brochures or consult providers before choosing a plan.
- *Diabetic supplies*—Some plans cover drugs but do not cover the cost of syringes and/or special testing supplies and kits needed by diabetics. Even for the plans listed as "Yes," a diabetic should check brochures to determine the precise coverage the plans provide.
- *Durable medical equipment*—All national plans pay for prostheses, or artificial limbs. Some plans limit such coverage. Some plans also fail to pay for the purchase or rental costs of hospital beds, walkers, and other equipment you may need while recuperating from surgery or illness. Others pay only a limited benefit, such as 50 percent of the cost. This is another area to compare brochures and consult providers.
- *Nurse advice*—Most plans let you call a service to discuss medical problems that confuse you. Nurse advisors can greatly assist you in deciding, for example, whether to call a doctor and, if so, which specialty you need. Nurses can also advise you on handling minor medical problems of all kinds, on compliance with your medication needs, and diet and health, and on other issues. For plans that offer this, we enter the telephone number of the advisory service.

Chapter 7

Dental, Vision and Hearing

The Federal government offers standalone "FEDVIP" dental and vision plans, separate and distinct from the FEHB program. These plans share the same Open Season dates as the health insurance plans, but you join them separately. To enroll, you can use the special OPM Web site at *www.benefeds.com*, or call 1-877-888-3337. In sharp contrast to regular health insurance benefits, there is no direct Federal government contribution to the cost of the premium. You pay it all, though with substantial tax savings to employees (but not annuitants).

While these plans do have an element of insurance, in that they protect you against some unforeseen dental or vision expenses, they are best thought of as primarily pre-paid care. Most people enroll in these kinds of plans because they know roughly what kinds of expenses to expect, and plan to do a little better than breaking even. In effect, you pay for those new contact lenses or your recurring dental expenses on the biweekly or monthly installment plan, with protection against some unanticipated expense.

The dental and vision plans save you money in two ways. First, they use affiliated providers who provide discounts because of the increased business the plans attract. Second, because employees (but not retirees) pay the premiums with "pre-tax" dollars, you save approximately one-third of the premium cost. As explained in our analysis of "Costs and Taxes" almost all Federal employees face a marginal tax rate close to or above 33 percent, taking into account Federal income tax, State income tax, the Medicare tax and, for FERS employees, the Social Security tax. Any money an employee spends on dental or vision insurance is not subject to these taxes and employees get what amounts to a one-third discount on the premium, depending on their tax bracket.

On the other hand, these plans charge a premium, ranging from about $200 to $400 a year for self-only dental and about $130 a year for self-only vision, with family premiums about three times as high. Also, the companies that underwrite these plans know that they will attract persons who are heavy users of these services. This means that the premiums have to be higher than would otherwise be the case.

(Text continues on page 110)

Dental Plan Ratings for Employees—Single Person*

Plan code	Plan name	Plan type	Extra yearly premium	Approximate yearly cost ($) to you if your dental usage is:			Maximum benefit per person ($)
				Low	Average	High	
DC Area Health Plans When You Use Preferred Providers							
F51	Aetna HealthFund CDHP	Official	$0	$120	$600	$2,200	$300+prev
JN1	Aetna Open Access-Hi	Official	$0	$140	$630	$2,230	Unlim
JN4	Aetna Open Access Basic	Official	$0	$140	$630	$2,230	Unlim
2G1	CareFirst-Hi	Unofficial	$0	$120	$400	$1,200	Unlim
2G4	CareFirst-Std POS	Unofficial	$0	$120	$400	$1,200	Unlim
B61	CareFirst HDHP	Unofficial	$0	$80	$330	$1,130	Unlim
E31	Kaiser-Hi	Both	$0	$90	$400	$1,400	Unlim
E34	Kaiser-Std	Both	$0	$90	$400	$1,400	Unlim
JP1	MD-IPA	Both	$0	$120	$600	$2,200	$500
LR1	UnitedHealthcare Choice	Unofficial	$0	$150	$750	$2,750	$500
L91	UnitedHealthcare Choice Plus	Unofficial	$0	$150	$750	$2,750	$500
V41	UnitedHealthcare HDHP	Unofficial	$0	$150	$750	$2,750	$500
National Health Plans When You Use Preferred Providers							
224	Aetna HealthFund HDHP	Official	$0	$150	$750	$2,750	Unlim
471	APWU-Hi	Both	$0	$140	$530	$1,730	Unlim
111	Blue Cross Basic	Official	$0	$170	$780	$2,780	Unlim
104	Blue Cross-Std	Official	$0	$270	$950	$2,950	Unlim
421	Compass Rose	Unofficial	$0	$170	$580	$1,780	Unlim
401	Foreign Service	Official	$0	$270	$900	$2,700	Unlim
311	GEHA-Hi	Official	$0	$260	$880	$2,680	Unlim
314	GEHA-Std	Official	$0	$210	$800	$2,600	Unlim
341	GEHA HDHP	Official	$0	$140	$680	$2,480	Unlim
321	NALC-Hi	Unofficial	$0	$210	$700	$2,100	Unlim
KM1	NALC Value Plan	Unofficial	$0	$210	$700	$2,100	Unlim
324	NALC CDHP	Unofficial	$0	$210	$700	$2,100	Unlim
381	Rural Carrier	Official	$0	$310	$930	$2,730	Unlim
Supplemental Dental Plans When You Use Preferred Providers							
	Aetna Dental	FEDVIP	$280	$380	$740	$1,940	$25,000
	Delta Dental High	FEDVIP	$430	$510	$810	$1,810	$30,000
	Delta Dental Std	FEDVIP	$210	$300	$660	$1,860	$1,500
	Dominion Dental High	FEDVIP	$220	$280	$460	$1,060	Unlim
	Dominion Dental Std	FEDVIP	$140	$210	$450	$1,250	Unlim
	FEP BlueDental High	FEDVIP	$400	$480	$780	$1,780	Unlim
	FEP BlueDental Std	FEDVIP	$230	$320	$680	$1,880	$1,500
	GEHA Dental High	FEDVIP	$380	$460	$760	$1,760	$35,000
	GEHA Dental Std	FEDVIP	$220	$300	$660	$1,860	$2,500
	Humana Dental	FEDVIP	$190	$240	$420	$1,020	$15,000
	Metlife Dental High	FEDVIP	$400	$470	$770	$1,770	$35,000
	Metlife Dental Std	FEDVIP	$230	$320	$680	$1,880	$1,500
	United Concordia Dental	FEDVIP	$310	$370	$610	$1,410	$15,000

* Ratings reflect tax savings available to employees.

Dental Plan Ratings for Employees—Family of Three or More*

Plan code	Plan name	Extra yearly premium	Approximate yearly cost ($) to you if your dental usage is:			Maximum benefit per person ($)	Child ortho- dontic
			Low	Average	High		
DC Area Health Plans When You Use Preferred Providers							
F52	Aetna HealthFund CDHP	$0	$280	$1,680	$4,080	$300+prev	No
JN2	Aetna Open Access-Hi	$0	$330	$1,750	$4,150	Unlim	Some
JN5	Aetna Open Access Basic	$0	$330	$1,750	$4,150	Unlim	Some
2G2	CareFirst-Hi	$0	$320	$1,200	$2,400	Unlim	No
2G5	CareFirst-Std POS	$0	$320	$1,200	$2,400	Unlim	No
B62	CareFirst HDHP	$0	$180	$970	$2,170	Unlim	No
E32	Kaiser-Hi	$0	$220	$1,200	$2,700	Unlim	Some
E35	Kaiser-Std	$0	$220	$1,200	$2,700	Unlim	Some
JP2	MD-IPA	$0	$280	$1,840	$4,240	$500	No
LR2	UnitedHealthcare Choice	$0	$350	$2,300	$5,300	$500	No
L92	UnitedHealthcare Choice Plus	$0	$350	$2,300	$5,300	$500	No
V42	UnitedHealthcare HDHP	$0	$350	$2,300	$5,300	$500	No
National Health Plans When You Use Preferred Providers							
225	Aetna HealthFund HDHP	$0	$350	$2,300	$5,300	Unlim	No
472	APWU-Hi	$0	$350	$1,530	$3,330	Unlim	No
112	Blue Cross Basic	$0	$400	$2,370	$5,370	Unlim	No
105	Blue Cross-Std	$0	$700	$2,840	$5,840	Unlim	No
422	Compass Rose	$0	$440	$1,730	$3,530	Unlim	No
402	Foreign Service	$0	$710	$2,700	$5,400	Unlim	Yes
312	GEHA-Hi	$0	$680	$2,630	$5,330	Unlim	No
315	GEHA-Std	$0	$540	$2,420	$5,120	Unlim	No
342	GEHA HDHP	$0	$320	$2,070	$4,770	Unlim	No
322	NALC-Hi	$0	$560	$2,100	$4,200	Unlim	No
KM2	NALC Value Plan	$0	$560	$2,100	$4,200	Unlim	No
325	NALC CDHP	$0	$560	$2,100	$4,200	Unlim	No
382	Rural Carrier	$0	$830	$2,780	$5,480	Unlim	No
Supplemental Dental Plans When You Use Preferred Providers							
	Aetna Dental	$850	$1,060	$2,190	$3,990	$25,000	Wait
	Delta Dental High	$1,300	$1,470	$2,400	$3,900	$30,000	Wait
	Delta Dental Std	$640	$850	$2,000	$3,800	$1,500	Wait
	Dominion Dental High	$670	$780	$1,320	$2,220	Unlim	Yes
	Dominion Dental Std	$430	$570	$1,330	$2,530	Unlim	Yes
	FEP BlueDental High	$1,210	$1,390	$2,320	$3,820	Unlim	Wait
	FEP BlueDental Std	$680	$900	$2,050	$3,850	$1,500	Wait
	GEHA Dental High	$1,140	$1,320	$2,230	$3,730	$35,000	Wait
	GEHA Dental Std	$650	$860	$2,010	$3,810	$2,500	Wait
	Humana Dental	$580	$690	$1,250	$2,150	$15,000	Yes
	Metlife Dental High	$1,240	$1,420	$2,350	$3,850	$35,000	Yes
	Metlife Dental Std	$690	$900	$2,050	$3,850	$1,500	Yes
	United Concordia Dental	$920	$1,060	$1,800	$3,000	$15,000	Wait

* Ratings reflect tax savings available to employees.

Dental Plan Ratings for Annuitants—Single Person

Plan code	Plan name	Plan type	Extra yearly premium	Approximate yearly cost ($) to you if your dental usage is:			Maximum benefit per person ($)
				Low	Average	High	
DC Area Health Plans When You Use Preferred Providers							
F51	Aetna HealthFund CDHP	Official	$0	$120	$600	$2,200	$300+prev
JN1	Aetna Open Access-Hi	Official	$0	$140	$630	$2,230	Unlim
JN4	Aetna Open Access Basic	Official	$0	$140	$630	$2,230	Unlim
2G1	CareFirst-Hi	Unofficial	$0	$120	$400	$1,200	Unlim
2G4	CareFirst-Std POS	Unofficial	$0	$120	$400	$1,200	Unlim
B61	CareFirst HDHP	Unofficial	$0	$80	$330	$1,130	Unlim
E31	Kaiser-Hi	Both	$0	$90	$400	$1,400	Unlim
E34	Kaiser-Std	Both	$0	$90	$400	$1,400	Unlim
JP1	MD-IPA	Both	$0	$120	$600	$2,200	$500
LR1	UnitedHealthcare Choice	Unofficial	$0	$150	$750	$2,750	$500
L91	UnitedHealthcare Choice Plus	Unofficial	$0	$150	$750	$2,750	$500
V41	UnitedHealthcare HDHP	Unofficial	$0	$150	$750	$2,750	$500
National Health Plans When You Use Preferred Providers							
224	Aetna HealthFund HDHP	Official	$0	$150	$750	$2,750	Unlim
471	APWU-Hi	Both	$0	$140	$530	$1,730	Unlim
111	Blue Cross Basic	Official	$0	$170	$780	$2,780	Unlim
104	Blue Cross-Std	Official	$0	$270	$950	$2,950	Unlim
421	Compass Rose	Unofficial	$0	$170	$580	$1,780	Unlim
401	Foreign Service	Official	$0	$270	$900	$2,700	Unlim
311	GEHA-Hi	Official	$0	$260	$880	$2,680	Unlim
314	GEHA-Std	Official	$0	$210	$800	$2,600	Unlim
341	GEHA HDHP	Official	$0	$140	$680	$2,480	Unlim
321	NALC-Hi	Unofficial	$0	$210	$700	$2,100	Unlim
KM1	NALC Value Plan	Unofficial	$0	$210	$700	$2,100	Unlim
324	NALC CDHP	Unofficial	$0	$210	$700	$2,100	Unlim
381	Rural Carrier	Official	$0	$310	$930	$2,730	Unlim
Supplemental Dental Plans When You Use Preferred Providers							
	Aetna Dental	FEDVIP	$430	$520	$880	$2,080	$25,000
	Delta Dental High	FEDVIP	$650	$730	$1,030	$2,030	$30,000
	Delta Dental Std	FEDVIP	$320	$410	$770	$1,970	$1,500
	Dominion Dental High	FEDVIP	$340	$390	$570	$1,170	Unlim
	Dominion Dental Std	FEDVIP	$220	$280	$520	$1,320	Unlim
	FEP BlueDental High	FEDVIP	$600	$680	$980	$1,980	Unlim
	FEP BlueDental Std	FEDVIP	$340	$430	$790	$1,990	$1,500
	GEHA Dental High	FEDVIP	$570	$650	$950	$1,950	$35,000
	GEHA Dental Std	FEDVIP	$320	$410	$770	$1,970	$2,500
	Humana Dental	FEDVIP	$290	$340	$520	$1,120	$15,000
	Metlife Dental High	FEDVIP	$590	$670	$970	$1,970	$35,000
	Metlife Dental Std	FEDVIP	$340	$430	$790	$1,990	$1,500
	United Concordia Dental	FEDVIP	$460	$520	$760	$1,560	$15,000

Dental Plan Ratings for Annuitants—Self Plus One

Plan code	Plan name	Extra yearly premium	Approximate yearly cost ($) to you if your dental usage is:			Maximum benefit per person ($)	Child ortho-dontic
			Low	Average	High		
DC Area Health Plans When You Use Preferred Providers							
F53	Aetna HealthFund CDHP	$0	$200	$1,200	$2,800	$300+prev	No
JN3	Aetna Open Access-Hi	$0	$230	$1,250	$2,850	None	Some
JN6	Aetna Open Access Basic	$0	$230	$1,250	$2,850	None	Some
2G3	CareFirst-Hi	$0	$200	$800	$1,600	None	No
2G6	CareFirst-Std POS	$0	$200	$800	$1,600	None	No
B63	CareFirst HDHP	$0	$130	$650	$1,450	None	No
E33	Kaiser-Hi	$0	$150	$800	$1,800	None	Some
E36	Kaiser-Std	$0	$150	$800	$1,800	None	Some
JP3	MD-IPA	$0	$200	$1,200	$2,800	$500	No
LR3	UnitedHealthcare Choice	$0	$250	$1,500	$3,500	$500	No
L93	UnitedHealthcare Choice Plus	$0	$250	$1,500	$3,500	$500	No
V43	UnitedHealthcare HDHP	$0	$250	$1,500	$3,500	$500	No
National Health Plans When You Use Preferred Providers							
226	Aetna HealthFund HDHP	$0	$250	$1,500	$3,500	None	No
473	APWU-Hi	$0	$230	$1,050	$2,250	None	No
113	Blue Cross Basic	$0	$280	$1,550	$3,550	None	No
106	Blue Cross-Std	$0	$450	$1,900	$3,900	None	No
423	Compass Rose	$0	$280	$1,150	$2,350	None	No
403	Foreign Service	$0	$450	$1,800	$3,600	None	Yes
313	GEHA-Hi	$0	$430	$1,750	$3,550	None	No
316	GEHA-Std	$0	$350	$1,600	$3,400	None	No
343	GEHA HDHP	$0	$230	$1,350	$3,150	None	No
323	NALC-Hi	$0	$350	$1,400	$2,800	None	No
KM3	NALC Value Plan	$0	$350	$1,400	$2,800	None	No
326	NALC CDHP	$0	$350	$1,400	$2,800	None	No
383	Rural Carrier	$0	$530	$1,850	$3,650	None	No
Supplemental Dental Plans When You Use Preferred Providers							
	Aetna Dental	$850	$1,000	$1,750	$2,950	$25,000	Wait
	Delta Dental High	$1,300	$1,430	$2,050	$3,050	$30,000	Wait
	Delta Dental Std	$640	$790	$1,540	$2,740	$1,500	Wait
	Dominion Dental High	$670	$750	$1,120	$1,720	Unlim	Yes
	Dominion Dental Std	$430	$530	$1,030	$1,830	Unlim	Yes
	FEP BlueDental High	$1,210	$1,340	$1,960	$2,960	Unlim	Wait
	FEP BlueDental Std	$650	$800	$1,550	$2,750	$1,500	Wait
	GEHA Dental High	$1,140	$1,270	$1,890	$2,890	$35,000	Wait
	GEHA Dental Std	$650	$800	$1,550	$2,750	$2,500	Wait
	Humana Dental	$580	$660	$1,030	$1,630	$15,000	Yes
	Metlife Dental High	$1,240	$1,370	$1,990	$2,990	$35,000	Yes
	Metlife Dental Std	$680	$830	$1,580	$2,780	$1,500	Yes
	United Concordia Dental	$920	$1,020	$1,520	$2,320	$15,000	Wait

(Continued from page 105)

Virtually all FEHB health insurance plans provide insurance coverage for accidental dental or vision injuries. Typical brochure language says, "We cover services and supplies necessary to promptly repair sound natural teeth" when services are needed due to an "accidental injury." For vision services, typical brochure language says the plan will cover testing and evaluation and fitting for implanted ocular lenses or contact lenses when the impairment is "caused by accident or illness." Most FEHB plans also have some routine dental and vision benefits. These are often substantial benefits (though never as good as in these supplemental plans). By joining a health insurance plan with better than average dental or vision benefits, you can eliminate much of the need for a supplemental plan. As an example, the Aetna Consumer-Driven plan offers a special $300 fund for self-only enrollees (and double that for families) that covers dental costs.

You can also use a Flexible Spending Account to provide prepaid dental or vision care. By earmarking several hundred or even several thousand dollars of your salary, you avoid paying taxes on that income and effectively gain the same one-third discount that the FEDVIP plans provide. To set up an FSA, you estimate your likely spending for dental, vision, or other anticipated out of pocket expenses. You create an FSA during the same Open Season used for selecting health plans and FEDVIP plans.

You can use all three approaches simultaneously. For example, suppose you enroll in a health insurance plan that pays for preventive dental care and an annual eye exam. You can also enroll in a supplemental vision or dental plan, or both. The health insurance plan will be "primary" and pay first, and the FEDVIP plan pay second. You can then use your FSA account to pay the residual that the first two sources do not cover. This three-part approach may, of course, require more planning and more paperwork than you are willing to tolerate. There is the further complication that your favorite provider may not be a plan participant under either the FEHB or FEDVIP plan. But it does give you maximum wrap-around coverage.

Annuitants do not get the same tax advantages as employees. They may sign up for supplemental dental or vision plans, but do not get the pre-tax "discount." They are not allowed to create FSAs. However, annuitants do get the government contribution towards their FEHB plans, which averages about 70 percent. A health insurance plan with a good dental benefit may be an excellent choice for retirees with low to moderate dental or vision expenses, and with heavy anticipated expenses a FEDVIP plan is a sensible choice even without the taxpayer subsidy.

Consumer-Driven and High Deductible health plans are particularly flexible and comprehensive options for funding dental and vision expenses. These plans allow you to shelter from taxes a personal savings account that you can use for dental and vision expenses, and carry over from year to year. Several of them have special dental funds, and all of them allow employees (but not annuitants) to augment savings accounts during the year if unanticipated expenses arise. These accounts may be used for dental or vision expenses quite apart from those expenses that the plan normally covers, and without restrictions on provider choice (though you may lose discounts if you use non-plan providers). If you already know your dental expenses will be high next year, you can even set up a special account called a Limited Expense Health Care FSA (LEX HCFSA) during Open Season. This will provide dental and vision funding over and above the normal limits on your tax-free contributions to personal savings accounts.

Dental and vision benefits are areas in which you can plan, and in which it pays to plan. Unlike true insurance, where your main need is to guard against large and unpredictable expenses, you probably have a pretty good idea what you are likely to spend on dental and eye care expenses. You can structure your decision around those predictable costs, keeping in mind of course that a tooth, crown, or bridge can break unexpectedly, or some other dental emergency arise. Be careful to read the fine print of the plan brochures carefully, however. The plan may be unlikely to pay for a denture if the need arose before you joined the plan, for example.

The dental and vision plans offer a three-part premium structure—self only, self plus one, and family of three or more. The premiums for families of two or three are almost always about double or triple the self-only premium. If you have a family of three (or more) you may enroll as self plus one and designate which two persons will be eligible for benefits.

Dental Care

Plans' dental benefits differ widely in details, and many of the brochures use technical terminology such as "gingival" (gum, in English), "alveolar" (the part of the jawbone that holds teeth in place), and "amalgam restorations" (filling cavities). Moreover, many plans use schedules of allowances so you don't know if the full charge will be paid (usually not). Since most of the plans limit coverage to the items listed in the schedule of allowances, the particular problem you have may not be covered at all. Worst of all, no plans offer a catastrophic dental benefit that would cover you if, for example, you developed a chronic infection of the jaw and required dental procedures costing thousands of dollars. If you are not sure that a plan adequately covers the particular dental problems of your family, or to be sure you get the network discount, you should talk to your dentist before choosing that plan. For example, most dental plans now cover dental implants, a very expensive procedure. But exactly which parts of the procedure are covered for sure, which options are best, which of these parts or options require plan

National Vision Plans								
Plan name	Aetna Vision		FEP BlueVision		United-Healthcare		VSP	
	High	Std	High	Std	High	Std	High	Std
Web site	aetnafeds.com		fepbluevision.com		myuhcvision.com		choosevsp.com	
Telephone	855-347-6899		888-550-2583		866-249-1999		800-877-7195	
Annual Cost for Employees (with tax savings of one-third)								
Self only	$100	$60	$100	$70	$80	$50	$120	$60
Self plus one	$200	$110	$200	$140	$150	$100	$230	$120
Self and family	$300	$170	$290	$210	$230	$150	$350	$180
Annual Cost for Annuitants (published premium without tax savings)								
Self only	$150	$80	$150	$100	$120	$80	$170	$90
Self plus one	$300	$170	$290	$210	$230	$150	$350	$180
Self and family	$450	$250	$440	$310	$340	$230	$520	$270
Copayments								
Deductible	None	None	None	None	None	None	None	None
Annual eye exam	$0	$0	$0	$0	$10	$10	$10	$10
Eyeglass lenses (single, bifocal, tri.)	$0	$10	$0	$0	$10	$25	Included	$20
One pair inexpensive frames	$0	$0	$0	$0	$10	$25	Included	Included
Contact lenses (daily or replacement)	$0	$0	$0	$0	$10	$25	$0	$0
Lens and Frame Benefits								
Replace lost/broken lenses?	No	No	No	No	No	No	No	No
Frequency of lenses	Annual	Annual	Annual	Annual	Annual	Annual	Annual	Annual
Frequency of frames	Annual	Biannual	Annual	Biannual	Annual	Annual	Annual	Annual
Frame allowance	$230	$140	$150	$130	$150	$150	$150	$120
Premium frames allowance /discount	$230/20%	$140/15%	$150/20%	$130/20%	$150/0%	$150/0%	$150/20%	$120/20%
Anti-reflective coating cost	$20	$45	$20	$35	Included	$40	$21	$41
UV coating cost	Included	$15	Included	Included	Included	$16	Included	$16
Progressive lenses	Pay more	Pay more	Pay more	Pay more	Yes	Yes	Pay more	Pay more

approval, and how likely a case like yours is to get plan approval, varies from plan to plan. You can call the plan to discuss your case, but the best way to find out which dental plan will cover your implant at least cost to you is to ask your dental surgeon what his patients' experience has been.

In recent years OPM has not allowed most health plans to expand dental benefits. However, OPM has allowed plans to offer "non-FEHB" benefits to plan members, as shown on a special page in brochures. In many cases, extra dental benefits are offered, usually through a panel of dentists who provide discounts for the extra business the plan brings. When these do not involve an extra premium, and represent a significant benefit that can be determined from the brochure, we have included their value in our ratings and tables. While they are not part of the OPM contract and will not be enforced by OPM, they are nonetheless plan commitments to you.

The new standalone dental plans give you a good deal more advance assurance about what is covered and how much you are likely to pay than most of the health plans. However, how much each plan will cover depends importantly on whether your expenses are mainly for children or for adults, and whether for preventive and diagnostic services, or for more expensive restorative services (including surgical, endodontic, prosthodontic, etc.).

Our dental benefit tables help you sort this out. First, we provide estimates of the cost to you under each plan that provides dental benefits, organized by type of plan. There are no extra premiums under the health plans, but there are for the standalone dental plans and we show the annual premium cost together with the likely out of pocket cost under low, average, and high usage scenarios. Because the premium cost is a "for sure" expense we include it in each column.

We also show which plans cover roughly how much on average for child preventive, child restorative, adult preventive, and adult restorative services. These estimates are based on a market basket of dental procedures that are among the most common in each category. For example, we assume that children receive the following preventive and diagnostic services through an annual visit: periodic examination, prophylaxis, bitewing x-rays, and fluoride treatment. For adult restorative services, our index includes fillings, extractions, crowns, root canal treatment, periodontal treatment, and dentures. We also provide estimates for some individual procedures. Although the tables show specific percentages, these are rough estimates, based on national average prices. Your dentist may charge more or less. Also, we had to translate varied plan reimbursement approaches into the "percent you pay," and sometimes this is only an approximation. However, these data can steer you towards particular plans' brochures if there are particular benefits you want to check out in detail for the best coverage.

We also show you the maximum benefit levels (if any) of each plan. Most health plans do not have maximums because their benefits are low enough that they do not face substantial cost exposure. However, most of the standalone plans impose maximum ceilings on what they will pay. If you expect very high expenses, consider a plan with a high or even unlimited maximum, but expect to pay more in premium.

Orthodontic coverage is important to some. All of the standalone dental plans have a substantial orthodontic benefit, as does the Foreign Service plan. The coverage terms vary, so you should compare them carefully. Especially importantly, the dental plans try to discourage you from joining at the last minute to take advantage of these benefits, usually by imposing 24 month waiting periods on eligibility. Humana Dental, however, imposes no waiting period and uses a schedule of benefits without any limit on overall spending, and the Dominion and Metlife plans have no waiting period. Orthodontics is the perfect dental expense for combining a dental plan with an FSA account for expenses the plan doesn't cover. It is

Hearing Aid Benefits—Adults

Plan code	Plan name	Hearing aids coverage for adults?	Frequency of replacement	Most plan will pay for one ear ($)	Most plan will pay for two ears ($)
DC Area Plans When You Use Preferred Providers					
F51-3	Aetna HealthFund CDHP	No	NA	NA	NA
JN1-3	Aetna Open Access-Hi	Some	3 years	1400	2800
JN4-6	Aetna Open Access Basic	Some	3 years	1400	2800
F54-6	Aetna Value Plan	No	NA	NA	NA
B61-3	CareFirst HDHP	Yes	No limit	No limit	No limit
2G1-3	CareFirst-Hi	Yes	3 years	No limit	No limit
2G4-6	CareFirst-Std POS	Yes	3 years	No limit	No limit
T71-3	Kaiser Basic	No	NA	NA	NA
E31-3	Kaiser-Hi	No	NA	NA	NA
E34-6	Kaiser-Std	No	NA	NA	NA
JP1-3	MD-IPA	No	NA	NA	NA
LR1-3	UnitedHealthcare Choice	No	NA	NA	NA
L91-3	UnitedHealthcare Choice Plus	No	NA	NA	NA
V41-3	UnitedHealthcare HDHP	Yes	No limit	No limit	No limit
National Plans When You Use Preferred Providers					
N61-3	Aetna Direct CDHP	Yes	3 years	3000	3000
224-6	Aetna HealthFund HDHP	No	NA	NA	NA
474-6	APWU CDHP	Some	3 years	1500	1500
471-3	APWU-Hi	Some	3 years	1500	1500
111-3	Blue Cross Basic	Yes	3 years	2500	2500
104-6	Blue Cross-Std	Yes	3 years	2500	2500
421-3	Compass Rose	Some	5 years	1200	2400
401-3	Foreign Service	Yes	5 years	4000	4000
341-3	GEHA HDHP	No	NA	NA	NA
311-3	GEHA-Hi	Yes	3 years	2500	2500
314-6	GEHA-Std	Yes	3 years	2500	2500
481-3	MHBP HDHP	Some	5 years	1500	1500
414-6	MHBP Value	Some	5 years	1500	1500
454-6	MHBP-Std	Some	5 years	2000	2000
324-6	NALC CDHP	Some	3 years	500	1000
KM1-3	NALC Value	Some	3 years	500	1000
321-3	NALC-Hi	Some	3 years	500	1000
381-3	Rural Carrier	Yes	5 years	3000	3000
441-3	SAMBA-Hi	Some	3 years	500	1000
444-6	SAMBA-Std	Some	3 years	500	1000

Hearing Aid Benefits—Children

Plan code	Plan name	Hearing aids coverage for children?	Age limit for child	Frequency of replacement	Most plan will pay for one ear ($)	Most plan will pay for two ears ($)
DC Area Plans When You Use Preferred Providers						
F51-2	Aetna HealthFund CDHP	No	NA	NA	NA	NA
JN1-2	Aetna Open Access-Hi	Some	None	3 years	1400	2800
JN4-5	Aetna Open Access Basic	Some	None	3 years	1400	2800
F54-5	Aetna Value Plan	No	NA	NA	NA	NA
B61-2	CareFirst HealthyBlue-HDHP	Yes	18	No limit	No limit	No limit
2G1-2	CareFirst BlueChoice-Hi	Yes	18	3 years	No limit	No limit
2G4-5	CareFirst BlueChoice-Std POS	Yes	18	3 years	No limit	No limit
E31-2	Kaiser-Hi	Yes	19	3 years	No limit	No limit
E31-2	Kaiser-Hi	Yes	19	3 years	No limit	No limit
E34-5	Kaiser-Std	Yes	19	3 years	No limit	No limit
JP1-2	M.D. IPA	Some	19	3 years	700	1400
LR1-3	UnitedHealthcare Choice	No	NA	NA	NA	NA
L91-2	UnitedHealthcare Choice Plus	Yes	18	3 years	2500	5000
V41-3	UnitedHealthcare HDHP	Yes	No limit	No limit	No limit	No limit
National Plans When You Use Preferred Providers						
N61-2	Aetna Direct CDHP	Yes	None	3 years	3000	3000
224-5	Aetna HealthFund HDHP	No	NA	NA	NA	NA
474-5	APWU CDHP	Some	None	3 years	1500	1500
471-2	APWU-Hi	Some	None	3 years	1500	1500
111-2	Blue Cross Basic	Yes	22	1 year	2500	2500
104-5	Blue Cross-Std	Yes	22	1 year	2500	2500
421-2	Compass Rose	Yes	22	No limit	No limit	No limit
401-2	Foreign Service	Yes	22	No limit	No limit	No limit
341-2	GEHA HDHP	No	NA	NA	NA	NA
311-2	GEHA-Hi	Yes	22	1 year	2500	2500
314-5	GEHA-Std	Yes	22	1 year	2500	2500
481-2	MHBP HDHP	Some	None	5 years	1500	1500
414-5	MHBP Value Plan	Some	None	5 years	1500	1500
454-5	MHBP-Std	Some	None	5 years	2000	2000
324-5	NALC CDHP	Some	None	3 years	500	1000
KM1-2	NALC Value	Some	None	3 years	500	1000
321-2	NALC-Hi	Some	None	3 years	500	1000
381-2	Rural Carrier	No	NA	NA	NA	NA
441-2	SAMBA-Hi	Some	18	3 years	1000	2000
444-5	SAMBA-Std	Some	18	3 years	1000	2000

also an area where it makes sense to talk to providers about getting the lowest cost, taking into account which networks and plans they have joined.

In sum, even if you and your family do not need substantial dental work, one of the health plans may be worth several hundred dollars per year, or more, a benefit that costs you no additional premium. The standalone dental plans provide a distinctly better benefit than almost all health plans, but at a premium cost that largely offsets their better benefits. The dental plans make the most sense for persons who are sure they will have moderately or very high dental expenses, want some protection against an unexpected expense, and like the predictability of paying a regular premium and reducing wide fluctuations from month to month in what they may pay.

Before selecting a dental plan, be sure to check with your family dentist as to which plan(s) he or she affiliates with. Our estimates are based on the assumption that you use network providers. But plan coverage out of network loses you the network discount. These plans are good buys only when you use network providers.

Vision Care

All FEHB plans pay for medically necessary care of your eyes, such as cataract surgery. Many pay for annual refractive examinations to determine your prescription for eye glasses or contact lens, and some pay for part of the cost for the lens and frame, or arrange for a discount at plan-affiliated providers (this is often stated as an unofficial non-FEHB benefit in brochures.) Our Cost and Coverage Features table indicates which health plans pay the most toward vision services. In addition, some of the new FEDVIP dental plans, including Aetna and GEHA, provide discounts for lens and frames as "unofficial" benefits.

The nation-wide standalone FEDVIP vision plans provide tax-advantaged premiums for employees (but not retirees), and use the purchasing power of their enrollees to obtain discounts for all enrollees. They are not true insurance plans, and will pay neither for lost or broken glasses nor for medical or surgical care. Instead, they are a way to prepay your anticipated and routine costs for refractive eye examination, glasses and frames, contact lenses, and related services and supplies. If you plan to purchase unusually expensive frames, or multiple pairs of glasses, you will need to rely on discounts rather than direct plan benefits.

Unfortunately, the vision plan brochures do not present benefits in a consistent format, making them very hard to compare. We have attempted to capture most of the important features of the plans in our table on "National Vision Plans" to help you decide whether, and which, plans you may want to examine in depth. In general, their benefits and premiums are similar, but most offer both high and standard options with differences in both premiums and cost sharing. If you have a preferred optician or eyewear outlet you should ask which plan(s) if any it affiliates with in order to inform your decision.

You have several alternatives to enrolling in these plans. You can simply decide to pay for your predictable dental and vision expenses without the bother of using a plan, or being restricted to its providers. If you combine this with prudent shopping, you can achieve substantial savings. For example, *Washington Consumers' Checkbook* magazine has rated dozens of DC area providers for optical services and found that prices one-fourth or more below (or above) the average for glasses or contact lenses were not uncommon. Also, most FEHB health insurance plans have unofficial plan benefits and discounts for eyewear from particular chains, without paying any extra premium.

You have two other major alternatives for vision care. As for other categories of expense, employees (but not retirees) can establish a Flexible Spending Account that covers vision along with other expenses. Or you can join a Consumer-Driven or High Deductible plan and use its savings account feature to pay for vision costs. You can even supplement a High Deductible plan's savings account with a LEX HCFSA. Either of these options gives employees the same tax advantage—about a one third saving—as a separate vision plan. If you use any FEHB plan, of course, the government pays most of the premium.

The primary advantages of joining a vision plan are that it enables you to lock in a provider discount as well as a tax saving while budgeting for your eye wear. You pay roughly $10, $20, or $30 a month (depending on your family size and which plan you select) knowing that each covered family member will be able to get a good deal on a refractive examination and one good set of eyewear equipment.

Hearing Aids

All plans cover medical problems, such as infections, that affect any part of your body, including your ears. All plans cover routine hearing testing for children. Almost all will pay most of the cost for hearing-related medical procedures, such as cochlear implants. But only in recent years have plans begun to cover the cost of hearing aids to compensate for deafness. Coverages vary widely, with some plans covering only children, ages of child coverage varying, frequency of replacement varying, and big differences in the cost amount the plan will cover. We compare these coverages in our table on hearing aid benefits. Before selecting a plan on this basis, it is worth checking with providers for special discounts, some tailored to specific plans. Publications read by Federal employees or annuitants, such as the magazine of the National Active and Retired Federal Employees Association, often carry ads that promise high quality hearing aids at no cost to enrollees in specific plans.

Chapter 8
Plan Types and Flexibility

All FEHB plans impose restraints on provider choice, using networks as a key strategy to reduce payments and hold down premium costs. The only significant exception to this pattern is for retirees with Medicare Parts A and B, who in most national plans and some HMOs can go to almost any hospital or physician at no cost. This flexibility is allowed because Medicare pays first for these enrollees, and the Federal government uses its legal power to force Medicare-participating providers to accept government fee limitations regardless of their actual costs.

Although all plans, not just HMOs, now provide significantly reduced benefits if you do not use "preferred" or "network" providers, there remain significant differences between PPO plans, PPO plans with fee-for-service (FFS) benefits for using out-of-network providers, local HMOs, and the Consumer-Driven (CDHP) and High Deductible (HDHP) plans. All national plans use PPO networks and no HMOs are national, but each type of plan can be found in local offerings in most large cities.

Type of Plan

In national plans—whether PPO/FFS, HDHP, or CDHP—you generally get a much larger selection of preferred providers, national as well as local. In addition, in all national plans except for Blue Cross Basic you can go to virtually any doctor or hospital you choose—provided you are willing to pay much more (often half or more) of the bill. Under this FFS coverage of providers outside the network, you are covered if you choose to use a world-famous facility, such as the Mayo Clinic, even if it is not a preferred provider. This flexibility gives you maximum freedom of choice, but imposes higher costs on you. The national plans offering broad PPO networks and out of network coverage usually but not always charge higher premiums than most local HMOs, although the gap has narrowed in recent years. HDHP and CDHP plans also provide this flexibility, usually at lower premiums than traditional plans.

Most HMO plans are quite different. They operate through a relatively limited group or network of physicians who share your fees, regardless of which doctor you use. Our analysis below on "Joining an HMO" presents their important advantages and disadvantages in detail. Although cost and benefit comparisons are the key considerations in assessing most plans, other factors are important in deciding whether to enroll in an HMO plan and, if so, which one. Most HMOs will not cover you at all outside of their provider network except in emergencies, but some offer fee-for-service coverage for non-network providers, similar to the national plan (see the point-of-service discussion that follows). Others offer non-emergency out of area benefits to students or, in some cases, to your whole family.

HDHP and CDHP present yet another dimension of choice. These plans provide incentives to you to hold costs down by prudent shopping. The plans provide savings accounts, which, if not fully used, roll over their balances so they can be used in future years. In fact, in some of these plans the amount in your savings account at the end of the year will exceed what you paid in premium (after Premium Conversion savings), if your usage is low. However, once the savings account is used up, you face a high deductible before complete health insurance kicks in. Thus, these plans seemingly present more risk than traditional PPO or HMO plans, as described below in "Joining a High Deductible Plan." However, they have significant tax advantages that largely negate their seemingly higher risk, and their catastrophic cost protection is generally as good or better than in other plans.

Cost Controls

Plans engage in many forms of cost control. All plans now use networks of preferred providers, who agree to accept lower fees and avoid unnecessary utilization. All plans also engage in other measures, such as second opinions before surgery, penalties for non-emergency hospital admissions without a "preadmission certification," priori approval of expensive services or products, case management, or a combination. Some cost control measures, such as second opinions before elective surgery, are good for both you and the plan since neither wants you to have an unnecessary operation. Another "win-win" measure is high discounts on generic drugs that are therapeutically equivalent to name brand drugs. Others pose problems if you are not careful.

In the national PPO and FFS plans, there is a $500 penalty for any non-emergency hospital admission without a "preadmission certification." HMOs normally refuse to pay for unauthorized non-emergency admissions. This means that you must obtain permission from the plan, not just your doctor, before you enter a hospital. Likewise, with the major exceptions of routine visits and emergencies, some HMOs do not pay for care that is not arranged through, or approved by, the plan. In recent years most plans have begun to actively supervise this way certain kinds of extraordinarily expensive treatments, such as "specialty" drugs for cancer or other diseases. Plans also use "case management" to reduce expenses in costly cases. For example, if you have a stroke, the plan may authorize extra home health benefits in lieu of prolonged hospitalization. This can benefit you as well as the plan, but you must use the procedure specified by the plan.

Preferred Providers

All national plans obtain reduced rates from "preferred providers," operating through PPO networks. You share in these savings through elimination of deductibles or lower copayments if you use one of these preferred providers. These providers also guarantee that their fee will be accepted by the plan. Such PPO plans are similar in some ways to HMOs. The main difference is that the number of preferred providers in each community is often much larger. At any time, you can switch to a provider of your choice rather than a preferred provider. However, you get the low copayments only from preferred providers, and the plans will not recognize costs above their fee schedule.

Each national plan, except Blue Cross Basic, allows you to use non-preferred providers on a fee-for-service basis, but limits reimbursement for doctors who are not in the network to a schedule of charges. These schedules often reflect usual rates (or less), but never allow higher rates. The problem is that your doctor may be one who charges much more than the plan will allow. Moreover, in recent years most plans have reduced the generosity of the fee schedules they use with non-participating doctors. **You should never use a non-preferred provider without first checking to be sure that the provider will accept the plan's payment level, including your coinsurance or copayment, as payment in full.** The way to find out is simple: **BEFORE** incurring an expensive procedure, ask the provider point blank if he or she will accept your plan's payment level. Do not accept an equivocal answer—they know roughly what the plans pay and can offer in advance to accept that amount. Moreover, you can bargain for a network or Medicare rate. (Retirees over age 65 face little such risk, since by law almost all physicians must give them a Medicare rate.)

For provider choice, the value of the PPO benefit depends in part on how many doctors and hospitals participate. Blue Cross has agreements with about half of all physicians and most hospitals to be preferred providers. Most other plans also offer you a wide choice. For example, GEHA, APWU, NALC, and other national plans use UnitedHealthcare, Aetna, and other insurance firms to provide an almost equally broad selection of providers. However, it is prudent to check provider lists, particularly if you live in a rural area. The best way to check for overall choices is to use plan Web sites. For a specific provider, simply call the office and check not only whether he or she is currently participating, but also whether he or she intends to continue with the plan.

Point of Service

Some HMOs provide a Point of Service (POS) option under which you may, by paying a deductible and coinsurance, use any doctor or hospital. Our comparisons indicate which HMO plans offer this. In effect, these HMOs operate as dual plans, in which you can go to any doctor of your choice if you pay a deductible and coinsurance. In most cases the deductible is $250 or $300 and you pay coinsurance of 25 or 30 percent. These arrangements allow you to join an HMO, get most of your health care with little out-of-pocket cost, but preserve the ability to go out of plan "just in case" you want a doctor not participating in the plan. In other words, if you join an HMO with a POS benefit, you get essentially the same choices as if you join a national plan with both PPO and FFS benefits. Some HMOs offer this benefit limited to college students while away from home.

Joining a Traditional HMO

HMO plans provide not just insurance, but also a different approach to health care delivery from traditional fee-for-service medicine. Therefore, although cost and benefit comparisons are the key considerations in assessing most plans, other factors are important in deciding whether to enroll in an HMO plan and, if so, which one.

There are two main types of HMO plans. One is the facility-based group practice where enrollees agree to receive their health care from a group of doctors working together at the plan's facilities and at hospitals chosen by the plan. The doctors usually are on salary or in a form of partnership. They generally are paid no more if their patients receive more extensive surgery or other medical treatment, thus, their incentives are different from those of doctors working in the traditional fee-for-service system, who can increase their incomes by increasing the amount of care. The Kaiser plans are the largest of this type.

A much more common type of HMO plan is the individual practice association (IPA). In IPAs, physicians agree to share costs and premium income. Each physician continues to practice in his or her own office and continues to serve some patients who are not plan members. All IPAs have a system to assure that physicians do not give costly, excessive service. In a typical system, each physician negotiates a fee schedule with the plan. After seeing a patient, the physician bills the plan for the agreed fee, but the plan pays only part of the bill, such as 80 percent. The remaining 20 percent is kept in a reserve. If costs are held down, the plan will later distribute the reserve to the physicians. To protect against physicians who might deliver excessive services, a committee of physicians regularly reviews treatment practices of each physician. Joining an individual practice association plan is a more modest departure from the fee-for-service system than joining a group practice plan. Some have both groups and individual physicians. Each HMO brochure describes which of these models it uses, and how you get service.

Some features of HMO plans considered desirable by many consumers are:

- They generally have systems for doctors to review each other's practices.
- They eliminate the inconvenience of submitting claims for costs of services.
- They assure you access to a group of doctors.
- They prevent a doctor charging more than the plan will reimburse for a procedure.

Some features of HMO plans considered undesirable by many consumers are:

- The IPA plans often have many participating physicians and hospitals, but rarely a majority of those in the community, and rarely prestigious facilities in

Plan Flexibility: National Plans and DC Area Plans

Plan code	Plan name (Listed in alphabetical order within group)	Get regular benefits anywhere?	Payment for out of network providers (non-emergency)?		Specialist visits covered without referral?		Open formulary?	Company offers a local Medicare Advantage Plan?
			Without Medicare Part B?	Cost-free with Part B?	Gynecologist	Other specialist		
DC Area Plans When You Use Preferred Providers								
F51-3	Aetna HealthFund CDHP	Many Areas	Reduced	No	Yes	Yes	Pay More	Many Areas
JN1-3	Aetna Open Access-Hi	Many Areas	No	No	Yes	Yes	Pay More	Yes
JN4-6	Aetna Open Access Basic	Many Areas	No	No	Yes	Yes	Pay More	Yes
F54-6	Aetna Value Plan	Many Areas	Reduced	No	Yes	Yes	Pay More	Yes
B61-3	CareFirst HDHP	Some Areas	Reduced	Yes	Yes	Yes	Pay More	No
2G1-3	CareFirst-Hi	Some Areas	No	Yes	Yes	Yes	Pay More	No
2G4-6	CareFirst-Std POS	Some Areas	Reduced	Yes	Yes	Yes	Pay More	No
T71-3	Kaiser Basic	Some Areas	No	No	Yes	Some	Pay More	Yes
E31-3	Kaiser-Hi	Some Areas	No	No	Yes	Some	Pay More	Yes
E34-6	Kaiser-Std	Some Areas	No	No	Yes	Some	Pay More	Yes
JP1-3	MD-IPA	No	No	Yes	Yes	No	Pay More	No
LR1-3	UnitedHealthcare Choice	Some Areas	Reduced	No	Yes	Yes	Pay More	Yes
L91-3	UnitedHealthcare Choice Plus	Some Areas	Reduced	No	Yes	Yes	Pay More	Yes
National Plans When You Use Preferred Providers								
N61-3	Aetna Direct CDHP	Many Areas	Reduced	Yes	Yes	Yes	Pay More	Many Areas
224-6	Aetna HealthFund HDHP	Many Areas	Reduced	No	Yes	Yes	Pay More	Many Areas
474-6	APWU CDHP	Nationwide	Reduced	No	Yes	Yes	Yes	No
471-3	APWU-Hi	Nationwide	Reduced	Yes	Yes	Yes	Yes	No
111-3	Blue Cross Basic	Nationwide	No	No	Yes	Yes	Pay More	Many Areas
104-6	Blue Cross-Std	Nationwide	Reduced	Yes	Yes	Yes	Pay More	Many Areas
421-3	Compass Rose	Nationwide	Reduced	Yes	Yes	Yes	Pay More	No
401-3	Foreign Service	Nationwide	Reduced	Yes	Yes	Yes	Pay More	No
341-3	GEHA HDHP	Nationwide	Reduced	No	Yes	Yes	Yes	No
311-3	GEHA-Hi	Nationwide	Reduced	Yes	Yes	Yes	Pay More	No
314-6	GEHA-Std	Nationwide	Reduced	Yes	Yes	Yes	Pay More	No
481-3	MHBP HDHP	Nationwide	Reduced	Yes	Yes	Yes	Pay More	No
454-6	MHBP Value	Nationwide	Reduced	No	Yes	Yes	Pay More	No
454-6	MHBP-Std	Nationwide	Reduced	Yes	Yes	Yes	Pay More	No
324-6	NALC CDHP	Nationwide	Reduced	No	Yes	Yes	Pay More	No
KM1-3	NALC Value	Nationwide	Reduced	No	Yes	Yes	Pay More	No
321-3	NALC-Hi	Nationwide	Reduced	Yes	Yes	Yes	Pay More	No
381-3	Rural Carrier	Nationwide	Reduced	Yes	Yes	Yes	Yes	No
441-3	SAMBA-Hi	Nationwide	Reduced	Yes	Yes	Yes	Pay More	No
444-6	SAMBA-Std	Nationwide	Reduced	Yes	Yes	Yes	Pay More	No

other states, such as the Lombardi Center or Mayo Clinic. In contrast, the preferred provider panels offered by the national plans are generally far broader, and cover many facilities around the country.

- The group plans require you to go to one of their office locations except in emergencies. Some group plans have only a few locations. They limit your choice of doctor even further: to those who work for the plan. You will have to give up your existing doctors when you join a group plan. In contrast, IPA plans use doctors in private practice and your physician may well participate in one or more IPA HMOs.

- Both types of plan impose barriers to obtaining care as rapidly as you might like, such as waits for the next available appointment for "non-urgent" visits or obtaining the approval of a "gatekeeper" primary care physician in order to see a specialist.

Some features that you may or may not like are:

- Some HMOs rely very heavily on mid-level professionals such as nurse practitioners and physician assistants.

- HMOs generally put patients in hospitals less frequently and keep them there for a shorter time than fee-for-service physicians. This is the major reason HMOs usually have lower costs. A number of studies have found no overall difference in medical outcomes between HMOs and traditional practice. On the other hand, if you want quick surgery to relieve a painful but not life-threatening problem, you may not want to wait while an HMO tries more conservative therapies.

- Few HMOs offer the extra benefits to Medicare enrollees that are found in most national plans, although the number that do so is increasing.

Joining a High Deductible Plan

Several national companies and some local HMO organizations now offer High Deductible or Consumer-Driven plans. Aetna offers such plans in almost all parts of the country, and UnitedHealthcare in many places. These plans differ in details, but all share two main features. First, they provide some form of savings account for health care expenses, financed on a tax-free basis through the premium paid to the plan and, in some cases, additional contributions. This account is typically about $750 to $1,000 for a self-only enrollment, and twice as much for a family enrollment, although a few are higher. During the year, you can use this account to pay for any of your qualified health care expenses, including expenses that the plan does not otherwise cover, such as a hearing aid. Second, if you use up the account on other expenses (or decide to save it rather than use it), you face a high deductible, usually about $1,000 to $2,000 for a self-only enrollment and twice as much for a family enrollment. Thereafter, you typically pay 10 or 15 percent of expenses, up to an out-of-pocket spending limit, though some plans pay everything above the deductible. The main focus of these plans is to encourage you to be a prudent purchaser. If you are relatively healthy and spend wisely, you may avoid any out of pocket expenses. Furthermore, your unused account balances "roll over" and you can build up a substantial cushion that even earns interest. Your total cost under these plans can be LESS than your tax-preferred premium share.

Because of this design, there is no simple answer to "what is my copayment" or "what is my deductible." If you stay within your spending account both are zero. After your account is used up you pay 100 percent, until you pass your deductible amount. In our tables, we provide the percentage that applies after your deductible and until you hit the catastrophic limit.

Two other important features that these plans share is that routine preventive care does not count against either the spending account or the deductible, and you have good catastrophic expense protection. Most of these plans' limits have none of the loopholes found in other plans.

The High Deductible plans offer two kinds of spending accounts. Which one you get depends on your eligibility. A "Health Savings Account" (HSA) not only lets you accumulate funds, but also lets you retain the savings account when you change plans or retire. Moreover, you can earn interest, tax-free, for decades to come. The HSA is your property. In contrast, a "Health Reimbursement Arrangement" (HRA), or "Personal Care Account" as it is called in some plans, works almost the same but terminates when you change plans. In that case, the unspent balance remains with the plan. The Consumer-Driven plans offer only HRAs. Unlike HSAs, HRAs do not let you grow the account through interest. You can use an HRA, but not an HSA, if you are covered by other health insurance, such as TRICARE, a spouse's plan, or Medicare. In the HDHP plans, annuitants with Medicare get an HRA in the same amount as the HSA received by other enrollees. To fully understand these complex plans, you should read the explanations in their brochures carefully, and you may want to consult material on the OPM Web site.

The other important characteristic of an HSA account (in contrast to an HRA) is that you can make voluntary contributions to it during the year. This feature comes into play if your expenses are much higher than you expected, but you can make contributions regardless of your expected expenses. In an HSA you can make voluntary contributions up to the amount of the deductible, less the personal account amount funded by the plan. Your contributions are tax preferred. Thus, if you need to spend an extra thousand dollars, rather than pay it directly to providers you can contribute it to the HSA account, lower your taxable income by a thousand dollars, and pay providers from the HSA account. If you are in a 33 percent tax bracket, this saves you over three hundred dollars compared to traditional health insurance plans. This is a better arrangement for you than under Flexible Spending Accounts, because there is no "use or lose" penalty. HSA accounts are sometimes described as "Trifecta" benefits because the contribution is tax-free, the account grows tax-free, and disbursements from the account are tax-free when spent for health care.

Annuitants are eligible for these plans, but most of these plans do not provide extra benefits for having Medicare Parts A and B (significant exceptions are the Aetna Direct CDHP and MHBP HDHP national plans). However, these spending accounts cover many expenses that Medicare does not, and Medicare protects you from substantial copayment expense. For hospital expenses, you will almost always get the zero percent Medicare rate (after deductible) rather than the plan's rate of cost sharing. Therefore, they work well for retirees with Medicare. Once you have Medicare the law allows you to contribute only to an HRA, not to an HSA, and the HDHP plans all allow for that.

Plan Flexibility

Our comparisons of flexibility capture as best as we can the features of each plan that affect your ability to select the providers of your preference. We would like to display the number of affiliated providers in each local area, but such data are not available for many plans. Of course, staff model HMOs would always show a relatively low number, because they ordinarily limit you to primary care providers on their staff.

In our comparisons, we show first which HMOs allow you to get regular plan benefits from providers located outside the plan's main service area. For example, the Kaiser plans allow you to use Kaiser facilities and providers anywhere they are located. Of course, national plans all cover the entire nation. All plans cover emergencies throughout the world (not shown). Second, we show how plans deal with providers who are not preferred. National plans and some HMOs let you use non-preferred providers with a significantly higher cost sharing. Third, we show which plans provide annuitants with Medicare Parts A and B wrap around benefits to make all hospital and doctor care cost-free, in or out of network.

We show which plans allow women to visit a gynecologist without having to be referred by a primary care provider. Almost all HMOs now allow self-referral, at least for an annual exam (those which allow only an examination without referral are marked "Exam"). Unfortunately, some HMOs do not allow self-referral to other specialists, though the number that do so is growing.

Our entry for "open formulary" indicates whether the plan will pay for any name brand drug that your physician prescribes, or just for those that are on the plan's list of approved drugs (commonly called a "formulary"). Most plans will pay for any drug but require higher copays for non-formulary drugs. We indicate these with a "Pay More" entry.

Finally, we indicate whether each company sponsors a Medicare Advantage (MA) plan, so that Medicare participants can elect to stay with their health plan while paying only one premium. However, even though we enter "Yes" you have to check further to see if the Medicare Advantage plan covers the exact area where you live. Not shown, all Medicare Parts A and B enrollees have access to at least some MA plans, and most have access to dozens.

Chapter 9

Quality and Service

For traditional fee-for-service insurance plans, service quality used to be a minor issue. The main service concerns were how easily you could get help from plan representatives regarding coverage questions and how fairly and promptly claims were paid.

However, even fee-for-service plans now have some involvement in the quality of your health care. All of these plans require you to get authorization before hospitalization or surgery. And almost all have assembled networks of preferred providers and have prescription drug formularies. Because you save money by using providers from these networks and preferred drugs in these formularies, the availability and quality of preferred providers and the lists of preferred drugs are important.

Meanwhile, many prepaid (HMO) plans are available and now substantial numbers of Federal employees have selected these plans. Your choice of HMO can have a big effect on the quality of medical care and service you receive. Not only does an HMO offer you a selected list of providers to choose among; your HMO may be set up so that your primary care doctor is a "gatekeeper" who decides whether to authorize you to get specialist, hospital, and other types of services. In addition, an HMO may be able to manage care so that members get better service than they would get in a less structured system. For example, some HMOs have succeeded in reducing asthma problems by having doctors, nurses, pharmacists, and other HMO staff work together to train patients and families in self-medication and other self-care techniques.

Customer Satisfaction Ratings

The table beginning on page 128 reports plan-by-plan customer satisfaction ratings reported by OPM. These ratings come from a 2017 survey in which a standardized questionnaire was sent to a sample of each plan's members. The table tells you how plans compare for several categories of service, based on answers given to various questions asked on the survey. OPM reports scores for:

- Overall quality of the plan
- Overall rating of personal doctors
- Getting needed care
- Getting care quickly

- Coordination of care
- Claims processing
- Plan's customer service

For each of these aspects of care, the table reports how OPM scored the survey results for each plan. OPM used the following scale:

● = Outstanding (plan's score was in the 90th percentile)

◕ = Excellent (plan's score was in the 75th-89th percentile)

◑ = Good (plan's score was in the 50th-74th percentile)

◔ = Fair (plan's score was in the 25th to 49th percentile)

○ = Poor (plan's score was worse than the 25th percentile)

Blanks indicate no data was reported for the measure

We advise that you keep several points in mind when using the customer ratings:

- Some of the ratings are based on opinions. Your opinions might not be the same as those of survey respondents.
- The way enrollees rate their plans can be affected by their age, education level, state of health, and other characteristics. For example, older individuals tend to rate their plans relatively high. If one plan has attracted a large proportion of members over age 65, its ratings might be high for that reason. The scores reported here have not been adjusted for member characteristics. Within the group of HMO and POS plans, it does not appear that such differences in member characteristics had much effect on scores; very few plans' overall scores would change by more than two percentage points if the scores were adjusted for member differences. But the effects might be greater among fee-for-service plans.
- Since the survey included only a sample of plan members, it is possible that a plan's ratings were affected by "the luck of the draw": a disproportionately large number of satisfied or dissatisfied members happened to respond.
- Some enrollees did not return the questionnaire. It is possible that those who responded are more satisfied or less satisfied than those who did not. Our analysis of these and similar survey data has indicated that younger members and men are less likely to respond than women and older members. Young male members also tend to give somewhat lower ratings than older members of either gender. Fortunately, with roughly 40 percent of surveyed members responding for most plans, the respondents do at least represent a substantial portion of members. And we have some evidence from follow-up survey tests we have done that scores would not have changed much even if an additional 10 or 15 percent of surveyed members had responded.

(Text continues on page 141)

Plan Quality

See chapter text for discussion of these data and their limitations

	Enrollment code	Overall rating of plan	Overall rating of personal doctors	Getting needed care	Getting care quickly	Coordination of care	Claims processing	Customer service
				Ratings from consumers				
National Plans								
Aetna HealthFund HDHP (PPO)	N6	◔	◔	◑	◕	●	○	
APWU (PPO)	47	●	◑	○	◔	◕	◑	◑
APWU CDHP (PPO)	47	●	○	◔	◑	○	○	
Blue Cross-Basic (PPO)	11	●	◑	◑	◑	◔	◕	◑
Blue Cross-Std (PPO)	10	●	◑	◕	◕	◔	◕	◑
Compass Rose (PPO)	42	●	◔	●	●	◔	◔	◕
Foreign Service (PPO)	40	●	○	◕	●	○	◔	◑
GEHA HDHP (PPO)	34	◑	○	○	◔	○	◔	○
GEHA-Hi (PPO)	31	◕	◑	◑	◔	◔	◑	◑
GEHA-Std (PPO)	31	◕	◑	●	◔	◔	○	
MHBP HDHP (PPO)	48	◕	○	◑	●	◑	◕	◑
MHBP Value Plan (PPO)	41	◕	◕	●	●	●	◕	◕
MHBP-Std (PPO)	45	●	●	●	●	●	●	◑
NALC HDHP (PPO)	32	●	◔	◕	●	◔	◕	◕
NALC Value Plan (PPO)	KM	●	◔	◕	●	◔	◕	◕
NALC-Hi (PPO)	32	●	◔	◕	●	◔	◕	◕
Panama Canal (POS)	43	●	●	◕	●	◑		◔
Rural Carrier (PPO)	38	●	◕	●	●	●	●	●
SAMBA-Hi (PPO)	44	●	◑	●	◕	◔	◕	◑
SAMBA-Std (PPO)	44	●	◔	◑	◕	◔	◑	◑
Local Plans and National Plans with Scores from Members in Specific States								
Alabama								
Blue Cross-Basic (PPO)	11	●	◑	◕	◔	○	●	
Blue Cross-Std (PPO)	10	●	◕	●	●	◔	●	
UnitedHealthcare (HDHP)	LS	○	◔	○	◔	○	○	
UnitedHealthcare Choice (PPO)	KK	○	◔	○	◔	○	○	
Alaska								
Blue Cross-Std (PPO)	10	●	◑	○	●	◔	◑	◕

Plan Quality

See chapter text for discussion of these data and their limitations

	Enrollment code	Ratings from consumers						
		Overall rating of plan	Overall rating of personal doctors	Getting needed care	Getting care quickly	Coordination of care	Claims processing	Customer service
Arizona								
Aetna Open Access (HMO/POS)	WQ	◔	○	◔	◔	○		
Blue Cross-Basic (PPO)	11	●	◔	◔	◐	◔	●	
Blue Cross-Std (PPO)	10	●	◔	◔	●	○	●	◕
Health Net (HMO)	A7	◔	○	◔	◔	◔	◔	○
Humana (HMO/POS) (Phoenix)	BF	○	○	○	○			
Humana (HMO/POS) (Tucson)	C7	○	○	○	○			
UnitedHealthcare (HDHP)	LU	◐	◔	◐	◔	○	◔	◔
UnitedHealthcare Choice (PPO)	KT	◐	◔	◐	◔	○	◔	◔
Arkansas								
Blue Cross-Basic (PPO)	11	●	◔	◕	◐	○	●	◐
Blue Cross-Std (PPO)	10	●	◐	◕	●	◔	●	●
QualChoice (HMO/POS)	DH	◔	◔	◐	◔	◔	◔	○
UnitedHealthcare (HDHP)	LS	◔	◔	◕	◔	◕	◔	
UnitedHealthcare Choice (PPO)	KK	◔	◔	◕	◔	◕	◔	
California								
Aetna (HMO/POS)	2X	◐	○	○	○			
Aetna (PPO)	JS	◐	○	◐	◐			
Anthem Blue Cross (HMO/POS)	B3	◕	○	○	○	◐		
Blue Cross-Basic (PPO)	11	◕	○	○	○	○		
Blue Cross-Std (PPO)	10	◕	◐	◔	◐	◔	○	
Blue Shield of California (HMO/POS)	SI	◕	○	○	○	○		◔
GEHA (PPO)	31	◐	◔	○	○	○	○	
Health Net (HMO/POS)	P6	◐	○	○	○	○	○	○
Health Net (HMO/POS) (Northern CA)	LB	◐	○	○	○	○	○	○
Health Net (HMO/POS) (Southern CA)	LP	◐	○	○	○	○	○	○
Kaiser (HMO) (Fresno)	NZ	◐	◔	◐	◔	◐	○	◔

● = Outstanding (score was in the 90th percentile)
◕ = Excellent (score was in the 75th-89th percentile)
◐ = Good (score was in the 50th-74th percentile)
◔ = Fair (score was in the 25th to 49th percentile)
○ = Poor (score was worse than the 25th percentile)
Blanks indicate no data was reported for the measure

Plan Quality *See chapter text for discussion of these data and their limitations*	Enrollment code	Ratings from consumers						
		Overall rating of plan	Overall rating of personal doctors	Getting needed care	Getting care quickly	Coordination of care	Claims processing	Customer service
Kaiser (HMO) (Northern CA)	59	◑	◕	◑	◕	◑	○	◕
Kaiser (HMO) (Southern CA)	62	◕	◕	◕	○	◕	○	◑
Kaiser Basic (HMO) (Northern CA)	KC	◑	◕	◑	◕	◑	○	◕
UnitedHealthcare (HMO)	CY	◑	◑	◕	◕	◕		◑
Colorado								
Aetna HealthFund CDHP & Value (PPO)	G5	○	○	○	○	○	◑	
Blue Cross-Basic (PPO)	11	●	◑	○	◕	◕	●	
Blue Cross-Std (PPO)	10	●	◑	◑	◕	○	●	●
Humana (HMO/POS) (Colorado Springs)	NR	○	○					
Humana (HMO/POS) (Denver)	NT	○	○					
Kaiser (HMO)	65	◕	○	○	◕	○		◕
Kaiser Basic (student POS)	N4	◕	○	○	◕	○		◕
UnitedHealthcare (HDHP)	LU	◕	○	○	○			
UnitedHealthcare Choice (PPO)	KT	◕	○	○	○			
Connecticut								
Blue Cross-Basic (PPO)	11	●	●	◑	●	○	●	
Blue Cross-Std (PPO)	10	●	◕	●	●	◑	◑	◕
Delaware								
Aetna (HMO/POS)	P3	○	○	◕	◑	◕	○	
District of Columbia								
Aetna (HMO/POS)	JN	◑	◑	◕	◕	◕	◕	○
Aetna HealthFund (HDHP)	22	◕	◕	◑	◕	●	○	
Aetna HealthFund CDHP & Value (PPO)	F5	◕	◕	◑	◕	●	○	
Blue Cross-Basic (PPO)	11	◑	○	○	○	○	◑	
Blue Cross-Std (PPO)	10	◕	◕	◕	◕	○	○	
CareFirst (HMO)	2G	◕	◕	◑	●	◕	◕	◑
CareFirst HDHP (HMO)	B6	◕	◕	◑	●	◕	◕	◑
Kaiser (HMO)	E3	◕	◕	◕	◕	◑		○
M.D. IPA (HMO/POS)	JP	●	◑	◑	●	◕	◑	◑

Plan Quality — See chapter text for discussion of these data and their limitations	Enrollment code	Ratings from consumers						
		Overall rating of plan	Overall rating of personal doctors	Getting needed care	Getting care quickly	Coordination of care	Claims processing	Customer service
UnitedHealthcare (PPO)	L9	◔	○	○				
UnitedHealthcare Choice (PPO)	LR	◔	○	○				
Florida								
Av-Med Health Plan (HMO/POS)	ML	●	◑	◔	○	○	◑	
Blue Cross-Basic (PPO)	11	●	◕	◑	●	○	●	
Blue Cross-Std (PPO)	10	●	◑	◑	◕	○	◕	◔
Capital Health Plan (HMO)	EA	●	◑	◕	●	◔		◕
GEHA (PPO)	31	●	◑	◑	◔	○	◕	◔
Humana (HMO/POS) (South FL)	QP	◔	◔					
Humana (HMO/POS) (Tampa)	MJ	◔	◔					
Humana Medical (HMO/POS) (Daytona)	EX	◔	◔					
Humana Medical (HMO/POS) (Orlando)	E2	◔	◔					
Humana Medical (HMO/POS) (South FL)	EE	◔	◔					
Humana Medical (HMO/POS) (Tampa)	LL	◔	◔					
UnitedHealthcare (PPO)	LV	◕	◕	◔	○	◔		
Georgia								
Aetna (HMO/POS)	2U	◔	◔	◕	◑			
Blue Cross-Basic (PPO)	11	●	○	◕	●	○	●	
Blue Cross-Std (PPO)	10	●	◕	●	◕	◑	●	◕
GEHA (PPO)	31	◕	◔	◑	◑	○	○	
Humana CoverageFirst (HMO/POS) (Atlanta)	AD	○	◔	○				
Humana Employers (HMO/POS) (Atlanta)	DG	○	◔	○				
Humana Employers (HMO/POS) (Columbus)	CB	○	◔	○				
Humana Employers (HMO/POS) (Macon)	DN	○	◔	○				
Kaiser (HMO)	F8	◑	◑	○	○	◔		◔
UnitedHealthcare (PPO)	LV	◑	◕	◔	○			

● = Outstanding (score was in the 90th percentile)　　◕ = Excellent (score was in the 75th-89th percentile)
◑ = Good (score was in the 50th-74th percentile)　　◔ = Fair (score was in the 25th to 49th percentile)
○ = Poor (score was worse than the 25th percentile)　　Blanks indicate no data was reported for the measure

131

Plan Quality *See chapter text for discussion of these data and their limitations*	Enrollment code	**Ratings from consumers**						
		Overall rating of plan	Overall rating of personal doctors	Getting needed care	Getting care quickly	Coordination of care	Claims processing	Customer service
Guam								
TakeCare (HMO)	JK	◐	◕	○	○			
TakeCare HDHP (HMO)	KX	◐	◕	○	○			
Hawaii								
HMSA (HMO/POS)	87	●	●	●	●	◕	●	◐
Kaiser (HMO)	63	◐	◐	○	○	◐		◕
Idaho								
Aetna-Hi and Aetna HDHP (HMO/POS)	9K	◐	●	◕	●	●	○	○
Aetna-Std (HMO/POS)	DK	◐	●	◕	●	●	○	○
Blue Cross-Basic (PPO)	11	●	○	◐	●	○	●	◐
Kaiser (HMO)	54	◐	◕	◕	◐	◕	◐	◐
Kaiser (HMO)	PT	◐	◕	◕	◐	◕	◐	◐
Illinois								
Aetna HealthFund CDHP & Value (PPO)	H4	◕	◐	◐	◕	◐	○	
Anthem BCBS (HMO/POS)	9G	◕	◕	◕	◐	◕	◕	
Blue Cross-Basic (PPO)	11	●	◕	◐	○	◕	●	◐
Blue Cross-Std (PPO)	10	●	●	◕	◐	◕	●	◐
Health Alliance (HMO/POS)	K8	●	●	◐	◕	◐	◕	◕
Humana CoverageFirst (HMO) (Central IL)	GB	◕	◐	○	○	◐		
Humana CoverageFirst (HMO/POS) (Chicago)	MW	◕	◐	○	○	◐		
Humana Health (HMO/POS) (Chicago)	75	◐	◕	○	○	◐		
Humana-Hi (HMO) (Rockford/NW IL)	9F	◐	◕	○	○	◐		
Humana-Std (HMO) (Rockford/NW IL)	AB	◐	◕	○	○	◐		
Union Health Service (HMO)	76	◐	◕	○	○	◕		
UnitedHealthcare (HMO/POS)	YH	◕	◐	◐	◐	◕	◕	
UnitedHealthcare (PPO)	L9	◐	●	◕	○			◐
Indiana								
Blue Cross-Basic (PPO)	11	●	◐	◐	◕	○	◕	◕
Blue Cross-Std (PPO)	10	●	◕	◕	◐	◕	●	◐

Plan Quality *See chapter text for discussion of these data and their limitations*	Enrollment code	Ratings from consumers						
		Overall rating of plan	Overall rating of personal doctors	Getting needed care	Getting care quickly	Coordination of care	Claims processing	Customer service
Health Alliance (HMO/POS)	K8	●	●	◑	◕	◑	◔	◔
Humana CoverageFirst (HMO/POS)	MW	◕	◑	○	○	◑		
Humana Health (HMO/POS) (Chicago area)	75	◑	◔	○	○	◑		
Humana Health (HMO/POS) (Cincinnati)	A6	○	◕					
Humana Health (HMO/POS) (Louisville)	MH	◔	◑	◔	○	○	◔	
Iowa								
Aetna (PPO/CDHP)	H4	◔	◑	◑	○	◑	◔	
Blue Cross-Basic (PPO)	11	●	◑	●	●	◕	●	●
Blue Cross-Std (PPO)	10	●	●	●	●	●	●	●
Health Alliance (HMO/POS)	K8	●	●	◑	◕	◑	◔	◔
HealthPartners (HMO/POS)	V3	◑	◑	◑	●	◕	◑	●
UnitedHealthcare (HDHP)	N7	◔	◑	◕	◑	○	◑	
UnitedHealthcare (HMO/POS)	YH	◔	◑	◑	◑	◕	◔	
UnitedHealthcare Choice (PPO)	LJ	◔	◑	◕	◑	○	◑	
Kansas								
Blue Cross-Basic (PPO)	11	●	◔	◔	●	◔	◕	●
Blue Cross-Std (PPO)	10	●	◕	●	◕	◑	●	◑
Coventry (HMO/POS)	HA	○	◔	◑	◑	◑	○	
Humana CoverageFirst (HMO/POS)	PH	◑	◑	●	◑	◑		
Humana Health Plan (HMO/POS)	MS	◑	◑	●	◑	◑		
Kentucky								
Blue Cross-Basic (PPO)	11	●	◕	◑	◕	◔	●	
Blue Cross-Std (PPO)	10	●	◔	●	●	◑	●	◕
Humana CoverageFirst (PPO)	6N	○	○	○	○			
Humana (HMO/POS) (Lexington/central)	MI	◔	◑	◔	○	○	◔	
Humana (HMO/POS) (Louisville)	MH	◔	◑	◔	○	○	◔	
Humana (HMO/POS) (Northern KY)	A6	○	◕					

● = Outstanding (score was in the 90th percentile)   ◕ = Excellent (score was in the 75th-89th percentile)
◑ = Good (score was in the 50th-74th percentile)   ◔ = Fair (score was in the 25th to 49th percentile)
○ = Poor (score was worse than the 25th percentile)   Blanks indicate no data was reported for the measure

Plan Quality *See chapter text for discussion of these data and their limitations*	Enrollment code	Ratings from consumers						
		Overall rating of plan	Overall rating of personal doctors	Getting needed care	Getting care quickly	Coordination of care	Claims processing	Customer service
UnitedHealthcare (HDHP)	N7	◕	◑	◑	○	◕	◔	
UnitedHealthcare Choice (PPO)	LJ	◕	◑	◑	○	◕	◕	
Louisiana								
Blue Cross-Basic (PPO)	11	●	◑	◑	◕	◕	●	
Blue Cross-Std (PPO)	10	●	◕	◕	◕	○	●	
Humana (HMO/POS) (Baton Rouge)	AE	◑	◕	○	○	◕		
Humana (HMO/POS) (New Orleans)	BC	◑	◕	○	○	◕		
UnitedHealthcare (HDHP)	LS	◕	●	◕	◑	◑	◑	
UnitedHealthcare Choice (PPO)	KK	◕	●	◕	◑	◑	◑	
Maine								
Blue Cross-Basic (PPO)	11	◕	◑	◕	●	●	●	
Maryland								
Aetna (HMO/POS)	JN	◑	◑	◕	◕	◕	◕	○
Aetna HealthFund (HDHP)	22	◕	◕	◑	◕	●	○	
Aetna HealthFund CDHP & Value (PPO)	F5	◕	◕	◑	◕	●	○	
Blue Cross-Basic (PPO)	11	●	◑	◑	◑	○		
Blue Cross-Std (PPO)	10	●	◕	●	◑	◕	◑	
CareFirst (HMO)	2G	◕	◕	◑	●	◕	◕	◑
CareFirst HDHP (HMO)	B6	◕	◕	◑	●	◕	◕	◑
GEHA (PPO)	31	◕	○	○	◕	○	○	◑
Kaiser (HMO)	E3	◕	◕	◕	◕	◑		○
M.D. IPA (HMO/POS)	JP	●	◑	◑	●	◕	◑	◑
UnitedHealthcare (PPO)	L9	◕	○	◕	◕	◕	○	
UnitedHealthcare Choice (PPO)	LR	◕	○	◕	◕	◕	○	
Massachusetts								
Blue Cross-Basic (PPO)	11	●	◕	◑	◕	◕	◕	◑
Blue Cross-Std (PPO)	10	●	◑	◑	●	◑	◕	◑
Michigan								
Blue Cross-Basic (PPO)	11	◕	◑	◕	◑	◕	●	

Plan Quality

See chapter text for discussion of these data and their limitations

	Enrollment code	Ratings from consumers						
		Overall rating of plan	Overall rating of personal doctors	Getting needed care	Getting care quickly	Coordination of care	Claims processing	Customer service
Blue Cross-Std (PPO)	10	●	◕	◑	●	◔	◕	◕
Bluecare (HMO) (Detroit)	LX	◔	◔	◑	◔	◔	◕	◑
Bluecare (HMO) (Flint/Saginaw)	K5	◔	◔	◑	◔	◔	◕	◑
Health Alliance-Hi (HMO/POS)	52	◑	●	◑	◑	◕	◑	◔
Health Alliance-Std (HMO/POS)	GY	◑	●	◑	◑	◕	◑	◔
Priority Health (HMO/POS)	LE	◑	●	◑	◑	●	◕	◑
Minnesota								
Blue Cross-Basic (PPO)	11	●	◑	◑	●	◔	◕	◑
Blue Cross-Std (PPO)	10	●	●	●	●	◔	◑	◑
HealthPartners (HMO/POS)	V3	◑	◑	◑	●	◕	◑	●
Mississippi								
Blue Cross-Basic (PPO)	11	●	◕	◔	◔	○	●	
Blue Cross-Std (PPO)	10	●	●	●	●	◔	●	◕
UnitedHealthcare (HDHP)	LS	◕	●	◕	◑	◔	◑	
UnitedHealthcare Choice (PPO)	KK	◕	●	◕	◑	◔	◑	
Missouri								
Aetna (HMO/POS)	HA	○	◔	◑	◑	◑	○	
Anthem BCBS (HMO/POS)	9G	◕	◕	◕	◑	◔	◕	
Blue Cross-Basic (PPO)	11	●	◔	◔	◕	◔	◕	◕
Blue Cross-Std (PPO)	10	●	◑	●	◑	◑	●	◑
GEHA (PPO)	31	●	◔	◕	◑	◔	◔	◑
Humana CoverageFirst (HMO/POS)	PH	◑	◑	●	◑	◑		
Humana Health Plan (HMO/POS)	MS	◑	◑	●	◑	◑		
Montana								
Blue Cross-Std (PPO)	10	●	◑	◕	◑	◔	◕	◕
Nebraska								
Blue Cross-Basic (PPO)	11	●	◑	●	◕	◕	◕	◑

● = Outstanding (score was in the 90th percentile)   ◕ = Excellent (score was in the 75th-89th percentile)
◑ = Good (score was in the 50th-74th percentile)   ◔ = Fair (score was in the 25th to 49th percentile)
○ = Poor (score was worse than the 25th percentile)   Blanks indicate no data was reported for the measure

Plan Quality *See chapter text for discussion of these data and their limitations*	Enrollment code	Ratings from consumers						
		Overall rating of plan	Overall rating of personal doctors	Getting needed care	Getting care quickly	Coordination of care	Claims processing	Customer service
Nevada								
Blue Cross-Basic (PPO)	11	●	○	○	○	○	◔	◔
Health Plan of Nevada (HMO/POS)	NM	◔	○	○	○	○		
New Hampshire								
Blue Cross-Basic (PPO)	11	●	◕	●	○	◕	●	
New Jersey								
Aetna Health (HMO/POS)	JR	●	◕	●	◑	◕		◕
Aetna HealthFund CDHP & Value (PPO)	EP	◑	◕	○	◕	◕		
Aetna Open Access (HMO/POS)	P3	●	◕	●	◑	◕		◕
Blue Cross-Basic (PPO)	11	●	◑	◑	◑	○	◔	◑
Blue Cross-Std (PPO)	10	◕	◑	●	◕	◕	◕	◑
GHI (PPO)	80	◕	◑	◕	◕			
New Mexico								
Blue Cross-Basic (PPO)	11	●	○	○	◔	○	◑	
Blue Cross-Std (PPO)	10	●	○	◕	○	○	◕	
Presbyterian-Hi (HMO/POS)	P2	◑	◑	○	○	○	○	◑
Presbyterian-Std (HMO/POS)	PS	◑	◑	○	○	○	○	◑
New York								
Aetna Health (HMO/POS)	JC	◕	◑	◕	◑	●	◕	
Aetna HealthFund CDHP & Value (PPO)	EP	◕	◑	◕	◑	●	◕	
Blue Cross-Basic (PPO)	11	◕	○	◕	◕	◕	◕	
Blue Cross-Std (PPO)	10	◕	◑	◕	◑	◕	●	◑
CDHP (PPO)	SG	◕	◕	◑	◕	●	◑	
GHI (PPO)	80	◕	◑	◕	◕			
HIP (HMO/POS)	51	◑	○	○	○	○		
Independent Health (HMO/POS)	C5	◕	●	●	●	◕	●	●
Independent Health HDHP (HMO/POS)	QA	◕	●	●	●	◕	●	●
MVP (HMO/POS) (Bing/Syr/Utica)	M9	◕	◕	●	●	●	●	●
MVP (HMO/POS) (East-Schen/Troy)	GA	◕	◕	●	●	●	●	●

Plan Quality

See chapter text for discussion of these data and their limitations

	Enrollment code	Ratings from consumers						
		Overall rating of plan	Overall rating of personal doctors	Getting needed care	Getting care quickly	Coordination of care	Claims processing	Customer service
MVP (HMO/POS) (Hudson)	MX	◕	◕	●	●	●	●	●
MVP (HMO/POS) (Plattsburgh)	MF	◕	◕	●	●	●	●	●
MVP (HMO/POS) (Rochester)	GV	◕	◕	●	●	●	●	●
North Carolina								
Blue Cross-Basic (PPO)	11	●	◐	●	◕	◐	◔	
Blue Cross-Std (PPO)	10	●	◕	◐	◕	◐	◕	◕
North Dakota								
HealthPartners (HMO/POS)	V3	◐	◐	◐	●	◕	◐	●
Ohio								
AultCare (HMO)	3A	●	●	●	●	◕	●	●
Blue Cross-Basic (PPO)	11	●	●	◕	◐	●	●	●
Blue Cross-Std (PPO)	10	●	◐	●	●	◕	●	◕
GEHA (PPO)	31	●	○	◐	◔	○	◕	
Humana (HMO/POS)	A6	○	◕					
Medical Mutual of Ohio (HMO)	64	◔	◐	◐	◐	◐	◐	◕
Oklahoma								
Blue Cross-Basic (PPO)	11	●	○	◐	◐	○	●	
Blue Cross-Std (PPO)	10	●	◕	●	●	◔	●	◕
Globalhealth (HMO)	IM	◐	◔	◔	◐	○	○	◔
Oregon								
Blue Cross-Basic (PPO)	11	◕	◔	○	◔	◔	◔	◔
Blue Cross-Std (PPO)	10	◕	◔	◐	◕	◔	◔	◕
Kaiser (HMO)	57	◐	○	○	○	◔		◔
Pennsylvania								
Aetna Health (HMO/POS)	P3	◔	◔	◐	◔	◐		
Aetna HealthFund CDHP & Value (PPO)	H4	◔	◔	◕	◐	◐		
Aetna Open Access (HMO/POS)	YE	◔	◔	◐	◔	◐		

● = Outstanding (score was in the 90th percentile) ◕ = Excellent (score was in the 75th-89th percentile)
◐ = Good (score was in the 50th-74th percentile) ◔ = Fair (score was in the 25th to 49th percentile)
○ = Poor (score was worse than the 25th percentile) Blanks indicate no data was reported for the measure

Plan Quality — *See chapter text for discussion of these data and their limitations*	Enrollment code	Ratings from consumers						
		Overall rating of plan	Overall rating of personal doctors	Getting needed care	Getting care quickly	Coordination of care	Claims processing	Customer service
Blue Cross-Basic (PPO)	11	●	◔	◕	◑	◕	●	◑
Blue Cross-Std (PPO)	10	●	◕	●	●	◕	●	◕
Geisinger (HMO/POS)	GG	◑	◔	○	◔	◕		
Highmark (HMO)	NP	●	◑	◕	◑	◑		
UPMC-Hi (HMO)	8W	◑	◕	●	◕	●	◑	◕
UPMC-Std (HMO)	UW	◑	◕	●	◕	●	◔	◕
Puerto Rico								
Humana (HMO)	ZJ	◕	●	◑	◔			
Triple-S (PPO)	89	◕	●	○	◑	●		
South Carolina								
Blue Cross-Basic (PPO)	11	●	◑	◔	◔	○	◕	◑
Blue Cross-Std (PPO)	10	●	●	●	●	◕	●	◕
South Dakota								
HealthPartners (HMO/POS)	V3	◑	◑	◑	●	◕	◑	●
Tennessee								
Aetna (HMO/POS)	UB	◕	◑	◕	●	●	◑	◔
Blue Cross-Basic (PPO)	11	●	◑	●	◕	◑	●	
Blue Cross-Std (PPO)	10	●	●	●	●	◑	●	●
Humana (HMO/POS)	GJ	◕						
UnitedHealthcare (HDHP)	LS	◕	◔	◕	◑	◔	◑	
UnitedHealthcare Choice (PPO)	KK	◕	◔	◕	◑	◔	◑	
Texas								
Aetna HealthFund (HDHP)	22	◑	◕	◑	◔	◕	◔	
Aetna Value Plan (PPO)	JS	◑	◕	◑	◔	◕	◔	
Blue Cross-Basic (PPO)	11	●	◔	◑	◕	○	●	
Blue Cross-Std (PPO)	10	●	◑	◔	◔	◔	◕	
GEHA (PPO)	31	◕	◔	◔	○	○	◕	
Humana CoverageFirst (HMO/POS)	TV	◔	◕					
Humana Health (HMO/POS) (Austin)	UU	◔	◕					

Plan Quality

See chapter text for discussion of these data and their limitations

	Enrollment code	Overall rating of plan	Overall rating of personal doctors	Getting needed care	Getting care quickly	Coordination of care	Claims processing	Customer service
		Ratings from consumers						
Humana Health (HMO/POS) (Corpus Christi)	UC	◔	◑					
Humana Health (HMO/POS) (Houston)	EW	◔	◑					
Humana Health (HMO/POS) (San Antonio)	UR	◔	◔					
Scott & White (HMO/POS) (Austin/Central TX)	A8	◑	●	●	◔	●	◔	
Scott & White (HMO/POS) (Dallas/Ft Worth)	P8	◑	●	●	◔	●	◔	
UnitedHealthcare (PPO)	L9	◑	◔	◑	◑			
Utah								
Aetna-Hi and Aetna HDHP (HMO/POS)	9K	◑	●	◑	●	●	○	○
Aetna-Std (HMO/POS)	DK	◑	●	◑	●	●	○	○
Blue Cross-Basic (PPO)	11	●	◔	◔	◑	○	●	◑
Blue Cross-Std (PPO)	10	●	●	◑	●	◔	●	●
SelectHealth (HMO/POS)	SF	◑	◑	◔	◔	◔	◑	◑
Virgin Islands								
Triple-S (PPO)	85	◑	●	○	◑	●		
Virginia								
Aetna (HMO/POS)	JN	◑	◑	◑	◔	◔	◔	○
Aetna HealthFund CDHP & Value (PPO)	F5	◑	◑	◑	◔	◑	◑	
Blue Cross-Basic (PPO)	11	●	○	◑	◔	○	●	
Blue Cross-Std (PPO)	10	●	◑	◑	◑	◔	●	◑
CareFirst (HMO)	2G	◑	◔	◑	●	◔	◑	◑
CareFirst HDHP (HMO)	B6	◑	◔	◑	●	◔	◑	◑
GEHA (PPO)	31	◑	○	◑	○	○	◑	
Kaiser (HMO)	E3	◑	◔	◔	◔	◑		○
M.D. IPA (HMO/POS)	JP	●	◑	◑	◑	◔	◑	◑
Optima (HMO/POS)	PG	◔	◑	◔	◑	●	◑	
UnitedHealthcare (PPO)	L9	○	○	◑	◑			
UnitedHealthcare Choice (PPO)	LR	○	○	◑	◑			

● = Outstanding (score was in the 90th percentile)   ◕ = Excellent (score was in the 75th-89th percentile)
◑ = Good (score was in the 50th-74th percentile)   ◔ = Fair (score was in the 25th to 49th percentile)
○ = Poor (score was worse than the 25th percentile)   Blanks indicate no data was reported for the measure

Plan Quality

See chapter text for discussion of these data and their limitations

	Enrollment code	Ratings from consumers						
		Overall rating of plan	Overall rating of personal doctors	Getting needed care	Getting care quickly	Coordination of care	Claims processing	Customer service
Washington								
Aetna HealthFund CDHP & Value (PPO)	G5	◔	○	○	◑			
Blue Cross-Basic (PPO)	11	◕	○	○	◑	◔	◑	
Blue Cross-Std (PPO)	10	◕	◔	◑	◕	◔	◔	◕
GEHA (PPO)	31	◕	◔	○	○	○	○	◑
Kaiser (formerly Group Health) (HMO)	54	◑	◔	◔	◑	◕	◑	◑
Kaiser (HDHP)	PT	◑	◔	◔	◑	◕	◑	◑
Kaiser (HMO)	57	◑	○	○	○	◔		◔
KPS-Std (PPO)	L1	○	○	○	○	○		
West Virginia								
Blue Cross-Basic (PPO)	11	●	◔	◑	◕	○	●	
Blue Cross-Std (PPO)	10	●	◔	●	◕	◔	●	◕
Wisconsin								
Blue Cross-Basic (PPO)	11	●	◔	◕	◕	◑	●	◕
Blue Cross-Std (PPO)	10	●	◕	●	●	●	●	◕
Dean Health Plan (HMO/EPO)	WD	◑	●	◔	◕	●	◔	◔
Group Health Cooperative (HMO)	WJ	◕	◑	◔	◕	◑	◕	◕
HealthPartners (HMO/POS)	V3	◑	◑	◑	●	◕	◑	●
MercyCare HMO	EY	◔	◕	◔	◑	◔	○	◔
Physicians Plus (HMO/POS)	LW	◑	◔	◑	◕	◔	◕	
Wyoming								
Aetna-Hi and Aetna HDHP (HMO/POS)	9K	◑	●	◕	●	●	○	○
Aetna-Std (HMO/POS)	DK	◑	●	◕	●	●	○	○

● = Outstanding (score was in the 90th percentile)   ◕ = Excellent (score was in the 75th-89th percentile)
◑ = Good (score was in the 50th-74th percentile)   ◔ = Fair (score was in the 25th to 49th percentile)
○ = Poor (score was worse than the 25th percentile)   Blanks indicate no data was reported for the measure

(Continued from page 127)

In interpreting member ratings, also keep in mind that comparing across different *types* of plans is at best imperfect. First, it is not possible directly to compare regional plans (primarily HMO and POS plans) to national plans. For example, high or low ratings of "personal doctors" by enrollees in a national plan don't tell you how that plan's members in a particular region rate their doctors, and yet it is the national plan's doctors in that region who should be compared to the doctors of members of regional plans serving only that region. Second, for the national plans (and the ratings we report for Blue Cross and Blue Shield by state), the ratings are only from FEHBP enrollees, while the ratings for the regional HMO and POS plans include ratings from non-FEHBP enrollees.

Disputed Claims Per 10,000 Federal Enrollees Filed With the Office of Personnel Management
(National Plans With at Least 10,000 Enrollees)

October 1, 2016—September 30, 2017

Plan name	Disputed claims	Disputed claims in which plan's initial decision was changed or reversed
Blue Cross Blue Shield	3.79	0.60
Rural Carrier[†]	4.52	2.43
SAMBA	7.16	1.79
Foreign Service[†]	9.26	2.96
NALC	11.42	3.48
MHBP	11.72	3.33
GEHA	13.09	3.10
APWU	15.63	7.26
Aetna HealthFund	23.56	4.42
Compass Rose[†]	31.62	10.36

[†] These plans are not open to all.

Even among HMO and POS plans, the ratings given by non-federal members may have been given for a different variant of the plan. We have found, for example, that among members of the same plan, POS users are about two to three percentage points less likely than basic HMO users to give high ratings to the overall plan.

It should also be noted that differences in the way the survey was administered might explain small differences in plan scores. All of the plans are required to use an independent firm to conduct their surveys under the supervision of the nonprofit National Committee for Quality Assurance (NCQA) using standardized survey procedures. But there is some room for variation in procedures. For example, some plans allow members to respond by the Internet in addition to mail and phone calls, and Internet responders tend to give somewhat lower ratings. Also, some plans get a relatively high percentage of their responses by phone (as opposed to mail), and phone responders tend to give higher ratings than mail responders.

Disputed Claims

Along with the customer satisfaction survey results, we have another indicator of service quality for the fee-for-service plans. We checked "disputed claims" on file at OPM. A "disputed claim" is a case in which a plan member has been denied benefits and has followed the required procedure to appeal the denial to OPM.

The Disputed Claims table on page 141 shows disputed claims per 10,000 Federal enrollees for the period from October 2016 through September 2017. The table also shows in how many cases per 10,000 enrollees a plan's initial decision in a disputed claim was changed or reversed. The disputed claim information is shown for national plans.

There are several possible explanations for differences in incidence of disputed claims. For example, some plans may have an unusually large share of hypercritical members, be more aggressive than others in enforcing their policy limitations to prevent benefit abuses, or have benefit limits that enrollees tend not to notice or not to understand. Most of the disputed claims are resolved in favor of the plans on the grounds that they involve matters that are not within the plans' coverage. But do you want to be in a plan where you will feel the need to file a disputed claim? Everything else equal, it seems preferable to join a plan where the coverage limits are easily understood, communication is good, benefit limitations are interpreted broadly—and disputed claims are rare.

Clinical Quality of Care

At GuideToHealthPlans.org, we report additional ratings from OPM on how plans compared for clinical quality of care. These ratings indicate how well plans performed for prevention measures (immunizations, breast cancer screenings, etc.) and how well plans performed for treating chronic conditions (asthma, diabetes, etc.). OPM used the same scale to report these results as it did for the customer satisfaction survey results.

Accreditation

The National Committee for Quality Assurance (NCQA) is the largest organization that accredits health plans. The table at the end of the print Guide, and under the quality tab online, shows whether or not plans are accredited by NCQA or by URAC or AAAHC, two smaller accrediting organizations. These organizations have procedures to determine whether plans meet the organization's accreditation standards. The standards cover many areas of performance, such as whether the plan takes appropriate steps to check the credentials of its physicians, whether the plan has appropriate health promotion and disease prevention programs, and whether the plan has appropriate protections of patients' rights. NCQA includes in its accreditation process assessments of plan performance on member satisfaction survey measures and effectiveness of care measures, such as the percentage of two-year-olds who have had all recommended immunizations and the percentage of heart attack patients who are given a specific type of recommended medication.

All accredited plans are not of equal quality, and there are many aspects of quality that accreditation reviews can't measure. But accreditation is a plus, and absence of accreditation should raise concerns about quality.

Chapter 10
Premiums and Taxes

There are major tax advantages for health insurance. The "employer share" of health insurance—paid by agencies for employees and by OPM for annuitants—is part of employee compensation but by law is exempted from being counted as taxable income. For Federal employees and annuitants, the non-taxable premium share paid by employing agencies and OPM averages about $6,000 for self-only enrollments, over $12,000 for self plus one, and over $13,000 for families. The tax laws also allow employers to make the "employee share" of the premium tax-free to employees, and to set up tax advantaged Flexible Spending Accounts for employees. The average tax-sheltered employee share of premium for Federal self-only enrollees is about $2,000 and for families about $5,000. In total, employees in family plans shelter about $19,000 in employee compensation for health insurance from Federal, State, and local income taxes, as well as from OASDI taxes. This saves employees a tidy sum, about $6,000 per family on average. By law, only the tax benefits for the employer share, but not the annuitant share, are available to retirees in either the public or private sectors. But annuitants in Medicare Parts A and B also get over $9,000 per person of untaxed insurance benefits on top of their FEHB savings, for a total tax shelter of about $22,000 for a retired couple.

Tax Savings for Employee Premium Share

Federal employees shelter their share of the FEHB plan premium from income taxes through what is called "Premium Conversion." Employees have the right to opt out of this program. This increases very slightly future Social Security benefits. However, in what economists call "present value" terms, that offsetting amount is a very small fraction—a few pennies on the dollar—of the gains from the Premium Conversion program. We strongly advise all employees **NOT** to opt out of Premium Conversion tax savings.

How much employees gain from this tax subsidy varies depending on employee salary, spousal salary, other income, state income tax rate, number of dependents, amount of deductions, whether or not they file jointly, and whether or not they are in FERS (and hence paying Social Security taxes). We present two tables that show the likely percent of premiums that will be offset by tax savings under several typical scenarios. The tables show the marginal tax rate, which represents the rate that applies to dollars earned or premium dollars tax

Marginal Tax Rates for Single Earners With No Dependents	Gross annual income range				
	$19,000 to $48,000	$48,001 to $101,000	$101,001 to $129,000	$129,001 to $200,000	$200,001 to $422,000
GS Grades with steps within income range	GS-1 to GS-7	GS-7 to GS-12	GS-12 to GS-14	GS-14 to SES	Outside income
Taxable income range after personal exemption and standard deduction	$10,000 to $37,000	$37,001 to $91,000	$91,001 to $119,000	$119,001 to $189,000	$189,001 to $412,000
Marginal Federal income tax rate	15.0%	25.0%	25.0%	28.0%	33.0%
Marginal Medicare tax rate	1.45%	1.45%	1.45%	1.45%	1.45%
Net marginal state tax rate (assuming deductions are itemized and gross rate of seven percent)	6.0%	5.3%	5.3%	5.0%	4.7%
Total marginal tax rate for CSRS employees	22%	32%	32%	34%	39%
Social Security marginal tax rate	6.2%	6.2%	6.2%	0%	0%
Total marginal tax rate for FERS employees	29%	38%	38%	34%	39%

sheltered slightly above or slightly below current total income levels. When Social Security, Medicare, and state taxes are added, the overall marginal tax rate can reach 41 percent, or even more in some high tax states. Our tables on marginal tax rates for single and family earners present marginal tax rates at various income levels. For each income level, they also present equivalent General Schedule salary ranges using pay rates for the DC area.

At income ranges typical of Federal employees, whether in single- or dual-earner families, and whether in the FERS or CSRS retirement systems, these tables show that almost everyone will save at least 25 percent, and very few will save much more than 40 percent, from tax-sheltered health care premiums or other expenses.

How Much Tax-Sheltered Premiums Are Reduced
We provide a table showing how this tax shelter affects your total costs. This table present our estimates of the likely average premium cost to GS enrollees under some of the plans available in the Washington metropolitan area, including both local plans and national plans. As the table shows, the effects of Premium Conversion are substantial.

Because the effects of different marginal tax rates are relatively small in comparing plans, and never change our relative rankings or the general magnitude of plan-to-plan differences, we use a 33 percent premium savings estimate in all *Guide* tables for persons who are eligible for Premium Conversion. This simplifies presentation and gives you the essential information you need to compare plans. You can, of course, make your own calculation of marginal tax rate, but this is complicated and will not affect most plan comparisons substantially.

Marginal Tax Rates for Families of Four With Two Equal Earners	Gross annual income range				
	$47,000 to $104,000	$104,001 to $180,000	$180,001 to $259,000	$259,001 to $265,000	$265,001 to $440,000
GS Grades with steps half-way up to income range	GS-1 to GS-7	GS-7 to GS-12	GS-12 to GS-14	GS-14 to GS-15	GS-15 to SES
Taxable income range after exemptions and standard deduction	$29,000 to $75,000	$75,001 to $151,000	$151,001 to $230,000	$230,001 to $237,000	$237,001 to $412,000
Marginal Federal income tax rate	15.0%	25.0%	28.0%	28.0%	33.0%
Marginal Medicare tax rate	1.45%	1.45%	1.45%	1.45%	1.45%
Net marginal state tax rate (assuming deductions are itemized and gross rate of seven percent)	6.0%	5.3%	5.0%	5.0%	4.7%
Total marginal tax rate for CSRS employees	22%	32%	34%	34%	39%
Social Security marginal tax rate	6.2%	6.2%	6.2%	0%	0%
Total marginal tax rate for FERS employees	29%	38%	41%	34%	39%

Flexible Spending Accounts

Health Care Flexible Spending Accounts (FSAs) provide a way to shelter even more health care spending from taxes. FSAs allow you to shelter the out-of-pocket costs that you incur for copayments, coinsurance, deductibles, charges above customary and reasonable, and uncovered health care expenses. Under health reform, you can no longer use an FSA account to pay for over-the-counter drugs without a physician prescription (insulin is an exception) but all other categories of expense are unchanged. For most people, the favored categories for using FSAs are dental expenses, vision expenses, and your share of costs for services covered by the plan—for example, the coinsurance you pay for mental health services, or the annual deductible.

Under IRS rules, you have to set up your FSA account and amount in advance. OPM allows you to use the regular Open Season period for setting up your account. For health care, in 2018 you can elect to choose any amount from a minimum of $100 to a maximum of $2,650. (You can also elect to set aside additional amounts for "Dependent Care.") You establish the account by enrolling online at *www.fsafeds.com* or by calling 1-877-372-3337. Unlike Premium Conversion, you have to elect this benefit and will NOT be enrolled automatically. Until recently, enrollees in Consumer-Driven and High Deductible plans were not allowed to create FSAs. However, they may now set up "Limited Expense" FSAs that cover only dental and vision expenses that are not reimbursed by insurance.

You can carry up to $500 in unused FSA accounts into the next year. But any amount over $500 that you elect to set aside for an FSA must be spent by the end of the year, or it will be forfeited (a "grace period" of 2 1/2 months is no longer

Persons Who Pay GS Premiums		Effects of "Premium Conversion" Tax Savings for 2018					
		Single person			Family		
Plan code	Plan name (in order of premium cost for single person with no tax saving)	Published premium	Premium at marginal tax rate of 33%	Dollar saving	Published premium	Premium at marginal tax rate of 33%	Dollar saving
Selected DC Area Plans							
E3	Kaiser-Std	$1,510	$1,010	$500	$3,480	$2,320	$1,160
JN	Aetna Open Access Basic	$1,990	$1,330	$660	$4,640	$3,090	$1,550
JP	MD IPA	$2,650	$1,770	$880	$10,590	$7,060	$3,530
2G	CareFirst-Hi	$4,300	$2,870	$1,430	$10,820	$7,220	$3,600
Selected National Plans							
31	GEHA-Std	$1,430	$950	$480	$3,380	$2,250	$1,130
47	APWU CDHP	$1,660	$1,110	$550	$3,990	$2,660	$1,330
22	Aetna HealthFund HDHP	$1,820	$1,210	$610	$4,020	$2,680	$1,340
40	Foreign Service	$1,720	$1,150	$570	$4,250	$2,830	$1,420
48	MHBP-Std	$1,750	$1,170	$580	$4,060	$2,710	$1,350
11	Blue Cross Basic	$1,920	$1,280	$640	$4,710	$3,140	$1,570
44	SAMBA-Std	$2,540	$1,690	$850	$5,980	$3,990	$1,990
32	NALC-Hi	$2,050	$1,370	$680	$4,500	$3,000	$1,500
10	Blue Cross-Std	$2,940	$1,960	$980	$7,070	$4,720	$2,350

allowed). You should plan carefully based on your best "guesstimate" as to health care expenses that you are virtually certain to incur, such as maintenance prescription drugs, routine dental care, and routine eye care or any services for which you make multiple and foreseeable provider visits.

Only about one in five Federal employees are signing up each year for FSA accounts. This means that about four out of five employees are leaving money on the table each year. Almost everyone has at least a few hundred dollars in foreseeable out-of-pocket health care expenses. Those who don't sign up are throwing away a one-third discount on these costs. We recommend that ALL employees who are not in High Deductible plans establish an FSA if they have foreseeable expenses.

Health Savings Accounts

Both Health Reimbursement Arrangements (HRAs) and Health Savings Accounts (HSAs) provide significant tax advantages, beyond those available through Premium Conversion and FSAs. The simpler case involves HRAs, where your savings account can grow as long as you stay with the same plan (if you change plans the entire amount is lost), and you can also use an FSA to supplement the HRA amount set aside by the plan. For example, if you expect out of pocket drug and dental expenses of five hundred dollars next year, you could place that amount in an FSA in the expectation that the HRA amount paid through your premiums would remain available for unforeseen expenses next year or in future years. Unfortunately, retirees cannot use the FSA method of supplementing HRAs.

HSAs convey far larger advantages. First, you can add to your HSA account by advance planning, just as if it were an FSA. Second, while you can only establish an FSA account in advance, you can add to your HSA account at any time during the year. Thus, if you have unanticipated expenses late in the year of an extra thousand dollars, in most High Deductible plans you can have a thousand dollars transferred from your pay to your HSA, lower your taxable income by a thousand dollars, pay the bill through the HSA, and obtain what amounts to a one-third discount on your unplanned expenses. Or you can transfer the extra thousand dollars even if you don't have any unexpected expenses, saving one third in taxes, and build up your account for future years. Since you retain the HSA account for life, regardless of Open Season plan changes or retirement, and it can accumulate tax-free earnings, it can become a very substantial lifelong protection against health care expense.

This account augmentation advantage is dramatic if you consider the catastrophic guarantee provided by most FEHB plans. Consider a traditional plan, national or local, that holds self-only total out-of-pocket cost to $6,000, without significant loopholes. Compare that to a High Deductible plan, with a guarantee of $7,000 for a self-only enrollment, also without significant loopholes. The traditional plan seems better. However, under the High Deductible plan your plan-paid HSA account of $1,000 (a typical amount) can be used to defray large expenses, thereby reducing your potential loss to $6,000. Beyond that, you are allowed to make tax advantaged voluntary contributions of over $2,000 and pay your bills through your augmented account. This lets you save approximately $700 through lower tax payments if you face catastrophic expense. Hence, your total cost exposure is only about $5,300, lower than that claimed by the traditional plan, and reversing the conclusion as to which plan has a better guarantee. Most HDHP plans, evaluated this way, offer catastrophic expense protection as good as or better than most traditional plans.

While retirees over the age of 65 cannot establish HSAs, those nearing retirement not only can take advantage of HSAs, but also are eligible for "catch up" contributions after age 55, until enrolled in Medicare. These contributions can reduce after-tax expenses by hundreds of dollars a year more, or simply be added to the growing HSA balance. After retirement, the HSA balance remains available for the rest of your life, and continues to earn tax-free returns.

Chapter 11

Key Tips and Final Plan Selection

The data we have presented should help you to quickly and easily narrow your choice to two or three of the plans, out of the dozens you are offered. At this point, compare the brochures of these carefully. Underline key points, or parts of the plans that confuse you, and compare these points among the plans. It is very easy to use our online Web site, or OPMs, to find copies of plan brochures for your area. Then you can search on a word such as "maternity" or "surgery" "chiropractor" in the brochure for each plan and find the benefit details in seconds. Probably the plans will be similar on most things, so concentrate on differences that are important to you.

When you have figured out the major differences among the best plans, you are ready to make your final decision. One way to do this is to write out the most important ways in which the plans differ. These differences may not be strictly financial. For example, suppose it turns out that your choice is between a national plan and an HMO. Let's say that our ratings show that the HMO costs $1,000 dollars a year less on average, and has slightly better coverage for a benefit you need. But you are unwilling to give up a particular doctor you have been using for years. This seems to be an impasse, but there are several possible ways to resolve it. Perhaps your doctor is affiliated with the HMO—why not ask? Or consider using part of the money you will save by joining the HMO to continue going to your doctor and paying out-of-pocket (using a Flexible Spending Account will cut this cost by a third). Or you may have more than one doctor you want to keep and conclude that the national plan is well worth the higher cost.

Throughout this *Guide* we have argued that your best strategy is to make the primary factor in your plan selection the predicted cost of the plan for families like yours. This takes into account that none of us can predict whether or not we may have a heart attack, a stroke, a cancer, or other costly condition that strikes unexpectedly. You should use your known, predictable routine expenses to calculate how much to put in a Flexible Spending Account, not to choose an insurance plan whose main purpose is to protect you against unexpected and high expenses. There is an important exception to this general strategy. If you know that you will need some particular service next year, and it is very expensive (for example, hip surgery or maternity) and likely to cost you tens of thousands of dollars, it makes sense to select the physician you would like to use (or several you are considering) and ask two simple questions: "What plan networks are you in?" and "In your experience, which Federal employee health plan or plans pay best for the care I need?" Sometimes the answer will be that all of them pay well. But sometimes the answer will be that only a few plans pay well. In that case, look first at these plans and choose one of them after you complete your detective work by reading the brochure section on your procedure, calling the plan, or checking with other people who have been in your situation. But do not forget that some other disease may strike, so factor in both known problems and overall ratings in choosing among these few plans.

Flexible Spending Account

You can only establish your FSA during Open Season. Be sure to consider carefully this important option to reduce your health costs. Almost all employees should set up an FSA.

Whatever your personal decision turns on, you may be overwhelmed by details and confused by the choices you face. So here are some concluding thoughts based on some of the most common questions we have heard. Try to focus your decision on several key questions. Are you willing to join an HMO or a High Deductible plan? Do you expect big bills for a particular event such as surgery? Do you really want to have a particular benefit, such as chiropractic or hearing aid? Do you really "have to have" doctor sawbones in the plan network? (Hint: in the DC metro area, we have a "doc find" feature that tells you which plan networks include doctor sawbones.) Perhaps you can afford a higher premium to get the benefits you want, or perhaps you cannot and must pick a plan that at least gives you good catastrophic protection.

Tips

Throughout the *Guide* we have provided vital tips. We repeat some here:

- **Getting "Free" Health Insurance**—Some Consumer-Driven and High Deductible FEHB plans provide you a savings account larger than your actual premium cost after taxes. You can end the year with more money than you started if your medical costs are low.
- **Avoid a Big Risk**—Many people who are covered by their spouse's insurance drop FEHB insurance. This saves premium costs. However, if you are not enrolled and die suddenly, your spouse cannot ever enroll again. Your best option is to carry an FEHB family policy and drop the spousal insurance.
- **Protect Your Retirement**—It is not expensive to enroll in an FEHB plan or plans for the five years before retirement. Several plans have annual premiums that are about $1,500. These plans cost about $1,000 after tax savings. Some plans give you savings accounts higher than the tax advantaged premium cost.

- **Be Sure to Elect a Survivor Annuity for Your Spouse**—If you die and your spouse receives no Federal pension, your spouse will lose FEHB health insurance coverage forever. If you die while enrolled as self-only, your spouse will also lose coverage.

- **Be Wary of Misleading Catastrophic Cost Protection Claims in Plan Summaries**—Some plans exclude deductibles, physician copayments, or drug costs in the figure they claim for catastrophic limits. This can understate your risk by thousands of dollars.

- **Bargain with Out of Network Providers**—Most plans have very low payments for non-preferred providers. You MUST negotiate with these doctors before any expensive procedure in order to protect yourself. One good tactic is to ask for either their "preferred" or Medicare rate.

- **Check Your Brochure**—Do not stay in the same plan without reading at least "How We Change" for next year or join a new plan without checking any benefits of particular importance to your health care.

- **Flexible Spending Account**—You can only establish your FSA during Open Season. Be sure to consider carefully this important option to reduce your health costs. Almost all employees should set up an FSA.

- **You Can Keep Flexibility Only at a Price**—The best two arguments for paying the Medicare Part B premium are to preserve your choices over time, as both the FEHB and Medicare programs evolve, and to get you low costs for providers who are not in your plan network. However, this choice is costly.

- **Huge Annuitant Cost Saving**—Annuitants with Medicare Parts A and B can suspend their FEHB enrollment, join a Medicare Advantage plan, and pay only the Medicare premium. They can reenroll in an FEHB plan in the future without penalty, and in the meantime, enjoy good catastrophic protection, have low copays, and save thousands in premium costs.

- **Dealing with a Known High Expense**—There is an exception to our general advice about focusing on overall plan costs, not just one benefit category. If you know for sure that you will need an expensive service, you should look for the answer to "Which plans pay best?" If several plans pay equally well, then you can choose whichever of these is an overall better buy.

Questions and Answers

Here is a short list of frequent questions and their answers (we provide a far longer list in the online Guide):

- **What if I expect to have a baby?** What plan offers the best maternity benefits? Most plans offer low or no cost maternity coverage. Check brochures for this, and check network lists online to make sure you will have a good selection of obstetricians. Or select an obstetrician and then use her experience to steer you towards a few plans from which to choose.

- **What if I am going to have a major operation?** Pay particular attention to catastrophic limits. If you know for sure that you are going to face bills of

$25,000 or more, then pick a plan with a tight limit on your costs. In comparing catastrophic expense limits, use *Guide* figures. Our estimates include the "for sure" premium expense and adjust for inconsistencies among stated catastrophic limits, such as failing to include deductibles in the stated limit. If you are not sure what plans will work best in your case, check brochures and consult your surgeon to discuss which plans work best. Be sure your surgeon is in your plan network or will give you a network rate.

- **My two doctors aren't preferred providers for any plan. What should I do?** Set up an FSA account for about half the amount you expect to spend on those doctors. Then pick one of the top ranked plans that includes a fee-for-service benefit, use that benefit for whatever it will pay (which will probably be about half), and use the FSA to cover the rest. Or change doctors.

- **I need over 30 psychiatric visits. What plan is best?** The mental health parity requirement—which theoretically allows unlimited visits at a low cost—might arguably make all plans meet your needs. But plans require using preferred providers to get network rates. First, talk to your provider and see if he or she is "preferred" under any plan. If so, this plan is likely to be your best choice. Alternatively, most plans will pay sixty or seventy percent of the "plan allowance" for out of network visits. Since that is well below what most providers charge, you will likely pay half or more of the cost of each visit. Try making an arithmetic calculation. Estimate the number of visits you are likely to make and how much each of several plans will pay for these visits. Then add the annual premium cost to the amount that you will pay the doctor under each of those plans. If one of them stands out, you have an answer. If they are all about the same, choose on some other basis (like our overall ratings). Finally, you are a perfect candidate for a Flexible Spending Account, and your FSA tax savings will reduce your cost by about a third.

- **I really like the service from plan X. But it is rated halfway down your cost table. Would I be a sucker to stay with it?** No. Differences of several hundred dollars in estimated costs can move a plan up or down the table a long way. Our methods of estimating average costs are only approximations. Differences of $100 or less are not significant, and a national plan even halfway down the table is a perfectly acceptable deal. Furthermore, staying with the same plan will eliminate the hassle of changing doctors and of dealing with a plan bureaucracy that may not be as customer friendly as the one you have now.

- **You rated the plan I am in highly last year, but this year it has moved way down. Why did this happen and should I switch?** Premium differences are the biggest factor in our cost rankings, and premiums can swing widely from year to year. That is probably why your plan moved so far—but check the brochure's change page for a benefit cutback that could have affected our ratings. Or other plans could have improved their benefits. One of the big change factors, for example, is the catastrophic limit promised to you by the plan: these often move up or down by thousands of dollars and are big factors in our ratings. You can stick with your plan if it has not become unreasonably costly and has given you good service. But consider the possible savings from the plans we rank higher.

- **I don't have much money and can't afford an expensive premium. Is it safe to join one of the plans with a really low premium?** All plans are reputable, and all will pay the benefits they promise. Every plan, not just the ones with the lowest premiums, has gaps or loopholes of one kind or another. But the lower-premium national plans generally expose you to higher copayments and deductibles, so they may not save you as much money as you think. Look at our ratings tables and several brochures carefully, and then decide. A lower premium does not mean a worse plan, or a higher premium a better plan. Our estimates of average costs are a far better guide to likely costs than premiums alone.

- **I'm not very healthy and could easily have expenses of many thousands of dollars next year. I don't think that your rankings based on average costs are what I should use. What should I do?** A good method is to skip the average column and look at the column for high expenses of $30,000. Within that column, choose among several plans that our comparisons indicate are relatively low-cost. Another approach is to compare catastrophic limits. But keep in mind that our "average" columns include some very expensive years.

- **I can't decide whether I should get Medicare Part B and join a plan that guarantees I won't pay anything at all for medical bills, or plan to drop Medicare Part B and save about $1,600 a year in premium cost.** If your doctors are mostly preferred providers, consider dropping Part B. You won't save the entire amount of the Part B premium, but you will save most of it in most years. The main two arguments for getting Part B is that you have complete flexibility to use any doctor who accepts new Medicare patients, even if he is not preferred, and in the many plans with wraparound benefits you will pay nothing for hospital or doctor costs. But these savings and this flexibility costs you hundreds of dollars per year. Whatever you do, do not drop out of the FEHB program. If you decide to keep Part B, move to a low premium plan that waives cost sharing for those with Medicare Parts A and B, such as Aetna Direct, Blue Cross Basic, GEHA Standard, or in the DC area the CareFirst options. The first two of these not only provide a Medicare wraparound, but also pay part of the Part B premium.

- **My spouse has excellent family coverage from his or her employer and pays no premium. Is there any reason why I should not drop out of the Federal program?** If you are within five years of retirement, do not even consider dropping out. That private plan will go away sooner or later and you and your spouse will be stuck. You are not allowed to remain in the FEHB program after retirement without five years of continuous prior enrollment immediately preceding retirement (there are some narrow exceptions, such as layoffs).

- **I read that High Deductible plans are bad buys for older and less healthy individuals.** Nonsense. These plans are among the best deals in the program. Taking into account their tax advantages and savings accounts, they rival or beat many other plans. If you know for sure that your routine physician and drug expenses, priced at retail, will be three or four thousand dollars next year, you will probably do better in an HMO or national plan with low copayments. But high expense, in and of itself, is not an argument against High Deductible plans. They have some of the best catastrophic limit guarantees.

- **Some expensive plans have higher quality scores than some less expensive plans. How much weight should I put on quality?** The quality scores are driven by survey results from enrollees in each plan. Our ratings also show some of the particular factors those enrollees most like or dislike. Only you can judge how important these are to you. It may help to consider two things: most enrollees in just about all plans rate the plans quite favorably; and ultimately it is the doctors you choose, not the plan, that drives the quality of medical care you get. That said, the anecdotal evidence we get tells us that these scores measure things that are important and real.

- **I have an expensive condition that I am not sure is covered by several plans that you rank high. What should I do?** The first step is to get those plan brochures and compare them side-by-side. OPM's policy for standard brochure formats and clear English is immensely helpful. If you read and compare the specific language you may find the answer. If you do not, call at least one plan, and preferably several plans, and call again to protect yourself against mistakes that plan representatives sometimes make. If you are still not sure, consult providers who deal with your condition, or other patients with your condition, or both. Sometimes there is no way around doing your homework.

- **Skip all the details. What is the best plan?** There is no one best plan. Every plan is best for at least some people. Our rankings give you a good starting point, but only a starting point. If you don't want to be bothered with details, then check out only one or two plans carefully. But whatever else you do, read the "how we change" pages of the brochure, along with the "summary of benefits" near the end of the brochure, before you stay in the plan you are in or sign up for a new plan.

Cost & Special Features of All Plans

Average yearly cost in dollars (premiums and out-of-pocket expense)

Plan code	Plan name (primary service area)	Phone number	General Schedule			Annuitants 55 to 64		
			Self only	Self plus one	Family	Self only	Self plus one	Family of two
National Plans—Fee-for-Service, PPO, Consumer-Driven, and High-Deductible								
N61-3	Aetna Direct CDHP	888-238-6240	1840	**3720**	**4450**	3110	**6310**	6830
224-6	Aetna HealthFund HDHP	888-238-6240	1840	**3900**	**4280**	3080	6480	**6560**
474-6	APWU CDHP	800-222-2798	**1760**	**3600**	**4260**	3130	6500	6830
471-3	APWU-Hi	800-222-2798	2740	5100	6470	4040	7610	9330
111-3	Blue Cross Basic	800-411-2583	2190	4570	4980	3400	7110	7350
104-6	Blue Cross-Std	800-411-2583	3110	6530	7050	4650	9870	10240
421-3	Compass Rose	888-438-9135	2470	5340	6120	3720	7990	8870
401-3	Foreign Service	202-833-4910	1970	4350	4570	2980	6550	**6590**
311-3	GEHA-Hi	800-821-6136	2790	5820	6550	4260	8890	9620
314-6	GEHA-Std	800-821-6136	2100	**4030**	4540	3250	**6260**	**6570**
341-3	GEHA HDHP	800-821-6136	**1590**	**3280**	**3810**	**2720**	**5550**	**5880**
454-6	MHBP-Std	800-410-7778	2320	4530	4800	3490	6830	6870
414-6	MHBP Value Plan	800-410-7778	2610	5310	5730	3870	8000	8070
481-3	MHBP HDHP	800-694-9901	2080	4270	4800	3400	6980	7170
321-3	NALC-Hi	888-636-6252	2220	4690	4650	3330	7130	6760
KM1-3	NALC Value Plan	888-636-6252	2250	4530	4990	3440	7000	7050
324-6	NALC CDHP	888-636-6252	**1380**	**2670**	**3140**	**2710**	**5380**	**5450**
381-3	Rural Carrier	800-638-8432	2540	4300	4550	3730	6340	**6420**
441-3	SAMBA-Hi	800-638-6589	4520	9540	10750	6840	14470	15860
444-6	SAMBA-Std	800-638-6589	3030	6180	6530	4610	9490	9540
Local Plans—HMO, PPO, Consumer-Driven, and High-Deductible								
Alaska								
JS1-3	Aetna HealthFund CDHP	888-238-6240	4640	11020	10680	7400	17030	16520
JS4-6	Aetna Value Plan	888-238-6240	3290	7740	7350	5010	11350	10760
Alabama								
F51-3	Aetna HealthFund CDHP	888-238-6240	2740	6460	6360	4560	10620	10040
F54-6	Aetna Value Plan	888-238-6240	2310	4720	5100	3540	7310	7390
KK1-3	UnitedHealthcare Choice	877-835-9861	2110	4220	4880	3250	6530	7150
LS1-3	UnitedHealthcare HDHP	877-835-9861	**1680**	**3630**	**4350**	**2820**	**6110**	**6570**

Lowest costs are in **bold** type. Note that in some plans, family costs are lower than self-plus-one costs.

Avg. yearly cost (cont'd)					Pays for...					
Annuitants 65 or older with Medicare Parts A & B			Medicare wrap-around	Day limit in skilled nursing facility	Routine dental	Chiro-practic	Acupuncture	Hearing aids	Adult vision care	Accreditation
Self only	Self plus one	Family								
3380	**6590**	**7110**	Yes	60	No	No	Little	Yes	Exam	Yes
4970	10150	10230	No	60	Some	No	Little	No	Exam	Yes
5090	10280	10620	No	0	Yes	Some	Yes	Some	Some	Yes
5000	9630	11350	Yes	0	Yes	Some	Some	Some	No	Yes
3880	**8020**	**8260**	Network only	0	Some	Some	Some	Yes	No	Yes
5640	11610	11980	Yes	0	Some	Some	Some	Yes	No	Yes
4770	10060	10930	Yes	90	Yes	Yes	Yes	Some	Exam	No
4250	8940	8990	Yes	90	Some	Yes	Yes	Yes	No	Yes
5380	11120	11850	Yes	14	Yes	Some	Yes	Yes	No	Yes
4430	8500	8810	Yes	14	Yes	Some	Yes	Yes	No	Yes
4590	9230	9550	No	14	Yes	Some	Yes	No	Yes	Yes
4330	8690	8730	Yes	28	No	Yes	Yes	Yes	No	Yes
5850	11810	11880	No	28	No	Yes	Yes	Some	No	Yes
3690	**7220**	**7410**	Yes	28	No	Yes	Yes	Some	No	Yes
4490	9410	9040	Yes	0	Yes	Some	Some	Some	No	Yes
5280	10770	10820	No	0	Yes	Some	Some	Some	No	Yes
4460	9100	9170	No	0	Yes	Some	Some	Some	No	Yes
4380	**7770**	**7850**	Yes	60	Yes	Yes	Yes	Yes	No	No
7920	16610	18010	Yes	45	No	Yes	Some	Some	No	Yes
5570	11400	11450	Yes	30	No	Some	Some	Some	No	Yes
9160	20540	20030	No	60	Some	Yes	Little	No	Exam	Yes
6910	15130	14550	No	60	No	Yes	Little	No	Exam	Yes
6320	14130	13550	No	60	Some	Yes	Little	No	Exam	Yes
5450	11100	11170	No	60	No	Yes	Little	No	Exam	Yes
5110	10030	10660	No	60	Some	Some	Some	No	Exam	Yes
4800	10010	10470	No	60	Some	Yes	Some	Yes	Exam	Yes

Cost & Special Features of All Plans			Average yearly cost in dollars (premiums and out-of-pocket expense)					
			General Schedule			Annuitants 55 to 64		
Plan code	Plan name (primary service area)	Phone number	Self only	Self plus one	Family	Self only	Self plus one	Family of two
Arkansas								
F51-3	Aetna HealthFund CDHP	888-238-6240	2740	6460	6360	4560	10620	10040
F54-6	Aetna Value Plan	888-238-6240	2310	4720	5100	3540	7310	7390
DH1-3	QualChoice-Hi (Statewide) POS	800-235-7111	3020	4910	8580	4590	7510	12580
DH4-6	QualChoice-Std (Statewide)	800-235-7111	2180	**3990**	5000	3370	**6140**	7280
KK1-3	UnitedHealthcare Choice	877-835-9861	2110	4220	4880	3250	6530	7150
LS1-3	UnitedHealthcare HDHP	877-835-9861	**1680**	**3630**	**4350**	**2820**	**6110**	**6570**
Arizona								
G51-3	Aetna HealthFund CDHP	888-238-6240	2300	5460	5350	3890	9120	8530
WQ1-3	Aetna Open Access	800-537-9384	5830	14630	14520	8820	22110	21640
G54-6	Aetna Value Plan	888-238-6240	2250	4570	4940	3440	7080	7160
A74-6	Health Net-Std	800-289-2818	3390	9280	9040	5140	14130	13340
R61-3	Humana CoverageFirst CDHP (Ph'nix)	800-448-6262	1910	4620	5110	3340	7460	7660
R91-3	Humana CoverageFirst CDHP (Tuc'n)	800-448-6262	1870	4540	5020	3280	7340	7530
BF1-3	Humana Health-Hi (Ph'nix)	800-448-6262	6100	12810	13440	9200	19380	19940
C71-3	Humana Health-Hi (Tuc'n)	800-448-6262	3600	7430	7820	5460	11320	11510
BF4-6	Humana Health-Std (Ph'nix)	800-448-6262	3550	7240	7650	5420	11100	11260
C74-6	Humana Health-Std (Tuc'n)	800-448-6262	2620	5220	5540	4010	8080	8100
R64-6	Humana Value Plan (Ph'nix)	800-448-6262	2730	5390	5900	4050	8150	8310
R94-6	Humana Value Plan(Tuc'n)	800-448-6262	2670	5270	5780	3960	7980	8130
KT1-3	UnitedHealthcare Choice	877-835-9861	2150	4290	5080	3290	6630	7450
LU1-3	UnitedHealthcare HDHP	877-835-9861	**1770**	**3820**	4570	**2960**	6400	6910
California								
JS1-3	Aetna HealthFund CDHP	888-238-6240	4640	11020	10680	7400	17030	16520
JS4-6	Aetna Value Plan	888-238-6240	3290	7740	7350	5010	11350	10760
2X1-3	Aetna Open Access (LA/Bakersfield)	800-537-9384	2780	6680	6630	4240	10190	9810
B31-3	Anthem Blue Cross (Southern)	800-235-8631	3340	6390	7000	4950	9570	10080
SI1-3	Blue Shield Access (Southern)	800-880-8086	2740	6040	6320	4130	9150	9250
LB1-3	Health Net-Hi (Northern)	800-522-0088	7990	17370	19270	12020	26160	28680
LB4-6	Health Net-Std (Northern)	800-522-0088	7540	16490	18340	11350	24890	27230

Lowest costs are in **bold** type. Note that in some plans, family costs are lower than self-plus-one costs.

| Avg. yearly cost (cont'd) | | | | | Pays for... | | | | | |
| Annuitants 65 or older with Medicare Parts A & B | | | Medicare wrap-around | Day limit in skilled nursing facility | Routine dental | Chiro-practic | Acupunc-ture | Hearing aids | Adult vision care | Accredi-tation |
Self only	Self plus one	Family								
6320	14130	13550	No	60	Some	Yes	Little	No	Exam	Yes
5450	11100	11170	No	60	No	Yes	Little	No	Exam	Yes
5930	10190	15250	Yes	60	No	Some	No	Yes	Exam	Yes
4620	8610	9760	Yes	60	No	Some	No	Yes	Exam	Yes
5110	10030	10660	No	60	Some	Some	Some	No	Exam	Yes
4800	10010	10470	No	60	Some	Yes	Some	Yes	Exam	Yes
5650	12630	12040	No	60	Some	Yes	Little	No	Exam	Yes
10730	25820	25350	No	60	Yes	Yes	Some	No	Yes	Yes
5350	10870	10950	No	60	No	Yes	Little	No	Exam	Yes
6940	17590	16800	No	100	No	Some	No	No	Exam	No
3710	**8200**	**8390**	Yes	60	No	Some	Some	No	No	No
3660	**8070**	**8260**	Yes	60	No	Some	Some	No	No	No
10420	21510	22070	Yes	100	No	Yes	Some	No	Exam	Yes
6670	13460	13650	Yes	100	No	Yes	Some	No	Exam	Yes
6370	12800	12960	Yes	100	No	Some	Some	No	Exam	Yes
4960	9780	9800	Yes	100	No	Some	Some	No	Exam	Yes
4360	8430	8590	Yes	100	No	Yes	Some	No	No	No
4280	**8260**	**8410**	Yes	100	No	Yes	Some	No	No	No
5150	10130	10950	No	60	Some	Some	Some	No	Exam	Yes
4940	10290	10800	No	60	Some	Yes	Some	Yes	Exam	Yes
9160	20540	20030	No	60	Some	Yes	Little	No	Exam	Yes
6910	15130	14550	No	60	No	Yes	Little	No	Exam	Yes
6160	13900	13520	No	60	Yes	Yes	Some	No	Yes	Yes
6520	12270	12780	Yes	100	No	Yes	Yes	Yes	Exam	No
5760	12010	12110	No	100	No	Yes	No	Some	Yes	Yes
13960	29870	32390	No	100	No	Yes	Yes	Some	Exam	Yes
13330	28800	31140	No	100	No	Yes	Some	Some	Exam	Yes

Cost & Special Features of All Plans

Average yearly cost in dollars (premiums and out-of-pocket expense)

Plan code	Plan name (primary service area)	Phone number	General Schedule			Annuitants 55 to 64		
			Self only	Self plus one	Family	Self only	Self plus one	Family of two
T41-3	Health Net Basic (Northern)	800-522-0088	3470	7350	8370	5280	11230	12330
LP1-3	Health Net-Hi (Southern)	800-522-0088	4230	9100	10240	6380	13750	15150
LP4-6	Health Net-Std (Southern)	800-522-0088	4090	8900	10060	6180	13520	14830
P61-3	Health Net Basic (Southern)	800-522-0088	1890	**3520**	**3960**	**2930**	**5580**	**5770**
591-3	Kaiser-Hi (Northern)	800-464-4000	4020	10370	10030	6050	15630	14830
594-6	Kaiser-Std (Northern)	800-464-4000	3220	7760	7500	4800	11670	10870
KC1-3	Kaiser Basic (Northern)	800-464-4000	2610	6000	5790	3930	9110	8320
NZ1-3	Kaiser-Hi (Fresno)	800-464-4000	2370	5990	5650	3570	9060	8260
NZ4-6	Kaiser-Std (Fresno)	800-464-4000	1930	4190	**4450**	**2910**	6410	**6410**
621-3	Kaiser-Hi (Southern/Bakersfield)	800-464-4000	1970	4990	4650	**2960**	7550	6760
624-6	Kaiser-Std (Southern/Bakersfield)	800-464-4000	**1740**	**3740**	**4010**	2620	**5750**	**5750**
CY1-3	UnitedHealthcare-Hi (Southern)	866-546-0510	2510	4150	8550	3840	6390	12670
CY4-6	UnitedHealthcare-Std (Southern)	866-546-0510	2540	4890	8440	3740	7330	12220
Colorado								
G51-3	Aetna HealthFund CDHP	888-238-6240	2300	5460	5350	3890	9120	8530
G54-6	Aetna Value Plan	888-238-6240	2250	4570	4940	3440	7080	7160
R21-3	Humana Health Basic (Col Springs)	800-448-6262	2130	4250	4680	3300	6680	6830
RZ1-3	Humana Health Basic (Denv/Boulder)	800-448-6262	2180	4350	4790	3370	6840	6990
NR1-3	Humana Health-Hi (Col Springs)	800-448-6262	2270	4530	4920	3470	6980	7170
NT1-3	Humana Health-Hi (Denv/Boulder)	800-448-6262	2250	4480	4860	3430	6900	7090
NR4-6	Humana Health-Std (Col Springs)	800-448-6262	2140	4180	4580	3310	6510	6660
NT4-6	Humana Health-Std (Denv/Boulder)	800-448-6262	2200	4290	4690	3390	6680	6840
N41-3	Kaiser Basic student POS (Most of St)	800-632-9700	1840	**3630**	**3880**	2820	5620	**5620**
651-3	Kaiser-Hi student POS (Most of St)	800-632-9700	2440	5740	5450	3760	8850	8050
654-6	Kaiser-Std student POS (Most of St)	800-632-9700	2090	4230	4490	3130	6430	**6430**
LU1-3	UnitedHealthcare HDHP	877-835-9861	**1770**	**3820**	4570	**2960**	6400	6910
Connecticut								
EP1-3	Aetna HealthFund CDHP	888-238-6240	3480	8140	8060	5670	13140	12580
EP4-6	Aetna Value Plan	888-238-6240	2280	4650	5020	3490	7190	7260

Lowest costs are in **bold** type. Note that in some plans, family costs are lower than self-plus-one costs.

Avg. yearly cost (cont'd)			Medicare wrap-around	Day limit in skilled nursing facility	Pays for...					Accreditation
Annuitants 65 or older with Medicare Parts A & B					Routine dental	Chiro-practic	Acupunc-ture	Hearing aids	Adult vision care	
Self only	Self plus one	Family								
6270	13070	14160	No	100	No	Yes	Some	Some	Exam	Yes
8320	17460	18860	No	100	No	Yes	Yes	Some	Exam	Yes
8160	17430	18740	No	100	No	Yes	Some	Some	Exam	Yes
3730	**7100**	**7290**	Yes	100	No	Yes	Some	Some	Exam	Yes
7740	18670	17880	Some	100	No	Yes	Yes	No	Exam	Yes
6310	14240	13450	Some	100	No	Yes	Yes	No	Exam	Yes
4950	11690	10890	Some	100	No	Yes	Yes	No	Exam	Yes
5170	11800	11010	Some	100	No	Yes	Yes	No	Exam	Yes
4280	9150	9150	Some	100	No	Yes	Yes	No	Exam	Yes
4560	10310	9510	Some	100	No	Some	Yes	No	Exam	Yes
4020	8570	**8570**	Some	100	No	Some	Yes	No	Exam	Yes
5770	10110	16390	No	100	Yes	Yes	Yes	Yes	Yes	Yes
5470	10840	15730	No	100	Yes	Yes	Yes	Yes	Yes	Yes
5650	12630	12040	No	60	Some	Yes	Little	No	Exam	Yes
5350	10870	10950	No	60	No	Yes	Little	No	Exam	Yes
4210	**8120**	**8260**	Yes	100	No	Some	Some	No	Yes	Yes
4290	**8280**	**8420**	Yes	100	No	Some	Some	No	Yes	Yes
4710	9190	9380	Yes	100	No	Some	Some	No	Yes	Yes
4680	9110	9300	Yes	100	No	Some	Some	No	Yes	Yes
4300	**8310**	**8460**	Yes	100	No	Some	Some	No	Yes	Yes
4380	8480	8630	Yes	100	No	Some	Some	No	Yes	Yes
4200	8810	8810	No	100	No	Some	Some	No	Exam	Yes
5190	11530	10730	No	100	No	Some	Some	No	Exam	Yes
5000	10110	10110	No	100	No	Some	Some	No	Exam	Yes
4940	10290	10800	No	60	Some	Yes	Some	Yes	Exam	Yes
7430	16640	16090	No	60	Some	Yes	Little	No	Exam	Yes
5400	10980	11050	No	60	No	Yes	Little	No	Exam	Yes

Cost & Special Features of All Plans

Average yearly cost in dollars
(premiums and out-of-pocket expense)

Plan code	Plan name (primary service area)	Phone number	General Schedule			Annuitants 55 to 64		
			Self only	Self plus one	Family	Self only	Self plus one	Family of two
Delaware								
EP1-3	Aetna HealthFund CDHP	888-238-6240	3480	8140	8060	5670	13140	12580
P34-6	Aetna Open Access Basic (Phil)	800-537-9384	7710	17690	17620	11700	26730	26310
P31-3	Aetna Open Access-Hi (Philadelphia)	800-537-9384	9380	23130	23110	14130	34840	34500
EP4-6	Aetna Value Plan	888-238-6240	2280	4650	5020	3490	7190	7260
District of Columbia								
F51-3	Aetna HealthFund CDHP	888-238-6240	2740	6460	6360	4560	10620	10040
F54-6	Aetna Value Plan	888-238-6240	2310	4720	5100	3540	7310	7390
JN1-3	Aetna Open Access-Hi	800-537-9384	5480	12270	12100	8300	18550	18050
JN4-6	Aetna Open Access Basic	800-537-9384	2120	4200	4720	3290	6480	6940
2G1-3	CareFirst-Hi	888-789-9065	3770	6870	9100	5520	10170	13230
2G4-6	CareFirst-Std POS	888-789-9065	2300	4040	5550	3350	**5970**	8030
B61-3	CareFirst HDHP	888-789-9065	1870	**3730**	**4440**	2950	5910	**6600**
E31-3	Kaiser-Hi	877-574-3337	**1720**	4380	**3970**	2640	6710	**5920**
E34-6	Kaiser-Std	877-574-3337	**1630**	**3470**	**3660**	**2530**	**5430**	**5430**
T71-3	Kaiser-Basic	877-574-3337	1820	**3710**	**4160**	2780	5770	**6060**
JP1-3	MD-IPA	877-835-9861	2580	4250	8720	3960	6570	12950
LR1-3	UnitedHealthcare Choice	877-835-9861	2140	4280	5030	3290	6610	7370
L91-3	UnitedHealthcare Choice Plus	877-835-9861	2030	**4030**	5090	**2930**	**5950**	7140
V41-3	UnitedHealthcare HDHP	877-835-9861	1940	4190	4990	3210	6940	7540
Florida								
F51-3	Aetna HealthFund CDHP (State)	888-238-6240	2740	6750	6360	4560	10620	10040
F54-6	Aetna Value Plan (State)	888-238-6240	2310	5040	5100	3540	7310	7390
ML4-6	AvMed-Std (South)	800-882-8633	2930	5520	7930	4330	7810	11420
EA1-3	Capital Health (Tallahassee)	850-383-3311	2360	4590	7250	3600	6640	10640
QP1-3	Humana CoverageFirst CDHP (South)	800-448-6262	2120	5470	5490	3650	8210	8230
MJ1-3	Humana CoverageFirst CDHP (Tampa)	800-448-6262	3090	7550	7660	5110	11310	11480
EX1-3	Humana Medical-Hi (Daytona)	800-448-6262	2520	5360	5380	3850	7820	7850
E21-3	Humana Medical-Hi (Orlando)	800-448-6262	4050	8630	8810	6130	12730	12990
EE1-3	Humana Medical-Hi (South)	800-448-6262	4040	8610	8780	6120	12700	12960

Lowest costs are in **bold** type. Note that in some plans, family costs are lower than self-plus-one costs.

Avg. yearly cost (cont'd)					Pays for...					
Annuitants 65 or older with Medicare Parts A & B			Medicare wrap-around	Day limit in skilled nursing facility	Routine dental	Chiro-practic	Acupunc-ture	Hearing aids	Adult vision care	Accredi-tation
Self only	Self plus one	Family								
7430	16640	16090	No	60	Some	Yes	Little	No	Exam	Yes
13300	30140	29720	No	60	Yes	Yes	Little	No	Yes	Yes
16020	38460	38120	No	60	Yes	Yes	Little	No	Yes	Yes
5400	10980	11050	No	60	No	Yes	Little	No	Exam	Yes
6320	14130	13550	No	60	Some	Yes	Little	No	Exam	Yes
5450	11100	11170	No	60	No	Yes	Little	No	Exam	Yes
10180	22160	21660	No	60	Yes	Some	Little	Some	Yes	Yes
5240	10220	10680	No	60	Yes	Some	Little	Some	Yes	Yes
6550	12050	15120	Yes	Unlim	Yes	Some	Some	Yes	Exam	Yes
4390	**7940**	9990	Yes	Unlim	Yes	Some	Some	Yes	Exam	Yes
3410	**6600**	**7290**	Yes	Unlim	Yes	Some	Some	Yes	Exam	Yes
4140	9630	8830	No	100	Yes	Yes	Yes	No	Exam	Yes
4060	**8290**	**8290**	No	100	Yes	Some	Some	No	Exam	Yes
4520	8910	9200	No	100	No	Some	Some	No	Exam	Yes
5260	9120	15510	Yes	60	Yes	Some	Some	No	Yes	Yes
5150	10120	10870	No	60	Some	Some	Some	No	Exam	Yes
4770	9460	10650	No	60	Some	Some	Some	No	Exam	Yes
5190	10840	11430	No	60	Some	Yes	Some	Yes	Exam	Yes
6320	14130	13550	No	60	Some	Yes	Little	No	Exam	Yes
5450	11100	11170	No	60	No	Yes	Little	No	Exam	Yes
6370	11690	15310	No	30	No	Some	Some	Yes	No	No
5580	10430	14430	No	60	No	Some	No	No	Exam	Yes
4020	8940	8960	Yes	60	No	Some	Some	No	No	No
5480	12050	12210	Yes	60	No	Some	Soume	No	No	No
5090	10050	10090	Yes	100	No	Yes	Some	No	No	Yes
7370	14970	15220	Yes	100	No	Yes	Some	No	No	Yes
7360	14930	15190	Yes	100	No	Yes	Some	No	No	Yes

Cost & Special Features of All Plans

Average yearly cost in dollars (premiums and out-of-pocket expense)

Plan code	Plan name (primary service area)	Phone number	General Schedule			Annuitants 55 to 64		
			Self only	Self plus one	Family	Self only	Self plus one	Family of two
LL1-3	Humana Medical-Hi (Tampa)	800-448-6262	7920	16960	17520	11940	25210	26050
EX4-6	Humana Medical-St (Daytona)	800-448-6262	2350	4910	5030	3620	7150	7330
E24-6	Humana Medical-Std (Orlando)	800-448-6262	2300	4800	4920	3550	7000	7170
EE4-6	Humana Medical-Std (South)	800-448-6262	3260	6900	6980	4990	10140	10260
LL4-6	Humana Medical-Std (Tampa)	800-448-6262	3510	7440	7540	5360	10950	11110
MJ4-6	Humana Value (Tampa)	800-448-6262	2680	5680	5780	3970	7980	8130
QP4-6	Humana Value Plan (South)	800-448-6262	2670	5660	5760	3950	7950	8100
LV1-3	UnitedHealthcare Choice Plus	877-835-9861	2460	5180	7810	3540	7190	11140
LS1-3	UnitedHealthcare HDHP (State)	877-835-9861	**1680**	4040	**4350**	2820	**6110**	**6570**
Georgia								
F51-3	Aetna HealthFund CDHP	888-238-6240	2740	6750	6360	4560	10620	10040
2U1-3	Aetna Open Access (Atlanta/Athens)	800-537-9384	6460	15160	14850	9760	22590	22130
F54-6	Aetna Value Plan	888-238-6240	2310	5040	5100	3540	7310	7390
QM1-3	Blue Open Access POS (Atlanta/Ath)	844-423-9988	2070	4540	5200	3160	6580	7570
AD1-3	Humana CoverageFirst CDHP (Atl)	800-448-6262	2400	6060	6100	4070	9080	9140
S91-3	Humana CoverageFirst CDHP (Col)	800-448-6262	1900	4960	5090	3320	7430	7620
LM1-3	Humana CoverageFirst CDHP (Macon)	800-448-6262	1840	4820	4940	3230	7220	7400
Q71-3	Humana Employers Basic (Atlanta)	800-448-6262	2370	5080	5200	3650	7430	7600
RM1-3	Humana Employers Basic (Columbus)	800-448-6262	2330	5000	5120	3600	7310	7480
RJ1-3	Humana Employers Basic (Macon)	800-448-6262	2280	4900	5010	3530	7150	7310
DG1-3	Humana Employers-Hi (Atlanta)	800-448-6262	6690	14310	14750	10090	21240	21900
CB1-3	Humana Employers-Hi (Columbus)	800-448-6262	4270	9110	9300	6460	13440	13730
DN1-3	Humana Employers-Hi (Macon)	800-448-6262	2730	5800	5840	4160	8480	8540
DG4-6	Humana Employers-Std (Atlanta)	800-448-6262	3840	8150	8290	5860	12020	12220
CB4-6	Humana Employers-Std (Columbus)	800-448-6262	3850	8160	8290	5860	12020	12230
DN4-6	Humana Employers-Std (Macon)	800-448-6262	2630	5550	5560	4040	8110	8130
AD4-6	Humana Value Plan (Atlanta)	800-448-6262	2780	5910	6020	4130	8330	8490
S94-6	Humana Value Plan (Columbus)	800-448-6262	2700	5730	5830	4000	8050	8200
LM4-6	Humana Value Plan (Macon)	800-448-6262	2640	5600	5690	3910	7860	8000
F81-3	Kaiser-Hi (Most of St) student POS	888-865-5813	2220	5380	4850	3440	7960	7170

Lowest costs are in **bold** type. Note that in some plans, family costs are lower than self-plus-one costs.

Avg. yearly cost (cont'd)					Pays for...					
Annuitants 65 or older with Medicare Parts A & B			Medicare wrap-around	Day limit in skilled nursing facility	Routine dental	Chiro-practic	Acupuncture	Hearing aids	Adult vision care	Accreditation
Self only	Self plus one	Family								
13180	27450	28290	Yes	100	No	Yes	Some	No	No	Yes
4610	8970	9150	Yes	100	No	Yes	Some	No	No	Yes
4540	8820	8990	Yes	100	No	Yes	Some	No	No	Yes
5980	11960	12080	Yes	100	No	Yes	Some	No	No	Yes
6350	12770	12930	Yes	100	No	Yes	Some	No	No	Yes
4280	**8260**	**8410**	Yes	100	No	Yes	Some	No	No	No
4270	**8230**	**8380**	Yes	100	No	Yes	Some	No	No	No
5390	10950	14900	No	60	Some	Some	Some	No	Exam	Yes
4800	10010	10470	No	60	Some	Yes	Some	Yes	Exam	Yes
6320	14130	13550	No	60	Some	Yes	Little	No	Exam	Yes
11680	26300	25840	No	60	Yes	Yes	Some	No	Yes	Yes
5450	11100	11170	No	60	No	Yes	Little	No	Exam	Yes
5100	10400	11390	No	60	No	Yes	No	No	No	Yes
4440	9810	9870	Yes	60	No	Some	Some	No	No	No
3700	**8160**	**8350**	Yes	60	No	Some	Some	No	No	No
3600	**7950**	**8130**	Yes	60	No	Some	Some	No	No	No
4570	8880	9060	Yes	100	No	Some	Some	No	Yes	Yes
4510	8760	8930	Yes	100	No	Some	Some	No	Yes	Yes
4440	8600	8770	Yes	100	No	Some	Some	No	Yes	Yes
11330	23480	24130	Yes	100	No	Yes	Some	No	No	Yes
7700	15670	15970	Yes	100	No	Yes	Some	No	No	Yes
5400	10710	10780	Yes	100	No	Yes	Some	No	No	Yes
6850	13840	14040	Yes	100	No	Yes	Some	No	No	Yes
6850	13840	14050	Yes	100	No	Yes	Some	No	No	Yes
5030	9930	9960	Yes	100	No	Yes	Some	No	No	Yes
4440	8610	8770	Yes	100	No	Yes	Some	No	No	No
4310	**8330**	**8480**	Yes	100	No	Yes	Some	No	No	No
4220	**8140**	**8280**	Yes	100	No	Yes	Some	No	No	No
4780	10670	9880	No	100	Some	Yes	No	No	Exam	Yes

Cost & Special Features of All Plans

Average yearly cost in dollars (premiums and out-of-pocket expense)

Plan code	Plan name (primary service area)	Phone number	General Schedule			Annuitants 55 to 64		
			Self only	Self plus one	Family	Self only	Self plus one	Family of two
F84-6	Kaiser-Std (Most of St) student POS	888-865-5813	1990	4320	**4320**	3060	**6320**	6320
LV1-3	UnitedHealthcare Choice Plus	877-835-9861	2460	5180	7810	3540	7190	11140
Guam								
B41-3	Calvo's Selectcare-Hi	671-477-9808	**1620**	**3020**	**3890**	**2530**	**4730**	**5740**
B44-6	Calvo's Selectcare-Std	671-477-9808	**1720**	**3190**	**4040**	**2690**	**5100**	**5990**
JK1-3	TakeCare-Hi	671-647-3526	**1680**	**3240**	**3870**	**2630**	**5010**	**5730**
JK4-6	TakeCare-Std	671-647-3526	**1460**	**2770**	**3660**	**2320**	**4340**	**5380**
KX1-3	TakeCare HDHP	671-647-3526	**1430**	**2880**	**3490**	**2480**	**5300**	**5410**
Hawaii								
JS1-3	Aetna HealthFund CDHP	888-238-6240	4640	11020	10680	7400	17030	16520
JS4-6	Aetna Value Plan	888-238-6240	3290	7740	7350	5010	11350	10760
871-3	HMSA POS	800-776-4672	**1770**	**3710**	**3940**	**2710**	**5690**	**5800**
631-3	Kaiser-Hi student POS	808-432-5955	1970	4570	4480	3020	7050	**6600**
634-6	Kaiser-Std student POS	808-432-5955	**1670**	**3650**	**3910**	**2540**	**5690**	**5690**
Idaho								
9K4-6	Aetna Health/Altius HDHP	800-537-9384	**1750**	**3330**	**3690**	**2840**	**5420**	**5470**
9K1-3	Aetna Health/Altius-Hi	800-537-9384	3500	7580	7390	5320	11550	10980
DK4-6	Aetna Health/Altius-Std	800-537-9384	2200	4320	4590	3360	6610	6650
H41-3	Aetna HealthFund CDHP	888-238-6240	2880	6780	6670	4760	11100	10500
H44-6	Aetna Value Plan	888-238-6240	2300	4700	5070	3520	7270	7340
PT1-3	Kaiser Washington HDHP (WA/N ID)	888-901-4636	**1780**	**4010**	**4380**	**2900**	6570	**6570**
541-3	Kaiser Washington-Hi (WA/N ID)	888-901-4636	3440	7600	7290	5190	11500	10700
544-6	Kaiser Washington-Std (WA/N ID)	888-901-4636	2500	4940	5190	3690	7250	7250
SF1-3	SelectHealth-Hi student POS	844-345-3342	4520	10380	10030	6880	15750	14960
SF4-6	SelectHealth-Std student POS	844-345-3342	2120	4160	**4390**	3300	6460	**6460**
Illinois								
H41-3	Aetna HealthFund CDHP	888-238-6240	2880	6780	6670	4760	11100	10500
H44-6	Aetna Value Plan	888-238-6240	2300	4700	5070	3520	7270	7340
9G1-3	Blue Preferred-Hi POS (St L/Other)	888-811-2092	2870	5220	5610	4370	7990	8210
9G4-6	Blue Preferred-Std (St L/Other)	888-811-2092	2190	4760	5480	3350	7340	7980

Lowest costs are in **bold** type. Note that in some plans, family costs are lower than self-plus-one costs.

| Avg. yearly cost (cont'd) | | | Medicare wrap-around | Day limit in skilled nursing facility | Pays for... | | | | | Accredi-tation |
| Annuitants 65 or older with Medicare Parts A & B | | | | | Routine dental | Chiro-practic | Acupuncture | Hearing aids | Adult vision care | |
Self only	Self plus one	Family								
4530	9480	9480	No	100	Some	Some	No	No	Exam	Yes
5390	10950	14900	No	60	Some	Some	Some	No	Exam	Yes
3890	**7380**	**8400**	Yes	100	Some	Some	Some	Some	Exam	No
3940	**7520**	**8410**	Yes	100	Some	Some	Some	Some	Exam	No
4070	**7770**	**8490**	Some	100	Yes	Some	No	Some	Yes	No
4230	**7990**	9040	No	60	Some	Some	No	No	Yes	No
4500	9520	9620	No	100	Yes	Some	No	No	Yes	No
9160	20540	20030	No	60	Some	Yes	Little	No	Exam	Yes
6910	15130	14550	No	60	No	Yes	Little	No	Exam	Yes
4320	8780	8880	Some	100	Yes	Yes	No	Yes	Exam	Yes
4670	9980	9530	No	120	Some	No	No	Yes	Exam	Yes
4250	9090	9090	No	120	Some	No	No	Yes	Exam	Yes
4350	8500	**8550**	Yes	30	No	Some	No	Yes	Exam	Yes
6510	13860	13290	Yes	30	Yes	Some	No	Yes	Exam	Yes
4580	9000	9040	Yes	30	No	Some	No	Yes	Exam	Yes
6520	14610	14010	No	60	Some	Yes	Little	No	Exam	Yes
5430	11060	11130	No	60	No	Yes	Little	No	Exam	Yes
3530	**7920**	**7920**	Some	60	No	Yes	Some	No	Exam	Yes
7060	15250	14450	No	60	Some	Yes	Some	No	Exam	Yes
4510	9780	9780	Some	60	No	Yes	Some	No	Exam	Yes
8780	19380	18590	No	30	No	Yes	No	Yes	Exam	Yes
5070	10020	10020	No	30	No	Some	No	Yes	Exam	Yes
6520	14610	14010	No	60	Some	Yes	Little	No	Exam	Yes
5430	11060	11130	No	60	No	Yes	Little	No	Exam	Yes
6360	11790	12010	No	60	No	Some	No	No	Exam	No
5380	11240	11880	Yes	90	No	Some	No	No	Exam	No

Cost & Special Features of All Plans

Average yearly cost in dollars (premiums and out-of-pocket expense)

Plan code	Plan name (primary service area)	Phone number	General Schedule			Annuitants 55 to 64		
			Self only	Self plus one	Family	Self only	Self plus one	Family of two
K84-6	Health Alliance (So IL/So IN/Cen IA)	800-851-3379	3010	6350	9960	4470	9560	14370
GB1-3	Humana CoverageFirst CDHP (Cent'l)	800-448-6262	3650	8390	8920	5940	13110	13360
MW1-3	Humana CoverageFirst CDHP (Chi)	800-448-6262	2360	5620	6020	4010	8960	9020
RW1-3	Humana Health Basic (Chicago)	800-448-6262	2330	4570	4990	3590	7100	7280
AB1-3	Humana Health Basic (Rockford/NW)	800-448-6262	2310	4540	4950	3560	7050	7230
751-3	Humana Health-Hi (Chicago)	888-393-6765	7120	14990	15730	10740	22660	23370
9F1-3	Humana Health-Hi (Rockford/NW)	888-393-6765	9590	20300	21290	14440	30620	31710
754-6	Humana Health-Std (Chicago)	888-393-6765	4220	8680	9150	6430	13260	13520
AB4-6	Humana Health-Std (Rockford/NW)	888-393-6765	5340	11070	11660	8100	16850	17280
GB4-6	Humana Value Plan (Central)	800-448-6262	2720	5380	5880	4040	8130	8290
MW4-6	Humana Value Plan (Chicago)	800-448-6262	2800	5550	6070	4160	8390	8560
EY1-3	MercyCare HMO (Rockford/Janesville)	800-895-2421	3080	6170	8650	4640	9260	12690
761-3	Union Health (Chicago)	312-423-4200	2280	4750	6060	3460	7150	8840
YH1-3	UnitedHealthcare (Mol/Cedar R/D M)	800-747-1446	2860	4870	9190	4270	7380	13440
L91-3	UnitedHealthcare Choice Plus (Chi)	877-835-9861	2030	**4030**	5090	**2930**	**5950**	7140
Indiana								
JS1-3	Aetna HealthFund CDHP	888-238-6240	4640	11020	10680	7400	17030	16520
JS4-6	Aetna Value Plan	888-238-6240	3290	7740	7350	5010	11350	10760
K84-6	Health Alliance (So IL/So IN/Cen IA)	800-851-3379	3010	6760	9960	4470	9560	14370
GB1-3	Humana CoverageFirst CDHP (Cent'l)	800-448-6262	3650	8750	8920	5940	13110	13360
MW1-3	Humana CoverageFirst CDHP (Chi)	800-448-6262	2360	5980	6020	4010	8960	9020
TC1-3	Humana CoverageFirst CDHP (Lou)	800-448-6262	1840	4830	4950	3230	7230	7420
751-3	Humana Health-Hi (Chicago)	888-393-6765	7120	15250	15730	10740	22660	23370
A61-3	Humana Health-Hi (Cincinnati)	800-448-6262	5420	11630	11930	8180	17210	17670
MH1-3	Humana Health-Hi (Louisville)	800-448-6262	3460	7390	7500	5240	10860	11030
754-6	Humana Health-Std (Chicago)	888-393-6765	4220	8970	9150	6430	13260	13520
A64-6	Humana Health-Std (Cincinnati)	800-448-6262	3910	8330	8470	5940	12280	12490
MH4-6	Humana Health-Std (Louisville)	800-448-6262	2590	5460	5470	3970	7980	7990
MW4-6	Humana Value Plan (Chicago)	800-448-6262	2800	5950	6070	4160	8390	8560
L91-3	UnitedHealthcare Choice Plus (Chi)	877-835-9861	2030	4300	5090	**2930**	**5950**	7140

Lowest costs are in **bold** type. Note that in some plans, family costs are lower than self-plus-one costs.

| Avg. yearly cost (cont'd) | | | | | Pays for... | | | | | |
| Annuitants 65 or older with Medicare Parts A & B | | | Medicare wrap-around | Day limit in skilled nursing facility | Routine dental | Chiro-practic | Acupunc-ture | Hearing aids | Adult vision care | Accreditation |
Self only	Self plus one	Family								
4700	9770	14580	Yes	Unlim	No	Some	No	Some	Exam	Yes
6320	13840	14090	Yes	60	No	Some	Some	No	No	No
4390	9690	9750	Yes	60	No	Some	Some	No	No	No
4580	8900	9080	Yes	100	No	Some	Some	No	Yes	Yes
4550	8850	9020	Yes	100	No	Some	Some	No	Yes	Yes
11980	24870	25580	Yes	100	No	Some	Some	No	Yes	Yes
15680	32830	33920	Yes	100	No	Some	Some	No	Yes	Yes
7420	15060	15320	Yes	100	No	Some	Some	No	Yes	Yes
9090	18650	19080	Yes	100	No	Some	Some	No	Yes	Yes
4350	8410	**8570**	Yes	100	No	Yes	Some	No	No	No
4470	8670	8840	Yes	100	No	Yes	Some	No	No	No
6550	12920	16350	No	90	No	Yes	Some	Some	Exam	Yes
4670	10100	11790	Yes	60	No	Yes	No	No	Some	No
6120	11060	17120	No	Unlim	Yes	Yes	No	Yes	No	Yes
4770	9460	10650	No	60	Some	Some	Some	No	Exam	Yes
9160	20540	20030	No	60	Some	Yes	Little	No	Exam	Yes
6910	15130	14550	No	60	No	Yes	Little	No	Exam	Yes
4700	9770	14580	Yes	Unlim	No	Some	No	Some	Exam	Yes
6320	13840	14090	Yes	60	No	Some	Some	No	No	No
4390	9690	9750	Yes	60	No	Some	Some	No	No	No
3610	**7970**	**8150**	Yes	60	No	Some	Some	No	No	No
11980	24870	25580	Yes	100	No	Some	Some	No	Yes	Yes
9370	19260	19720	Yes	100	No	Some	Some	No	Exam	Yes
6460	13000	13160	Yes	100	No	Yes	Some	No	Exam	Yes
7420	15060	15320	Yes	100	No	Some	Some	No	Yes	Yes
6870	13880	14090	Yes	100	No	Some	Some	No	Exam	Yes
4920	9680	9690	Yes	100	No	Some	Some	No	Exam	Yes
4470	8670	8840	Yes	100	No	Yes	Some	No	No	No
4770	9460	10650	No	60	Some	Some	Some	No	Exam	Yes

			General Schedule			Annuitants 55 to 64		
Cost & Special Features of All Plans			*Average yearly cost in dollars (premiums and out-of-pocket expense)*					
Plan code	Plan name (primary service area)	Phone number	Self only	Self plus one	Family	Self only	Self plus one	Family of two
Iowa								
H41-3	Aetna HealthFund CDHP	888-238-6240	2880	6780	6670	4760	11100	10500
H44-6	Aetna Value Plan	888-238-6240	2300	4700	5070	3520	7270	7340
K84-6	Health Alliance (So IL/So IN/Cen IA)	800-851-3379	3010	6350	9960	4470	9560	14370
V31-3	HealthPartners-Hi (Statewide)	800-883-2177	3070	6730	7860	4740	10400	11700
V34-6	HealthPartners-Std (Statewide)	952-883-5000	2380	4750	5280	3500	7040	7350
YH1-3	UnitedHealthcare (Mol/Cedar R/D M)	800-747-1446	2860	4870	9190	4270	7380	13440
LJ1-3	UnitedHealthcare Choice	877-835-9861	2150	4290	5080	3290	6630	7450
N71-3	UnitedHealthcare HDHP	877-835-9861	1810	**3910**	4660	3010	6520	7050
Kansas								
G51-3	Aetna HealthFund CDHP	888-238-6240	2300	5460	5350	3890	9120	8530
HA1-3	Aetna Open Access-Hi (Kansas City)	800-537-9384	3340	8060	8010	4940	11890	11300
HA4-6	Aetna Open Access-Std (Kansas City)	800-537-9384	2910	6360	6750	4290	9300	9260
G54-6	Aetna Value Plan	888-238-6240	2250	4570	4940	3440	7080	7160
PH1-3	Humana CoverageFirst CDHP (KS City)	800-448-6262	**1790**	4360	4830	3150	7070	7240
MS1-3	Humana Health-Hi (Kansas City)	800-448-6262	10020	21240	22270	15080	32020	33170
MS4-6	Humana Health-Std (Kansas City)	800-448-6262	4170	8570	9050	6350	13100	13350
PH4-6	Humana Value Plan (Kansas City)	800-448-6262	2530	4960	5440	3740	7500	7630
Kentucky								
H41-3	Aetna HealthFund CDHP	888-238-6240	2880	7060	6670	4760	11100	10500
H44-6	Aetna Value Plan	888-238-6240	2300	5020	5070	3520	7270	7340
6N1-3	Humana CoverageFirst CDHP (Lex)	800-448-6262	1810	4750	4870	3180	7120	7300
TC1-3	Humana CoverageFirst CDHP (Lou)	800-448-6262	1840	4830	4950	3230	7230	7420
A61-3	Humana Health-Hi (Cincinnati)	800-448-6262	5420	11630	11930	8180	17210	17670
MI1-3	Humana Health-Hi (Lex/Central)	800-448-6262	5050	10810	11080	7630	15990	16390
MH1-3	Humana Health-Hi (Louisville)	800-448-6262	3460	7390	7500	5240	10860	11030
A64-6	Humana Health-Std (Cincinnati)	800-448-6262	3910	8330	8470	5940	12280	12490
MI4-6	Humana Health-Std (Lex/Central)	800-448-6262	3310	7020	7100	5050	10320	10440
MH4-6	Humana Health-Std (Louisville)	800-448-6262	2590	5460	5470	3970	7980	7990
N71-3	UnitedHealthcare HDHP	877-835-9861	1810	4310	4660	3010	6520	7050

Lowest costs are in **bold** type. Note that in some plans, family costs are lower than self-plus-one costs.

| Avg. yearly cost (cont'd) | | | | | Pays for... | | | | | |
| Annuitants 65 or older with Medicare Parts A & B | | | Medicare wrap-around | Day limit in skilled nursing facility | Routine dental | Chiro-practic | Acupunc-ture | Hearing aids | Adult vision care | Accredi-tation |
Self only	Self plus one	Family								
6520	14610	14010	No	60	Some	Yes	Little	No	Exam	Yes
5430	11060	11130	No	60	No	Yes	Little	No	Exam	Yes
4700	9770	14580	Yes	Unlim	No	Some	No	Some	Exam	Yes
5860	12450	13750	Yes	120	Some	Yes	Yes	Some	No	Yes
5360	10580	10890	No	120	No	Yes	Yes	No	No	Yes
6120	11060	17120	No	Unlim	Yes	Yes	No	Yes	No	Yes
5150	10130	10950	No	60	Some	Some	Some	No	Exam	Yes
5000	10410	10940	No	60	Some	Yes	Some	Yes	Exam	Yes
5650	12630	12040	No	60	Some	Yes	Little	No	Exam	Yes
6750	15690	15100	No	60	Yes	Yes	No	Yes	Exam	Yes
6190	13200	13150	No	60	Yes	Yes	No	Yes	Exam	Yes
5350	10870	10950	No	60	No	Yes	Little	No	Exam	Yes
3530	**7800**	**7970**	Yes	60	No	Some	Some	No	No	No
16300	34150	35300	Yes	100	No	Yes	Some	No	Exam	Yes
7300	14800	15050	Yes	100	No	Some	Some	No	Exam	Yes
4060	**7780**	**7910**	Yes	100	No	Yes	Some	No	No	No
6520	14610	14010	No	60	Some	Yes	Little	No	Exam	Yes
5430	11060	11130	No	60	No	Yes	Little	No	Exam	Yes
3560	**7850**	**8030**	Yes	60	No	Some	Some	No	No	No
3610	**7970**	**8150**	Yes	60	No	Some	Some	No	No	No
9370	19260	19720	Yes	100	No	Some	Some	No	Exam	Yes
8840	18120	18530	Yes	100	No	Yes	Some	No	Exam	Yes
6460	13000	13160	Yes	100	No	Yes	Some	No	Exam	Yes
6870	13880	14090	Yes	100	No	Some	Some	No	Exam	Yes
6000	12020	12140	Yes	100	No	Some	Some	No	Exam	Yes
4920	9680	9690	Yes	100	No	Some	Some	No	Exam	Yes
5000	10410	10940	No	60	Some	Yes	Some	Yes	Exam	Yes

Cost & Special Features of All Plans
Average yearly cost in dollars (premiums and out-of-pocket expense)

Plan code	Plan name (primary service area)	Phone number	General Schedule			Annuitants 55 to 64		
			Self only	Self plus one	Family	Self only	Self plus one	Family of two
Louisiana								
F51-3	Aetna HealthFund CDHP (State)	888-238-6240	2740	6460	6360	4560	10620	10040
F54-6	Aetna Value Plan (State)	888-238-6240	2310	4720	5100	3540	7310	7390
AE1-3	Humana Health-Hi (Baton Rouge)	800-448-6262	3350	6880	7240	5090	10510	10660
BC1-3	Humana Health-Hi (New Orleans)	800-448-6262	2570	5220	5500	3920	8000	8040
AE4-6	Humana Health-Std (Baton Rouge)	800-448-6262	2640	5280	5590	4060	8160	8190
BC4-6	Humana Health-Std (New Orleans)	800-448-6262	2290	4480	5330	3530	6970	7790
LS1-3	UnitedHealthcare HDHP (State)	877-835-9861	**1680**	**3630**	**4350**	**2820**	**6110**	**6570**
Maine								
EP1-3	Aetna HealthFund CDHP	888-238-6240	3480	8140	8060	5670	13140	12580
EP4-6	Aetna Value Plan	888-238-6240	2280	4650	5020	3490	7190	7260
Maryland								
F51-3	Aetna HealthFund CDHP	888-238-6240	2740	6460	6360	4560	10620	10040
F54-6	Aetna Value Plan	888-238-6240	2310	4720	5100	3540	7310	7390
JN4-6	Aetna Open Access Basic	800-537-9384	2120	12270	4720	3290	6480	6940
JN1-3	Aetna Open Access-Hi	800-537-9384	5480	4200	12100	8300	18550	18050
B61-3	CareFirst HDHP	888-789-9065	1870	6870	**4440**	**2950**	**5910**	**6600**
2G1-3	CareFirst-Hi	888-789-9065	3770	4040	9100	5520	10170	13230
2G4-6	CareFirst-Std POS	888-789-9065	2300	**3730**	5550	3350	**5970**	8030
T71-3	Kaiser-Basic	877-574-3337	1820	4380	**4160**	**2780**	**5770**	**6060**
E31-3	Kaiser-Hi	877-574-3337	**1720**	**3470**	3970	**2640**	6710	**5920**
E34-6	Kaiser-Std	877-574-3337	**1630**	3710	3660	2530	5430	5430
JP1-3	MD-IPA	877-835-9861	2580	4250	8720	3960	6570	12950
LR1-3	UnitedHealthcare Choice	877-835-9861	2140	4280	5030	3290	6610	7370
L91-3	UnitedHealthcare Choice Plus	877-835-9861	2030	**4030**	5090	**2930**	**5950**	7140
V41-3	UnitedHealthcare HDHP	877-835-9861	1940	4190	4990	3210	6940	7540
Massachusetts								
EP1-3	Aetna HealthFund CDHP	888-238-6240	3480	8140	8060	5670	13140	12580
EP4-6	Aetna Value Plan	888-238-6240	2280	4650	5020	3490	7190	7260

Lowest costs are in **bold** type. Note that in some plans, family costs are lower than self-plus-one costs.

Avg. yearly cost (cont'd) — Annuitants 65 or older with Medicare Parts A & B			Medicare wrap-around	Day limit in skilled nursing facility	Pays for...					Accreditation
Self only	Self plus one	Family			Routine dental	Chiro-practic	Acupuncture	Hearing aids	Adult vision care	
6320	14130	13550	No	60	Some	Yes	Little	No	Exam	Yes
5450	11100	11170	No	60	No	Yes	Little	No	Exam	Yes
6330	12710	12870	Yes	100	No	Some	Some	No	Exam	Yes
5160	10210	10250	Yes	100	No	Some	Some	No	Exam	Yes
5050	9960	9990	Yes	100	No	Some	Some	No	Exam	Yes
4520	8770	9590	Yes	100	No	Some	Some	No	Exam	Yes
4800	10010	10470	No	60	Some	Yes	Some	Yes	Exam	Yes
7430	16640	16090	No	60	Some	Yes	Little	No	Exam	Yes
5400	10980	11050	No	60	No	Yes	Little	No	Exam	Yes
6320	14130	13550	No	60	Some	Yes	Little	No	Exam	Yes
5450	11100	11170	No	60	No	Yes	Little	No	Exam	Yes
5240	10220	10680	No	60	Yes	Some	Little	Some	Yes	Yes
10180	22160	21660	No	60	Yes	Some	Little	Some	Yes	Yes
3410	**6600**	**7290**	Yes	Unlim	Yes	Some	Some	Yes	Exam	Yes
6550	12050	15120	Yes	Unlim	Yes	Some	Some	Yes	Exam	Yes
4390	**7940**	9990	Yes	Unlim	Yes	Some	Some	Yes	Exam	Yes
4520	8910	9200	No	100	No	Some	Some	No	Exam	Yes
4140	9630	8830	No	100	Yes	Yes	Yes	No	Exam	Yes
4060	**8290**	**8290**	No	100	Yes	Some	Some	No	Exam	Yes
5260	9120	15510	Yes	60	Yes	Some	Some	No	Yes	Yes
5150	10120	10870	No	60	Some	Some	Some	No	Exam	Yes
4770	9460	10650	No	60	Some	Some	Some	No	Exam	Yes
5190	10840	11430	No	60	Some	Yes	Some	Yes	Exam	Yes
7430	16640	16090	No	60	Some	Yes	Little	No	Exam	Yes
5400	10980	11050	No	60	No	Yes	Little	No	Exam	Yes

Cost & Special Features of All Plans			Average yearly cost in dollars (premiums and out-of-pocket expense)					
			General Schedule			Annuitants 55 to 64		
Plan code	Plan name (primary service area)	Phone number	Self only	Self plus one	Family	Self only	Self plus one	Family of two
Michigan								
G51-3	Aetna HealthFund CDHP	888-238-6240	2300	5460	5350	3890	9120	8530
G54-6	Aetna Value Plan	888-238-6240	2250	4570	4940	3440	7080	7160
LX1-3	Blue Care Network (Detroit)	800-662-6667	2190	5130	5530	3340	7760	8090
K51-3	Blue Care Network (Flint/Sag)	800-662-6667	4270	9910	10600	6460	14930	15690
521-3	Health Alliance-Hi (Det/Flint/Sag)	800-556-9765	2590	6050	6530	3970	9210	9600
GY4-6	Health Alliance-Std (Det/Flint/Sag)	800-556-9765	2460	5010	5480	3650	7570	7810
LE1-3	Priority Health-Hi (Lower Peninsula)	800-446-5674	3530	7470	8130	5360	11280	11950
LE4-6	Priority Health-Std (Lower Peninsula)	800-446-5674	2680	5250	5770	4010	7990	8250
Minnesota								
H41-3	Aetna HealthFund CDHP	888-238-6240	2880	6780	6670	4760	11100	10500
H44-6	Aetna Value Plan	888-238-6240	2300	4700	5070	3520	7270	7340
V31-3	HealthPartners-Hi	800-883-2177	3070	6730	7860	4740	10400	11700
V34-6	HealthPartners-Std	952-883-5000	2380	4750	5280	3500	7040	7350
Missouri								
G51-3	Aetna HealthFund CDHP	888-238-6240	2300	5460	5350	3890	9120	8530
HA1-3	Aetna Open Access-Hi (Kansas City)	800-537-9384	3340	8060	8010	4940	11890	11300
HA4-6	Aetna Open Access-Std (Kansas City)	800-537-9384	2910	6360	6750	4290	9300	9260
G54-6	Aetna Value Plan	888-238-6240	2250	4570	4940	3440	7080	7160
9G1-3	Blue Preferred-Hi POS (St L/Other)	888-811-2092	2870	5220	5610	4370	7990	8210
9G4-6	Blue Preferred-Std (St L/Other)	888-811-2092	2190	4760	5480	3350	7340	7980
PH1-3	Humana CoverageFirst CDHP (KS City)	800-448-6262	**1790**	4360	4830	3150	7070	7240
MS1-3	Humana Health-Hi (Kansas City)	800-448-6262	10020	21240	22270	15080	32020	33170
MS4-6	Humana Health-Std (Kansas City)	800-448-6262	4170	8570	9050	6350	13100	13350
PH4-6	Humana Value Plan (Kansas City)	800-448-6262	2530	4960	5440	3740	7500	7630
Mississippi								
H41-3	Aetna HealthFund CDHP	888-238-6240	2880	6780	6670	4760	11100	10500
UB1-3	Aetna Open Access (Memphis)	800-537-9384	5190	14230	14110	7860	21500	21020
H44-6	Aetna Value Plan	888-238-6240	2300	4700	5070	3520	7270	7340
LS1-3	UnitedHealthcare HDHP	877-835-9861	**1680**	**3630**	**4350**	**2820**	**6110**	**6570**

Lowest costs are in **bold** type. Note that in some plans, family costs are lower than self-plus-one costs.

Avg. yearly cost (cont'd)			Medicare wrap-around	Day limit in skilled nursing facility	Pays for...					Accreditation
Annuitants 65 or older with Medicare Parts A & B					Routine dental	Chiro-practic	Acupuncture	Hearing aids	Adult vision care	
Self only	Self plus one	Family								
5650	12630	12040	No	60	Some	Yes	Little	No	Exam	Yes
5350	10870	10950	No	60	No	Yes	Little	No	Exam	Yes
5160	11240	11570	No	Unlim	No	Some	No	Yes	Yes	Yes
8280	18420	19180	No	Unlim	No	Some	No	Yes	Yes	Yes
5920	12930	13320	Yes	Unlim	No	No	No	Yes	Exam	No
5500	11270	11510	Yes	100	No	No	No	Yes	Exam	No
6710	13960	14630	Yes	45	No	Yes	No	No	Exam	Yes
4820	9390	9660	Yes	45	No	Yes	No	No	Exam	Yes
6520	14610	14010	No	60	Some	Yes	Little	No	Exam	Yes
5430	11060	11130	No	60	No	Yes	Little	No	Exam	Yes
5860	12450	13750	Yes	120	Some	Yes	Yes	Some	No	Yes
5360	10580	10890	No	120	No	Yes	Yes	No	No	Yes
5650	12630	12040	No	60	Some	Yes	Little	No	Exam	Yes
6750	15690	15100	No	60	Yes	Yes	No	Yes	Exam	Yes
6190	13200	13150	No	60	Yes	Yes	No	Yes	Exam	Yes
5350	10870	10950	No	60	No	Yes	Little	No	Exam	Yes
6360	11790	12010	No	60	No	Some	No	No	Exam	No
5380	11240	11880	Yes	90	No	Some	No	No	Exam	No
3530	**7800**	**7970**	Yes	60	No	Some	Some	No	No	No
16300	34150	35300	Yes	100	No	Yes	Some	No	Exam	Yes
7300	14800	15050	Yes	100	No	Some	Some	No	Exam	Yes
4060	**7780**	**7910**	Yes	100	No	Yes	Some	No	No	No
6520	14610	14010	No	60	Some	Yes	Little	No	Exam	Yes
9780	25210	24730	No	60	Yes	Yes	Some	No	Yes	Yes
5430	11060	11130	No	60	No	Yes	Little	No	Exam	Yes
4800	10010	10470	No	60	Some	Yes	Some	Yes	Exam	Yes

Cost & Special Features of All Plans			Average yearly cost in dollars (premiums and out-of-pocket expense)					
			General Schedule			Annuitants 55 to 64		
Plan code	Plan name (primary service area)	Phone number	Self only	Self plus one	Family	Self only	Self plus one	Family of two
Montana								
H41-3	Aetna HealthFund CDHP	888-238-6240	2880	6780	6670	4760	11100	10500
H44-6	Aetna Value Plan	888-238-6240	2300	4700	5070	3520	7270	7340
Nebraska								
H41-3	Aetna HealthFund CDHP	888-238-6240	2880	6780	6670	4760	11100	10500
H44-6	Aetna Value Plan	888-238-6240	2300	4700	5070	3520	7270	7340
Nevada								
G51-3	Aetna HealthFund CDHP	888-238-6240	2300	5460	5350	3890	9120	8530
G54-6	Aetna Value Plan	888-238-6240	2250	4570	4940	3440	7080	7160
NM1-3	Health Plan of Nevada (Las Vegas)	877-545-7378	2010	**3700**	4460	3040	**5630**	**6490**
LU1-3	UnitedHealthcare HDHP	877-835-9861	**1770**	3820	4570	**2960**	6400	6910
New Hampshire								
EP1-3	Aetna HealthFund CDHP	888-238-6240	3480	8140	8060	5670	13140	12580
EP4-6	Aetna Value Plan	888-238-6240	2280	4650	5020	3490	7190	7260
New Jersey								
EP1-3	Aetna HealthFund CDHP	888-238-6240	3480	8420	8060	5670	13140	12580
JR4-6	Aetna Open Access Basic (Northern)	800-537-9384	6230	14490	14170	9480	21600	21130
P34-6	Aetna Open Access Basic (Phil)	800-537-9384	7710	17910	17620	11700	26730	26310
JR1-3	Aetna Open Access-Hi (Northern)	800-537-9384	8350	19560	19300	12590	29180	28780
P31-3	Aetna Open Access-Hi (Philadelphia)	800-537-9384	9380	23340	23110	14130	34840	34500
EP4-6	Aetna Value Plan	888-238-6240	2280	4970	5020	3490	7190	7260
801-3	GHI Health-Hi POS (NY State/N NJ)	212-501-4444	5020	13050	14810	7640	19460	22090
804-6	GHI Health-Std (NY State/N NJ)	212-501-4444	2720	6900	9840	4200	10210	14620
New Mexico								
G51-3	Aetna HealthFund CDHP	888-238-6240	2300	5460	5350	3890	9120	8530
G54-6	Aetna Value Plan	888-238-6240	2250	4570	4940	3440	7080	7160
P21-3	Presbyterian-Hi (NM/El Paso)	800-356-2219	3160	7130	7320	4820	10830	10780
PS4-6	Presbyterian-Std (NM/El Paso)	800-356-2219	2800	5830	6020	4150	8780	8610

Lowest costs are in **bold** type. Note that in some plans, family costs are lower than self-plus-one costs.

| Avg. yearly cost (cont'd) | | | | | Pays for... | | | | | |
| Annuitants 65 or older with Medicare Parts A & B | | | Medicare wrap-around | Day limit in skilled nursing facility | Routine dental | Chiro-practic | Acupuncture | Hearing aids | Adult vision care | Accreditation |
Self only	Self plus one	Family								
6520	14610	14010	No	60	Some	Yes	Little	No	Exam	Yes
5430	11060	11130	No	60	No	Yes	Little	No	Exam	Yes
6520	14610	14010	No	60	Some	Yes	Little	No	Exam	Yes
5430	11060	11130	No	60	No	Yes	Little	No	Exam	Yes
5650	12630	12040	No	60	Some	Yes	Little	No	Exam	Yes
5350	10870	10950	No	60	No	Yes	Little	No	Exam	Yes
4500	**8350**	9200	Yes	Unlim	No	Yes	No	Yes	Exam	Yes
4940	10290	10800	No	60	Some	Yes	Some	Yes	Exam	Yes
7430	16640	16090	No	60	Some	Yes	Little	No	Exam	Yes
5400	10980	11050	No	60	No	Yes	Little	No	Exam	Yes
7430	16640	16090	No	60	Some	Yes	Little	No	Exam	Yes
11090	25020	24540	No	60	Yes	Yes	Little	No	Yes	Yes
13300	30140	29720	No	60	Yes	Yes	Little	No	Yes	Yes
14480	32800	32400	No	60	Yes	Yes	Little	No	Yes	Yes
16020	38460	38120	No	60	Yes	Yes	Little	No	Yes	Yes
5400	10980	11050	No	60	No	Yes	Little	No	Exam	Yes
8960	22040	24670	Yes	30	Some	Yes	Yes	Yes	Yes	Yes
5320	12380	16780	Yes	30	Some	Some	Yes	Yes	Yes	Yes
5650	12630	12040	No	60	Some	Yes	Little	No	Exam	Yes
5350	10870	10950	No	60	No	Yes	Little	No	Exam	Yes
6040	13230	13180	Yes	60	No	Some	Some	No	Child Exam	Yes
5210	11010	10830	Yes	60	No	Some	Some	No	Child Exam	Yes

Cost & Special Features of All Plans			Average yearly cost in dollars (premiums and out-of-pocket expense)					
			General Schedule			Annuitants 55 to 64		
Plan code	Plan name (primary service area)	Phone number	Self only	Self plus one	Family	Self only	Self plus one	Family of two
New York								
EP1-3	Aetna HealthFund CDHP	888-238-6240	3480	8420	8060	5670	13140	12580
JC4-6	Aetna Open Access Basic (NYC/Upst)	800-537-9384	4000	10210	9850	6130	15190	14650
JC1-3	Aetna Open Access-Hi (NYC/Upst)	800-537-9384	6120	15940	15640	9240	23750	23290
EP4-6	Aetna Value Plan	888-238-6240	2280	4970	5020	3490	7190	7260
SG1-3	CDPHP-Hi (Alb/Sch) student POS	877-269-2134	3440	6240	12160	5210	9100	17970
SG4-6	CDPHP-Std (Alb/Sch) student POS	877-269-2134	2280	4580	7090	3470	6600	10370
801-3	GHI Health-Hi POS (NY State/N NJ)	212-501-4444	5020	13050	14810	7640	19460	22090
804-6	GHI Health-Std (NY State/N NJ)	212-501-4444	2720	6900	9840	4200	10210	14620
511-3	HIP HMO (NYC/Southeast)	800-447-8255	3230	4790	10220	4890	6940	15080
QA4-6	Independent Health HDHP (Buffalo)	800-501-3439	**1770**	4350	4540	3130	6810	7090
QA1-3	Independent Health-Hi POS (Buffalo)	800-501-3439	2800	8140	8470	4290	12000	12480
C54-6	Independent Health-Std POS (Buff)	800-501-3439	2630	7700	7980	4050	11330	11760
M91-3	MVP-Hi (Bing/Syr/Utica) std't POS	888-687-6277	3790	8990	9490	5720	13220	13960
GA1-3	MVP-Hi (East-Schen/Troy) std't POS	888-687-6277	4120	9760	10300	6210	14360	15180
MX1-3	MVP-Hi (Hudson) std't POS	888-687-6277	5650	13280	14050	8510	19640	20800
MF1-3	MVP-Hi (Plattsburgh) std't POS	888-687-6277	5420	12760	13500	8170	18860	19970
GV1-3	MVP-Hi (Roch) std't POS	888-687-6277	3300	7870	8290	4980	11530	12170
M94-6	MVP-Std (Bing/Syr/Utica) std't POS	888-687-6277	3080	7300	7610	4600	10520	10990
GA4-6	MVP-Std (East-Schen/Troy) std't POS	888-687-6277	3460	8170	8540	5170	11830	12390
MX4-6	MVP-Std (Hudson) std't POS	888-687-6277	4240	9980	10470	6350	14540	15270
MF4-6	MVP-Std (Plattsburgh) std't POS	888-687-6277	5190	12150	12780	7760	17790	18740
GV4-6	MVP-Std (Roch) std't POS	888-687-6277	3080	7300	7620	4610	10530	11000
North Carolina								
F51-3	Aetna HealthFund CDHP	888-238-6240	2740	6460	6360	4560	10620	10040
F54-6	Aetna Value Plan	888-238-6240	2310	4720	5100	3540	7310	7390
LS1-3	UnitedHealthcare HDHP	877-835-9861	**1680**	**3630**	**4350**	**2820**	**6110**	**6570**
North Dakota								
H41-3	Aetna HealthFund CDHP	888-238-6240	2880	6780	6670	4760	11100	10500
H44-6	Aetna Value Plan	888-238-6240	2300	4700	5070	3520	7270	7340

Lowest costs are in **bold** type. Note that in some plans, family costs are lower than self-plus-one costs.

Annuitants 65 or older with Medicare Parts A & B			Medicare wrap-around	Day limit in skilled nursing facility	Pays for...					Accreditation
Self only	Self plus one	Family			Routine dental	Chiro-practic	Acupuncture	Hearing aids	Adult vision care	
7430	16640	16090	No	60	Some	Yes	Little	No	Exam	Yes
7740	18600	18060	No	60	Yes	Yes	Little	No	Yes	Yes
11130	27370	26910	No	60	Yes	Yes	Little	No	Yes	Yes
5400	10980	11050	No	60	No	Yes	Little	No	Exam	Yes
7170	12820	21700	No	90	No	Yes	Some	Some	Exam	Yes
5420	10390	14160	No	90	No	Yes	Some	Some	Exam	Yes
8960	22040	24670	Yes	30	Some	Yes	Yes	Yes	Yes	Yes
5320	12380	16780	Yes	30	Some	Some	Yes	Yes	Yes	Yes
6770	10510	18650	Yes	Unlim	Yes	Yes	No	Yes	Exam	Yes
5240	10880	11160	No	45	Some	Yes	No	No	Some	Yes
6330	15870	16350	No	45	No	Yes	No	No	Some	Yes
6140	15300	15720	No	30	No	Yes	No	No	Some	Yes
7660	16920	17670	No	60	Some	Yes	Some	No	Exam	Yes
8160	18070	18880	No	60	Some	Yes	Some	No	Exam	Yes
10450	23350	24510	No	60	Some	Yes	Some	No	Exam	Yes
10110	22570	23670	No	60	Some	Yes	Some	No	Exam	Yes
6930	15240	15870	No	60	Some	Yes	Some	No	Exam	Yes
6670	14480	14950	No	60	Some	Yes	Some	No	Exam	Yes
7240	15790	16350	No	60	Some	Yes	Some	No	Exam	Yes
8420	18500	19230	No	60	Some	Yes	Some	No	Exam	Yes
9830	21750	22700	No	60	Some	Yes	Some	No	Exam	Yes
6680	14490	14960	No	60	Some	Yes	Some	No	Exam	Yes
6320	14130	13550	No	60	Some	Yes	Little	No	Exam	Yes
5450	11100	11170	No	60	No	Yes	Little	No	Exam	Yes
4800	10010	10470	No	60	Some	Yes	Some	Yes	Exam	Yes
6520	14610	14010	No	60	Some	Yes	Little	No	Exam	Yes
5430	11060	11130	No	60	No	Yes	Little	No	Exam	Yes

Cost & Special Features of All Plans			Average yearly cost in dollars (premiums and out-of-pocket expense)					
			General Schedule			Annuitants 55 to 64		
Plan code	Plan name (primary service area)	Phone number	Self only	Self plus one	Family	Self only	Self plus one	Family of two
V31-3	HealthPartners-Hi	800-883-2177	3070	6730	7860	4740	10400	11700
V34-6	HealthPartners-Std	952-883-5000	2380	4750	5280	3500	7040	7350
Ohio								
JS1-3	Aetna HealthFund CDHP	888-238-6240	4640	11020	10680	7400	17030	16520
JS4-6	Aetna Value Plan	888-238-6240	3290	7740	7350	5010	11350	10760
3A4-6	AultCare HDHP (Canton)	330-363-6360	**1410**	**2990**	**4380**	**2500**	**5340**	6760
3A1-3	AultCare-Hi (Canton)	330-363-6360	2650	5120	6950	4020	7770	10300
A61-3	Humana Health-Hi (Cincinnati)	800-448-6262	5420	11360	11930	8180	17210	17670
A64-6	Humana Health-Std (Cincinnati)	800-448-6262	3910	8020	8470	5940	12280	12490
UX1-3	Medical Mutual Basic (Cleve/Akron)	800-315-3144	2900	5790	6420	4270	8710	9070
641-3	Medical Mutual-Hi (Cleve/Akron)	800-315-3144	4170	9060	10200	6280	13670	15060
644-6	Medical Mutual-St (Cleve/Akron)	800-315-3144	3170	5620	6360	4800	8230	9260
Oklahoma								
JS1-3	Aetna HealthFund CDHP	888-238-6240	4640	11020	10680	7400	17030	16520
JS4-6	Aetna Value Plan	888-238-6240	3290	7740	7350	5010	11350	10760
IM1-3	GlobalHealth-Hi (Statewide)	877-280-2989	2020	**3780**	4560	3090	**5780**	6630
IM4-6	GlobalHealth-Std (Statewide)	877-280-2989	2320	4300	5110	3480	6470	7260
Oregon								
H41-3	Aetna HealthFund CDHP	888-238-6240	2880	6780	6670	4760	11100	10500
H44-6	Aetna Value Plan	888-238-6240	2300	4700	5070	3520	7270	7340
571-3	Kaiser Northwest-Hi (std't POS)	800-813-2000	2430	5500	5190	3700	8400	7600
574-6	Kaiser Northwest-Std (std't POS)	800-813-2000	2320	4790	5060	3470	7260	7260
LU1-3	UnitedHealthcare HDHP	877-835-9861	**1770**	**3820**	4570	**2960**	6400	6910
Panama Canal								
431-3	Panama Canal	800-424-8196	**1790**	**3360**	**3600**	**2710**	**5050**	**5210**
Pennsylvania								
H41-3	Aetna HealthFund CDHP	888-238-6240	2880	6780	6670	4760	11100	10500
P34-6	Aetna Open Access Basic (Phil)	800-537-9384	7710	17690	17620	11700	26730	26310
P31-3	Aetna Open Access-Hi (Philadelphia)	800-537-9384	9380	23130	23110	14130	34840	34500
H44-6	Aetna Value Plan	888-238-6240	2300	4700	5070	3520	7270	7340

Lowest costs are in **bold** type. Note that in some plans, family costs are lower than self-plus-one costs.

| Avg. yearly cost (cont'd) | | | Medicare wrap-around | Day limit in skilled nursing facility | Pays for... | | | | | Accreditation |
| Annuitants 65 or older with Medicare Parts A & B | | | | | Routine dental | Chiropractic | Acupuncture | Hearing aids | Adult vision care | |
Self only	Self plus one	Family								
5860	12450	13750	Yes	120	Some	Yes	Yes	Some	No	Yes
5360	10580	10890	No	120	No	Yes	Yes	No	No	Yes
9160	20540	20030	No	60	Some	Yes	Little	No	Exam	Yes
6910	15130	14550	No	60	No	Yes	Little	No	Exam	Yes
4500	9160	10590	Yes	Unlim	No	Yes	No	Some	Yes	Yes
5360	10480	13010	Yes	Unlim	Yes	Yes	No	Some	Yes	Yes
9370	19260	19720	Yes	100	No	Some	Some	No	Exam	Yes
6870	13880	14090	Yes	100	No	Some	Some	No	Exam	Yes
6210	12510	12860	No	100	No	No	No	No	Exam	Yes
8170	17340	18740	No	100	No	Yes	No	No	Exam	Yes
6800	11490	12530	No	100	No	No	No	No	Exam	Yes
9160	20540	20030	No	60	Some	Yes	Little	No	Exam	Yes
6910	15130	14550	No	60	No	Yes	Little	No	Exam	Yes
5040	9510	10360	No	Unlim	No	Yes	No	No	Exam	Yes
5520	10360	11150	No	Unlim	No	Some	No	No	Exam	Yes
6520	14610	14010	No	60	Some	Yes	Little	No	Exam	Yes
5430	11060	11130	No	60	No	Yes	Little	No	Exam	Yes
4420	10240	9450	Yes	100	No	Some	Some	No	Yes	Yes
4000	8630	8630	Yes	100	No	Some	Yes	No	Yes	Yes
4940	10290	10800	No	60	Some	Yes	Some	Yes	Exam	Yes
4410	**8350**	**8510**	Yes	60	Yes	Yes	Yes	Some	No	Yes
6520	14610	14010	No	60	Some	Yes	Little	No	Exam	Yes
13300	30140	29720	No	60	Yes	Yes	Little	No	Yes	Yes
16020	38460	38120	No	60	Yes	Yes	Little	No	Yes	Yes
5430	11060	11130	No	60	No	Yes	Little	No	Exam	Yes

Cost & Special Features of All Plans			Average yearly cost in dollars (premiums and out-of-pocket expense)					
			General Schedule			Annuitants 55 to 64		
Plan code	Plan name (primary service area)	Phone number	Self only	Self plus one	Family	Self only	Self plus one	Family of two
GG4-6	Geisinger-Std (Harr/York/Lanc/N'th)	800-447-4000	2970	6090	6610	4380	9150	9410
NP1-3	Highmark (Western)	866-283-4995	2470	4290	5230	3750	6560	7650
V41-3	UnitedHealthcare HDHP	877-835-9861	1940	4190	4990	3210	6940	7540
8W4-6	UPMC HDHP (Western)	888-876-2756	**1790**	**3710**	**4230**	3190	6620	6760
8W1-3	UPMC-Hi (Western)	877-648-9641	4180	9320	9790	6250	14090	14330
UW4-6	UPMC-Std (Western)	877-648-9641	2640	5390	5870	3970	8260	8450
Puerto Rico								
ZJ1-3	Humana Health POS	800-314-3121	**1100**	**2210**	**2380**	**1680**	**3360**	**3470**
891-3	Triple-S Salud POS	800-981-3241	**1210**	**2540**	**2690**	**1890**	**3890**	**3940**
Rhode Island								
EP1-3	Aetna HealthFund CDHP	888-238-6240	3480	8140	8060	5670	13140	12580
EP4-6	Aetna Value Plan	888-238-6240	2280	4650	5020	3490	7190	7260
South Carolina								
JS1-3	Aetna HealthFund CDHP	888-238-6240	4640	11020	10680	7400	17030	16520
JS4-6	Aetna Value Plan	888-238-6240	3290	7740	7350	5010	11350	10760
South Dakota								
G51-3	Aetna HealthFund CDHP	888-238-6240	2300	5460	5350	3890	9120	8530
G54-6	Aetna Value Plan	888-238-6240	2250	4570	4940	3440	7080	7160
V31-3	HealthPartners-Hi	800-883-2177	3070	6730	7860	4740	10400	11700
V34-6	HealthPartners-Std	952-883-5000	2380	4750	5280	3500	7040	7350
Tennessee								
F51-3	Aetna HealthFund CDHP	888-238-6240	2740	6750	6360	4560	10620	10040
UB1-3	Aetna Open Access (Memphis)	800-537-9384	5190	14430	14110	7860	21500	21020
F54-6	Aetna Value Plan	888-238-6240	2310	5040	5100	3540	7310	7390
TT1-3	Humana CoverageFirst CDHP (Knox)	800-448-6262	1910	4980	5110	3340	7470	7660
TC1-3	Humana CoverageFirst CDHP (Lou)	800-448-6262	1840	4830	4950	3230	7230	7420
GJ1-3	Humana Health-Hi (Knoxville)	800-448-6262	3910	8370	8520	5920	12320	12560
GJ4-6	Humana Health-Std (Knoxville)	800-448-6262	3460	7340	7430	5270	10790	10930
TT4-6	Humana Value Plan (Knoxville)	800-448-6262	2720	5780	5880	4030	8130	8280
LS1-3	UnitedHealthcare HDHP	877-835-9861	**1680**	4040	**4350**	**2820**	**6110**	**6570**

Lowest costs are in **bold** type. Note that in some plans, family costs are lower than self-plus-one costs.

Annuitants 65 or older with Medicare Parts A & B			Medicare wrap-around	Day limit in skilled nursing facility	Pays for...					Accreditation
Self only	Self plus one	Family			Routine dental	Chiro-practic	Acupuncture	Hearing aids	Adult vision care	
5340	10560	10820	Yes	60	No	Some	No	No	Exam	Yes
4940	8850	9940	Yes	100	No	Some	No	Yes	Exam	No
5190	10840	11430	No	60	Some	Yes	Some	Yes	Exam	Yes
5110	10410	10540	No	100	Yes	Yes	Some	Yes	Exam	Yes
8140	17800	18040	No	100	Yes	Yes	Some	Some	Exam	Yes
5080	10230	10410	Some	100	Yes	Yes	Some	Some	Exam	Yes
3320	**6580**	**6690**	Yes	60	Yes	Some	No	No	Exam	No
3460	**6990**	**7040**	Yes	Unlim	Yes	Yes	No	Some	Yes	No
7430	16640	16090	No	60	Some	Yes	Little	No	Exam	Yes
5400	10980	11050	No	60	No	Yes	Little	No	Exam	Yes
9160	20540	20030	No	60	Some	Yes	Little	No	Exam	Yes
6910	15130	14550	No	60	No	Yes	Little	No	Exam	Yes
5650	12630	12040	No	60	Some	Yes	Little	No	Exam	Yes
5350	10870	10950	No	60	No	Yes	Little	No	Exam	Yes
5860	12450	13750	Yes	120	Some	Yes	Yes	Some	No	Yes
5360	10580	10890	No	120	No	Yes	Yes	No	No	Yes
6320	14130	13550	No	60	Some	Yes	Little	No	Exam	Yes
9780	25210	24730	No	60	Yes	Yes	Some	No	Yes	Yes
5450	11100	11170	No	60	No	Yes	Little	No	Exam	Yes
3710	**8200**	**8390**	Yes	60	No	Some	Some	No	No	No
3610	**7970**	**8150**	Yes	60	No	Some	Some	No	No	No
7140	14460	14690	Yes	100	No	Yes	Some	No	Exam	Yes
6220	12490	12630	Yes	100	No	Some	Some	No	Exam	Yes
4350	8410	**8560**	Yes	100	No	Yes	Some	No	No	No
4800	10010	10470	No	60	Some	Yes	Some	Yes	Exam	Yes

Cost & Special Features of All Plans			Average yearly cost in dollars (premiums and out-of-pocket expense)					
			General Schedule			Annuitants 55 to 64		
Plan code	Plan name (primary service area)	Phone number	Self only	Self plus one	Family	Self only	Self plus one	Family of two
Texas								
JS1-3	Aetna HealthFund CDHP	888-238-6240	4640	11020	10680	7400	17030	16520
JS4-6	Aetna Value Plan	888-238-6240	3290	7740	7350	5010	11350	10760
TV1-3	Humana CoverageFirst CDHP (Austin)	800-448-6262	1990	5180	5230	3450	7760	7840
TP1-3	Humana CoverageFirst CDHP (C Ch)	800-448-6262	1820	4770	4890	3190	7150	7330
T31-3	Humana CoverageFirst CDHP (H'ton)	800-448-6262	1900	4960	5090	3330	7430	7620
TU1-3	Humana CoverageFirst CDHP (S Ant)	800-448-6262	1910	4980	5110	3340	7460	7650
QY1-3	Humana Health Basic (Austin)	800-448-6262	2360	5060	5180	3640	7400	7580
Q21-3	Humana Health Basic (Corpus Christi)	800-448-6262	2280	4760	4870	3510	6940	7110
Q61-3	Humana Health Basic (Houston)	800-448-6262	2270	4750	4860	3500	6920	7090
QX1-3	Humana Health Basic (San Antonio)	800-448-6262	2320	4850	4970	3570	7080	7250
UU1-3	Humana Health-Hi (Austin)	800-448-6262	8650	18540	19170	13030	27590	28540
UC1-3	Humana Health-Hi (Corpus Christi)	800-448-6262	4460	9520	9740	6750	14070	14390
EW1-3	Humana Health-Hi (Houston)	800-448-6262	4420	9450	9660	6690	13960	14280
UR1-3	Humana Health-Hi (San Antonio)	800-448-6262	7990	17130	17690	12050	25470	26320
UU4-6	Humana Health-Std (Austin)	888-393-6765	6660	14230	14650	10090	21130	21760
UC4-6	Humana Health-Std (Corpus Christi)	888-393-6765	3130	6630	6700	4790	9740	9840
EW4-6	Humana Health-Std (Houston)	888-393-6765	3110	6570	6640	4750	9660	9750
UR4-6	Humana Health-Std (San Antonio)	888-393-6765	4280	9090	9270	6510	13430	13700
T34-6	Humana Value Plan (Austin)	800-448-6262	2650	5630	5730	3930	7910	8060
TV4-6	Humana Value Plan (Austin)	800-448-6262	2770	5880	5990	4110	8280	8440
TP4-6	Humana Value Plan (Corpus Christi)	800-448-6262	2530	5360	5440	3740	7500	7630
TU4-6	Humana Value Plan (San Antonio)	800-448-6262	2700	5740	5840	4010	8070	8220
P21-3	Presbyterian-Hi (NM/El Paso)	800-356-2219	3160	7360	7320	4820	10830	10780
PS4-6	Presbyterian-Std (NM/El Paso)	800-356-2219	2800	6140	6020	4150	8780	8610
A81-3	Scott & White Basic (Austin/Central)	800-321-7947	2860	6120	6860	4310	8620	9740
P81-3	Scott & White Basic (Dallas/Ft W)	800-321-7947	3480	6600	8340	5240	9360	11960
A84-6	Scott & White-Std (Austin/Central)	800-321-7947	3350	5890	7750	5090	8620	11420
P84-6	Scott & White-Std (Dallas/Ft W)	800-321-7947	4090	7360	9510	6210	10830	14050
L91-3	UnitedHealthcare Choice Plus (S Ant)	877-835-9861	2030	4300	5090	**2930**	**5950**	7140

Lowest costs are in **bold** type. Note that in some plans, family costs are lower than self-plus-one costs.

| Avg. yearly cost (cont'd) | | | Medicare wrap-around | Day limit in skilled nursing facility | Pays for... | | | | | Accreditation |
| Annuitants 65 or older with Medicare Parts A & B | | | | | Routine dental | Chiro-practic | Acupuncture | Hearing aids | Adult vision care | |
Self only	Self plus one	Family								
9160	20540	20030	No	60	Some	Yes	Little	No	Exam	Yes
6910	15130	14550	No	60	No	Yes	Little	No	Exam	Yes
3830	8490	**8570**	Yes	60	No	Some	Some	No	No	No
3570	7890	**8060**	Yes	60	No	Some	Some	No	No	No
3700	8170	**8360**	Yes	60	No	Some	Some	No	No	No
3710	8190	**8380**	Yes	60	No	Some	Some	No	No	No
4550	8840	9010	Yes	100	No	Some	Some	No	Yes	Yes
4500	8740	8910	Yes	100	No	Some	Some	No	Yes	Yes
4490	8720	8890	Yes	100	No	Some	Some	No	Yes	Yes
4560	8870	9050	Yes	100	No	Some	Some	No	Yes	Yes
14280	29800	30750	Yes	100	No	Some	Some	No	Some	Yes
7990	16280	16600	Yes	100	No	Some	Some	No	Some	Yes
7940	16170	16490	Yes	100	No	Some	Some	No	Some	Yes
13290	27680	28530	Yes	100	No	Some	Some	No	Some	Yes
11080	22930	23560	Yes	100	No	Some	Some	No	Some	Yes
5780	11540	11640	Yes	100	No	Some	Some	No	Some	Yes
5740	11460	11550	Yes	100	No	Some	Some	No	Some	Yes
7500	15230	15500	Yes	100	No	Some	Some	No	Some	Yes
4250	**8190**	**8340**	Yes	100	No	Yes	Some	No	No	No
4420	8560	8720	Yes	100	No	Yes	Some	No	No	No
4060	**7780**	**7910**	Yes	100	No	Yes	Some	No	No	No
4320	**8350**	**8500**	Yes	100	No	Yes	Some	No	No	No
6040	13230	13180	Yes	60	No	Some	Some	No	Child Exam	Yes
5210	11010	10830	Yes	60	No	Some	Some	No	Child Exam	Yes
5960	11560	12670	Yes	Unlim	No	No	Little	No	Exam	Yes
6890	12290	14900	Yes	Unlim	No	No	Little	No	Exam	Yes
6390	11070	13870	Yes	Unlim	No	No	Little	No	Exam	Yes
7520	13270	16500	Yes	Unlim	No	No	Little	No	Exam	Yes
4770	9460	10650	No	60	Some	Some	Some	No	Exam	Yes

Cost & Special Features of All Plans			Average yearly cost in dollars (premiums and out-of-pocket expense)					
			General Schedule			Annuitants 55 to 64		
Plan code	Plan name (primary service area)	Phone number	Self only	Self plus one	Family	Self only	Self plus one	Family of two
Utah								
G51-3	Aetna HealthFund CDHP	888-238-6240	2300	5460	5350	3890	9120	8530
G54-6	Aetna Value Plan	888-238-6240	2250	4570	4940	3440	7080	7160
9K1-3	Aetna Health/Altius-Hi	800-537-9384	3500	7580	7390	5320	11550	10980
DK4-6	Aetna Health/Altius-Std	800-537-9384	2200	4320	4590	3360	6610	6650
9K4-6	Aetna Health/Altius HDHP	800-537-9384	**1750**	**3330**	**3690**	**2840**	**5420**	**5470**
SF1-3	SelectHealth-Hi student POS	844-345-3342	4520	10380	10030	6880	15750	14960
SF4-6	SelectHealth-Std student POS	844-345-3342	2120	4160	**4390**	3300	6460	**6460**
Vermont								
EP1-3	Aetna HealthFund CDHP	888-238-6240	3480	8140	8060	5670	13140	12580
EP4-6	Aetna Value Plan	888-238-6240	2280	4650	5020	3490	7190	7260
Virgin Islands								
851-3	Triple-S Salud POS	800-981-3241	**1650**	**3530**	**3700**	**2550**	**5370**	**5460**
Virginia								
F51-3	Aetna HealthFund CDHP	888-238-6240	2740	6460	6360	4560	10620	10040
JN4-6	Aetna Open Access Basic	800-537-9384	2120	4720	4720	3290	6480	6940
JN1-3	Aetna Open Access-Hi	800-537-9384	5480	12270	12100	8300	18550	18050
F54-6	Aetna Value Plan	888-238-6240	2310	4200	5100	3540	7310	7390
B61-3	CareFirst HDHP	888-789-9065	1870	6870	**4440**	**2950**	**5910**	**6600**
2G1-3	CareFirst-Hi	888-789-9065	3770	4040	9100	5520	10170	13230
2G4-6	CareFirst-Std POS	888-789-9065	2300	**3730**	5550	3350	**5970**	8030
T71-3	Kaiser-Basic	877-574-3337	1820	4380	**4160**	**2780**	**5770**	**6060**
E31-3	Kaiser-Hi	877-574-3337	**1720**	**3470**	3970	**2640**	6710	**5920**
E34-6	Kaiser-Std	877-574-3337	**1630**	**3710**	3660	**2530**	**5430**	**5430**
JP1-3	MD-IPA	877-835-9861	2580	4250	8720	3960	6570	12950
PG1-3	Optima Health (Hampton Roads)	800-206-1060	2970	6940	6750	4420	10480	9680
LR1-3	UnitedHealthcare Choice	877-835-9861	2140	4280	5030	3290	6610	7370
L91-3	UnitedHealthcare Choice Plus	877-835-9861	2030	**4030**	5090	**2930**	**5950**	7140
V41-3	UnitedHealthcare HDHP	877-835-9861	1940	4190	4990	3210	6940	7540

Lowest costs are in **bold** type. Note that in some plans, family costs are lower than self-plus-one costs.

| Avg. yearly cost (cont'd) | | | Medicare wrap-around | Day limit in skilled nursing facility | Pays for... | | | | | Accreditation |
| Annuitants 65 or older with Medicare Parts A & B | | | | | Routine dental | Chiro-practic | Acupunc-ture | Hearing aids | Adult vision care | |
Self only	Self plus one	Family								
5650	12630	12040	No	60	Some	Yes	Little	No	Exam	Yes
5350	10870	10950	No	60	No	Yes	Little	No	Exam	Yes
6510	13860	13290	Yes	30	Yes	Some	No	Yes	Exam	Yes
4580	9000	9040	Yes	30	No	Some	No	Yes	Exam	Yes
4350	8500	**8550**	Yes	30	No	Some	No	Yes	Exam	Yes
8780	19380	18590	No	30	No	Yes	No	Yes	Exam	Yes
5070	10020	10020	No	30	No	Some	No	Yes	Exam	Yes
7430	16640	16090	No	60	Some	Yes	Little	No	Exam	Yes
5400	10980	11050	No	60	No	Yes	Little	No	Exam	Yes
4120	8470	**8560**	Yes	Unlim	Yes	Yes	No	Some	Yes	No
6320	14130	13550	No	60	Some	Yes	Little	No	Exam	Yes
5240	10220	10680	No	60	Yes	Some	Little	Some	Yes	Yes
10180	22160	21660	No	60	Yes	Some	Little	Some	Yes	Yes
5450	11100	11170	No	60	No	Yes	Little	No	Exam	Yes
3410	**6600**	**7290**	Yes	Unlim	Yes	Some	Some	Yes	Exam	Yes
6550	12050	15120	Yes	Unlim	Yes	Some	Some	Yes	Exam	Yes
4390	**7940**	9990	Yes	Unlim	Yes	Some	Some	Yes	Exam	Yes
4520	8910	9200	No	100	No	Some	Some	No	Exam	Yes
4140	9630	8830	No	100	Yes	Yes	Yes	No	Exam	Yes
4060	**8290**	**8290**	No	100	Yes	Some	Some	No	Exam	Yes
5260	9120	15510	Yes	60	Yes	Some	Some	No	Yes	Yes
5300	12390	11590	Yes	100	No	No	No	No	Exam	No
5150	10120	10870	No	60	Some	Some	Some	No	Exam	Yes
4770	9460	10650	No	60	Some	Some	Some	No	Exam	Yes
5190	10840	11430	No	60	Some	Yes	Some	Yes	Exam	Yes

Cost & Special Features of All Plans			Average yearly cost in dollars (premiums and out-of-pocket expense)					
			General Schedule			Annuitants 55 to 64		
Plan code	Plan name (primary service area)	Phone number	Self only	Self plus one	Family	Self only	Self plus one	Family of two
Washington								
G51-3	Aetna HealthFund CDHP	888-238-6240	2300	5460	5350	3890	9120	8530
G54-6	Aetna Value Plan	888-238-6240	2250	4570	4940	3440	7080	7160
LU1-3	UnitedHealthcare HDHP	877-835-9861	**1770**	**3820**	4570	**2960**	6400	6910
571-3	Kaiser Northwest-Hi (std't POS)	800-813-2000	2430	5500	5190	3700	8400	7600
574-6	Kaiser Northwest-Std (std't POS)	800-813-2000	2320	4790	5060	3470	7260	7260
L11-3	Kaiser Washington Options-Std POS	888-901-4636	5290	10710	10820	6450	13760	13250
L14-6	Kaiser Washington Options HDHP POS	888-901-4636	1960	4140	4540	3240	6910	6910
541-3	Kaiser Washington-Hi (WA/N ID)	888-901-4636	3440	7600	7290	5190	11500	10700
544-6	Kaiser Washington-Std (WA/N ID)	888-901-4636	2500	4940	5190	3690	7250	7250
PT1-3	Kaiser Washington HDHP (WA/N ID)	888-901-4636	**1780**	**4010**	**4380**	**2900**	6570	**6570**
West Virgina								
F51-3	Aetna HealthFund CDHP	888-238-6240	2740	6460	6360	4560	10620	10040
F54-6	Aetna Value Plan	888-238-6240	2310	4720	5100	3540	7310	7390
Wisconsin								
JS1-3	Aetna HealthFund CDHP	888-238-6240	4640	11020	10680	7400	17030	16520
JS4-6	Aetna Value Plan	888-238-6240	3290	7740	7350	5010	11350	10760
WD1-3	Dean Health-Hi (Madison/Racine)	800-279-1301	5680	11370	12820	8610	17250	19020
WD4-6	Dean Health-Std (Madison/Racine)	800-279-1301	2580	5050	5840	3940	7780	8490
WJ1-3	Group Health Coop (Madison/S Cen)	608-828-4853	2140	**3660**	8600	3240	**5500**	12730
V31-3	HealthPartners-Hi	800-883-2177	3070	6730	7860	4740	10400	11700
V34-6	HealthPartners-Std	952-883-5000	2380	4750	5280	3500	7040	7350
EY1-3	MercyCare HMO (Rockford/Janesville)	800-895-2421	3080	6170	8650	4640	9260	12690
LW1-3	Physicians Plus-Hi (Madison/S Cen)	800-545-5015	2500	6050	9550	3840	9190	14130
LW4-6	Physicians Plus-Std (Madison/S Cen)	800-545-5015	2780	5790	6630	4130	8650	9500
Wyoming								
H41-3	Aetna HealthFund CDHP	888-238-6240	2880	6780	6670	4760	11100	10500
H44-6	Aetna Value Plan	888-238-6240	2300	4700	5070	3520	7270	7340
9K1-3	Aetna Health/Altius-Hi	800-537-9384	3500	7580	7390	5320	11550	10980
DK4-6	Aetna Health/Altius-Std	800-537-9384	2200	4320	4590	3360	6610	6650
9K4-6	Aetna Health/Altius HDHP	800-537-9384	**1750**	**3330**	**3690**	**2840**	**5420**	**5470**

Lowest costs are in **bold** type. Note that in some plans, family costs are lower than self-plus-one costs.

Avg. yearly cost (cont'd)			Medicare wrap-around	Day limit in skilled nursing facility	Pays for...					Accreditation
Annuitants 65 or older with Medicare Parts A & B					Routine dental	Chiro-practic	Acupunc-ture	Hearing aids	Adult vision care	
Self only	Self plus one	Family								
5650	12630	12040	No	60	Some	Yes	Little	No	Exam	Yes
5350	10870	10950	No	60	No	Yes	Little	No	Exam	Yes
4940	10290	10800	No	60	Some	Yes	Some	Yes	Exam	Yes
4420	10240	9450	Yes	100	No	Some	Some	No	Yes	Yes
4000	8630	8630	Yes	100	No	Some	Yes	No	Yes	Yes
8150	16870	16360	Yes	Unlim	Some	Some	Some	Some	Exam	No
5150	10640	10640	No	Unlim	Some	Some	Some	Some	Exam	No
7060	15250	14450	No	60	Some	Yes	Some	No	Exam	Yes
4510	9780	9780	Some	60	No	Yes	Some	No	Exam	Yes
3530	**7920**	**7920**	Some	60	No	Yes	Some	No	Exam	Yes
6320	14130	13550	No	60	Some	Yes	Little	No	Exam	Yes
5450	11100	11170	No	60	No	Yes	Little	No	Exam	Yes
9160	20540	20030	No	60	Some	Yes	Little	No	Exam	Yes
6910	15130	14550	No	60	No	Yes	Little	No	Exam	Yes
10510	20780	22550	Yes	120	No	Yes	Some	Yes	Exam	Yes
5840	11580	12290	Yes	120	No	Yes	Some	Yes	Exam	Yes
5040	8980	16200	No	30	Some	Yes	Yes	No	Exam	Yes
5860	12450	13750	Yes	120	Some	Yes	Yes	Some	No	Yes
5360	10580	10890	No	120	No	Yes	Yes	No	No	Yes
6550	12920	16350	No	90	No	Yes	Some	Some	Exam	Yes
5360	12170	17110	Yes	90	No	Yes	Some	Yes	Exam	No
5090	10430	11290	Yes	90	No	Yes	Some	Yes	Exam	No
6520	14610	14010	No	60	Some	Yes	Little	No	Exam	Yes
5430	11060	11130	No	60	No	Yes	Little	No	Exam	Yes
6510	13860	13290	Yes	30	Yes	Some	No	Yes	Exam	Yes
4580	9000	9040	Yes	30	No	Some	No	Yes	Exam	Yes
4350	8500	**8550**	Yes	30	No	Some	No	Yes	Exam	Yes

Appendix

Our Methods and Data Sources

We compare plans in terms of their likely dollar cost to you, including both the "for sure" expense of the premium and the out-of-pocket (OOP) expenses you face for costs the plan does not pay. We estimate OOP expenses using actuarial methods to evaluate the cost-sharing details of each plan for various categories of costs. All FEHB plans cover 80 percent or more of most types of expenses whenever your costs are high, and provide a reasonably solid catastrophic limit guarantee. Therefore, the premium covers not only true insurance for rare, high-cost situations, but also pre-payment of routine expenses. When your medical costs are zero the premium is the only expense, but when your medical costs run into the tens of thousands the catastrophic limit (which in most plans is between $6,000 and $12,000 a year) comes into play. Most of the analysis underlying the *Guide* is aimed at quantifying, and expressing in terms of annual costs, the various risks you face and the reimbursement provided by each plan at each level of risk. We calculate costs assuming that you use only preferred providers, or providers who will agree to network fees, both because sensible consumers will avoid leaving the network if they can, and also because there is no realistic way to estimate the many unknown rates that individual providers may charge.

We calculate likely out-of-pocket costs, taking into account the probabilities of families of various sizes and ages incurring relatively low, medium, or high levels of expense (we actually use eight different expense levels, but do not present detailed results for all of these). The low-cost situations are most common but, when weighted for dollar amounts, accounts for a relatively small portion of likely spending. In statistical terms, health care expenses are a highly "skewed" distribution, and the average (or "mean") is far higher than the typical (or "median") spending level.

Although most persons do not know whether they will incur large expenses or not—heart attacks, serious accidents, and most other costly scenarios are relatively unpredictable—some persons do have a pretty good idea of some future costs. For example, they may be planning major surgery for a congenital problem. We present data for both groups: persons with and without good information on next year's expenses and, for those with good prior information, estimated out-of-pocket expenses at several expense levels for each plan. We caution users, however, to beware of attempting to estimate the costs of "known usage" expenses for anything much beyond maintenance drugs. The problem is few are likely to know, and few to have access to, information on such simple questions as the number of visits involved in dealing with a pinched nerve, or with the mix among hospital, surgical, and rehabilitation costs for a condition such as a knee or hip replacement. No one is likely to know if he or she will have a heart attack, a stroke, or a case of Lyme disease next year. Our methods do not force you to make guesses over such matters, or to pretend that the worst will not happen.

Most of the data used in the *Guide* come from the plan brochures themselves. Plans have several different benefit levels: one for most enrollees when using preferred providers, one for enrollees with Medicare, and one for enrollees when using out-of-plan providers (for most HMOs, reimbursement is zero in this last case, except in emergencies). When analyzed carefully, taking into account the exact wording of benefit descriptions, the brochures tell a clear story. The premiums tell another clear story. However, more is needed to compare the plans usefully and completely.

The estimates of annual expenses we use in the cost tables are based on information taken from a number of sources. The most important of these is the Medical Expenditure Panel Survey (MEPS) of the Agency for Healthcare Research and Quality. This valuable survey produces information for researchers, health plans, and consumer advisors like us on what proportions of the population incur expenses of what kinds and at what dollar levels. We adjust MEPS data slightly to "smooth" the estimates and to cover persons most likely to approximate current FEHB plans' spending levels. Our cost tables also use rounded estimates to make them easier to read, and the cost headings represent ranges. For example, the entries for expenses of $3,000 represent a range from about $2,000 to $4,500.

Because some plans impose different deductibles and coinsurance for different services, the distribution of costs between hospital and other expenses can affect significantly the amount that a plan will require you to pay for a particular expense total. We model our comparisons closely to average experience. Though few persons or families will have exactly the same cost profile as used in our tables, most situations will be at least close. Our profile, when weighted for probability, corresponds closely to projected expenses of the employed and retired American population as a whole, both in total and in category of expense. Some of the details are shown in the table "Profile of Expenses Used for Cost Tables."

Our cost comparisons make several other simplifications. First, in analyzing most plans we have to make assumptions about the number of doctor visits and prescriptions to calculate the patient's share of expenses.

Second, we assume that all bills are for amounts negotiated between plans and preferred providers. Many doctors who are not in the plan network charge more than the plan allows, and all plans do not have the same "profiles" for calculating their maximums. Absent any basis for adjustment, we simply assume what is generally true: all preferred doctors have agreed to limit their charges to plan allowances, and some others will agree to meet that level (or will do so if you tell them what plan you have and explain your cost concerns). There are instances in which some plans' schedules for some procedures are well below those used by other plans. Unfortunately, there is no way to adjust for this in our tables, though you can protect yourself in the real world by using preferred providers or by getting your provider to promise to stay within your plan's payment level before getting any expensive service.

Third, we assume that you take advantage of the best cost-sharing rate in each plan. Specifically, we assume that you get network rates by using network providers rather than providers who are not preferred with that plan. For drugs, we assume you use those in the plan formulary.

Fourth, we make assumptions about how many family members incur expenses at each total cost level in a year to calculate deductibles. For example, we assume that in a year with $1,000 in expenses, a family of five will have expenses for three members, and in a year with $130,000 in expenses, for all family members. In the real world, no one's actual set of yearly expenses will exactly match our assumptions. For plans whose coinsurance rates and deductibles are low or the same for most services, a different mix of expenses would have little or no effect on the cost estimates we present. For other plans, such as those with 100 percent coverage of hospitalization and limited coverage of prescription drugs, a different mix of expenses could change the estimates considerably. However, a different mix would not likely change any cost entry at $3,000 by more than two or three hundred dollars, or any entry for the $30,000 column by more than one or two thousand dollars. (Highly expensive specialty prescription drugs, such as some AIDS, hemophilia, growth hormone, chemotherapy, and osteo-arthritis drugs are the most important potential exceptions.)

We apply our methodology consistently across plans, so that any estimating problem is likely to be small in its effects on the comparative information in the tables.

Profile of Expenses Used for Cost Tables (approximate)

Level of expense	$ 0	$1,000	$3,000	$6,000	$12,000	$30,000	$60,000	$130,000
Components of total expense:								
Hospital	$ 0	$ 0	$ 0	$ 0	$ 5,000	$10,000	$29,000	$86,000
Surgical & outpatient facility	0	0	0	0	0	3,000	8,000	8,000
Primary & specialist physician	0	500	1,500	3,000	3,000	8,000	10,000	20,000
Prescription drugs & other	0	500	1,000	2,500	3,000	7,000	11,000	14,000
Dental	0	0	500	500	1,000	2,000	2,000	2,000
Risk of expense at each level:								
Self under age 55	12.0%	49%	15%	11%	8%	5%	1%	0.3%
Family of two under age 55	1.0%	35%	18%	16%	16%	12%	1%	1.0%
Self age 55 to 64	5.0%	33%	20%	19%	12%	9%	1%	1.0%
Family of two age 55 to 64	0.3%	12%	14%	17%	27%	24%	3%	3.0%
Self age 65 and older	4.0%	24%	20%	21%	16%	13%	2%	1.0%
Family of two age 65 and older	0.1%	6%	9%	14%	28%	34%	5%	3.0%

Acknowledgments

*The Guide is dedicated to the memory of
David F. Lawton, a dedicated civil servant who
worked hard and well at creating and improving the
Federal Employees Health Benefits Program during
its formative years. Special thanks to many OPM
and plan staff who graciously provided information,
assistance, and answers at short notice.*

About the Authors

Walton Francis is a self-employed economist and policy analyst, expert in the analysis and evaluation of public programs. He has written on a wide range of subjects including program evaluation, statistical analysis, managed health care, and retirement benefits. His education includes Master's degrees from Yale and Harvard universities. He developed regulatory, budgetary, and legislative reforms for many policies and programs while working at the Office of Management and Budget and in the Office of the Secretary at the Department of Health and Human Services. He pioneered the systematic comparison of health insurance plans from a consumer perspective, starting with the 1979 edition of this guide. He has published articles and testified several times before Congress on the Federal Employees Health Benefits and Medicare programs. He evaluated both programs' performance in *Putting Medicare Consumers in Charge: Lessons from the FEHBP*.

Checkbook is a magazine and website produced by the nonprofit Center for the Study of Services. Checkbook rates the quality and prices of consumer services, ranging from auto repair shops to home improvement services to health-care providers in seven metropolitan areas: Washington, Boston, Chicago, Philadelphia, San Francisco, Seattle, and Minneapolis-St. Paul. In the health care field, Checkbook rates doctors, hospitals, dentists, and health insurance plans. The Center has a health care survey research arm that, in addition to conducting surveys for the Center's own publications and website, routinely conducts surveys under contract for government agencies, employer coalitions, and health plans, including many of the health plans evaluated in this book. The Center also produces national guides that evaluate surgeons and hospitals and provides comparison tools for several states' marketplace exchanges that help consumers choose health plans.